Organized Collapse: An Introduction to Discrete Morse Theory

GRADUATE STUDIES IN MATHEMATICS 207

Organized Collapse: An Introduction to Discrete Morse Theory

Dmitry N. Kozlov

AMERICAN MATHEMATICAL SOCIETY
Providence, Rhode Island

2010 *Mathematics Subject Classification.* Primary 57Q10;
Secondary 05C70, 06A07, 55U10, 57-02, 57Q05, 58E05.

For additional information and updates on this book, visit
www.ams.org/bookpages/gsm-207

Library of Congress Cataloging-in-Publication Data

Cataloging-in-Publication Data has been applied for by the AMS.
See http://www.loc.gov/publish/cip/.

∞ The paper used in this book is acid-free and falls within the guidelines
established to ensure permanence and durability.
Visit the AMS home page at `https://www.ams.org/`

10 9 8 7 6 5 4 3 2 1   25 24 23 22 21 20

Dedicated to David, Esther, Judith, and Eva-Maria

蜘殺すあとの淋しき夜寒哉

正岡 子規 (1867-1902)

After killing
a spider, how lonely I feel
in the cold of night!

Masaoka Shiki (1867-1902)

Contents

Preamble

Applied topology is a modern mathematical subject which appeared in recent years as a concentration point for many methods, topological in nature, which were used in a wide variety of applications, both within and outside of classical mathematics. While displaying an amazing breadth, these methods have at least one thing in common—the emphasis on the computational aspect.

Clearly, whenever computations are involved, there arises the question of their complexity. No application will be truly useful if it results in a computationally intractable problem. Accordingly, the simplification of the required computations takes center stage. Whether within a topological, combinatorial, or algebraic context, we need to be able both to define single elementary simplifications, as well as to manage their sequences, telling us for instance which sequence is permissible, and also what the final result will be of applying a certain sequence of simplifications.

In topological context, the tool of choice for handling these considerations came to be popularly known as *discrete Morse theory*, and this book grew out of the author's thoughts about the role discrete Morse theory should play within the wider context of applied topology.

Although some of the viewpoints and even some of the results presented here are new, this is not a research manuscript. When writing this book, we tried to produce a text which would be useful for a beginning graduate, as well as advanced undergraduate students. Due to the large differences in the master studies curricula in various educational systems, we have tried to keep the presentation self-contained.

As a result, we have included a brief introduction to the basics of algebraic topology. So, while our target audience consists of graduate students in applied topology, the book can also be used by anyone looking for a first textbook treatment of homology. Furthermore, we intended the book to be of interest to students and specialists in computer science and engineering who would like to learn about applications of topology to their fields, as well as for research mathematicians interested in learning about the subject and applying it in their context.

During the work on this book the author was supported by the University of Bremen, Germany, as well as by the Okinawa Institute of Science and Technology, Japan. He expresses his deepest gratitude to both of these wonderful institutions.

Herbert Edelsbrunner has been both an initiator and a strong supporter of this undertaking. Without him this book would probably never have been started.

Once it was, writing it was a long and excruciating process. During this time, the author had the great benefit of experiencing constant and friendly encouragement of the AMS Editor Ina Mette. This support is recognized and very much appreciated.

After a text reaches a certain size, it starts having a life of its own. It is only with the help of careful proofreaders that the author may proceed beyond a certain point. Here, the author would especially like to mention his graduate student Leonard Wienke, whose notational and typographic suggestions have been most helpful.

Last, but not least, I would like to express my gratitude to my family, to whom this book is dedicated. Without them the book would either have been finished much sooner, or not finished at all.

Preface

The idea of homology

The main idea of algebraic topology is to try to use *algebraic structures* to say something qualitative about *topological spaces*. Over time one developed many such algebraic invariants. Perhaps the simplest one to define is the so-called *fundamental group* of a space. Most probably the reader has seen its definition in one form or another. Roughly speaking, one chooses a point in space and then defines some calculus using all possible loops anchored at this point. A clear weakness of such an invariant is that it does not tell us anything beyond the first few dimensions: taking any space and then attaching balls of dimension 3 and higher to that space will not be detected by the fundamental group at all. That in itself can be fixed by introducing higher-dimensional homotopy groups. What is much worse, from the point of view of applied topology, is that not only are these invariants hard to compute, but the famous result of P.S. Novikov, [**No55**], actually tells us that it is not decidable whether or not the fundamental group is trivial.

All these problems are solved if one passes to the so-called *homology groups*. These are defined in all dimensions and, if the framework is right, can be computed using linear algebra.

Before talking about invariants, though, let us contemplate for a moment how topological spaces can be described. Many classic examples, including curves, surfaces, or more generally manifolds, are given by their defining equations in Euclidean spaces. While useful in many other fields of mathematics, such as differential geometry, as well as in physics, this will give us only a limited supply of spaces. Furthermore, the description using equations is indirect, making a constructive computation of algebraic invariants rather daunting.

An alternative approach is combinatorial in nature. Instead of using geometry as our guidance, we take some elementary building blocks, the so-called *simplices*, and then glue them together to produce a topological space, which we then call an abstract simplicial complex. This combinatorial gluing scheme then takes the role of the space description, and the actual topological space can be recovered from it, uniquely up to homeomorphism, using the so-called geometric realization construction.

In the opposite direction, the bridge from the continuous to the discrete is provided by the concept of triangulation. Although there is a number of underwater stones here, in essence well-behaved spaces can be triangulated so that an abstract simplicial complex can be produced. The main problem is that a triangulation, as opposed to the geometric realization, is in no way unique, and it is not feasible to combinatorially define a sensible equivalence relation on the set of simplicial complexes such that any two triangulations of the same topological space are equivalent. This conundrum can eventually be resolved, though not without using the technical tool of *simplicial approximation*.

One way to bypass these difficulties altogether is to take the idea of a combinatorial gluing scheme one step further, into the realm of abstract algebra. The sets of simplices are replaced by vector spaces or, more generally, by free abelian groups, and the gluing information gets baked into a linear map, the so-called *boundary operator*, leading to the concept of a *chain complex*. The resulting inter-relations between topology, combinatorics, and algebra are shown in Figure 0.1.

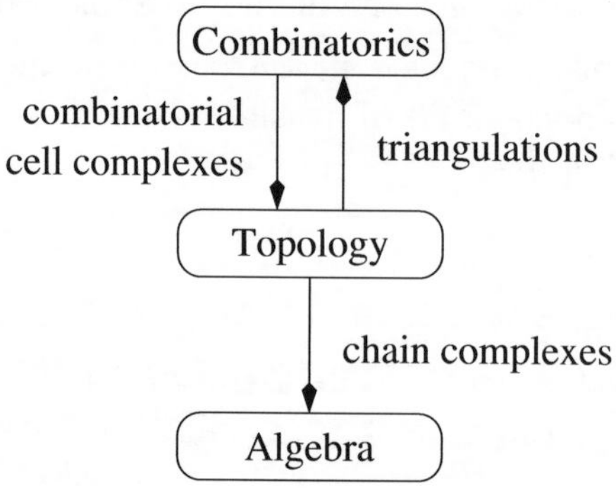

Figure 0.1. Inter-relations between topology, combinatorics, and algebra.

The idea of discrete Morse theory

In general, given two topological spaces, it is hard to tell whether they are homotopy equivalent. The intuitive picture of allowing stretchings of the space results in the formal concept of a *strong deformation retraction*, and it is possible to take it as a basis for an equivalence relation. Unfortunately, this is rather impractical, and completely useless from the computational point of view.

One is therefore sorely tempted to introduce such deformations in the combinatorial context of simplicial complexes. This leads to the so-called *simplicial collapses*, and their theory, known as *simple homotopy theory*, which was ingeniously developed by J.H.C. Whitehead in the 30s, [**Co73**, **Wh50**]. Unfortunately (or perhaps fortunately), it turned out that even when two topological spaces can be deformed to each other, in the desired way, the corresponding combinatorial deformation may not exist. In fact, there is a possible obstruction to the existence of such a deformation, the so-called *Whitehead torsion*, which can be found in the so-called *Whitehead group* of the appropriate fundamental group. On one hand, this leads to an interesting and subtle theory of combinatorial torsions. On the other, these "difficulties" led to the fact that the combinatorial track of development in topology was abandoned, to the advantage of the purely algebraic one.

In recent years, there arose many situations where the revival of combinatorial thinking could be of use. Many topological spaces are constructed not by starting from geometry, but rather directly as abstract simplicial complexes. Oftentimes, these are artificial objects which are associated to various situations in combinatorics, or other fields, constructed for the sole purpose of using the power of topology, where there was no topology to start with. One particular field, which has lately received a rather substantial development boost, is *applied topology*. Here simplicial complexes play an important role in many applied contexts, from data analysis to robotics. Just as in the combinatorial context, there is a renewed and natural desire to return to the theory of combinatorial deformations.

This is where *discrete Morse theory* comes in. This occurs on two levels. First, we would like to go beyond the usual simplicial collapses and to allow the sort of deformations which could be thought of as *internal collapses*. These will still yield homotopy equivalences, but will no longer preserve simplicial structure, producing more complicated gluing maps. Second, once we resign ourselves to perform sequences of such deformations, it is imperative to give conditions under which sequences are allowed, the so-called *acyclicity condition*, as well as to learn to do good book-keeping for collapsing sequences.

Once these objectives are achieved, we will have on our hands a theory which is very effective from the computational point of view. It can then be combined in a mutually profitable way with other tools of applied topology and combinatorics, see Table 0.1.

Field	Deformation
Topology	strong deformation retraction
Combinatorics	simplicial collapse
Algebra	change of basis

Table 0.1. The many faces of discrete Morse theory.

A sample application

To give an illustration of how discrete Morse theory works, let us consider the simplicial complex in Figure 0.2.

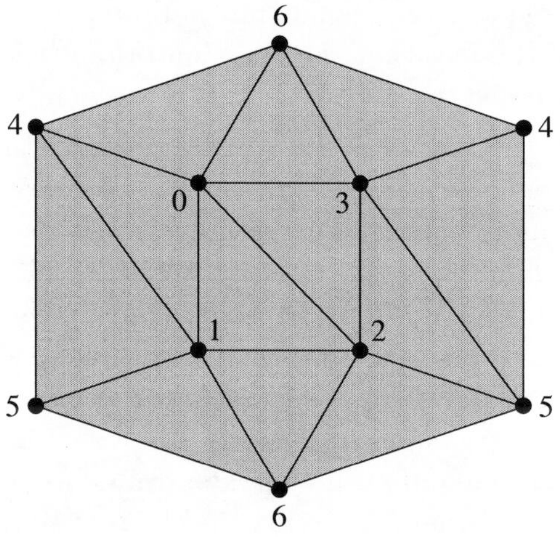

Figure 0.2. A triangulation of a pinched torus.

In this figure each set of vertices may span at most one simplex, so simplices with the same sets of vertices are to be identified. It is easy to see that we have a triangulation of a sphere with north and south poles identified, producing vertex 6. Alternatively, this can be viewed as the so-called *pinched torus*, obtained from a usual torus by shrinking an essential circle to a point.

In discrete Morse theory, we want to consider a sort of discrete flow, illustrated in Figure 0.3 by adding a number of arrows. This family of arrows

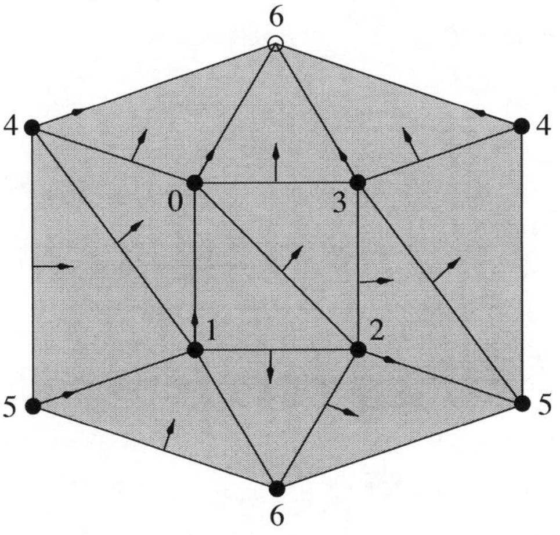

Figure 0.3. Acyclic simplex matching.

must satisfy an additional property—the acyclicity condition, which we will define later.

Later in the book, we will see that a fruitful way to work with such a discrete flow is to view it as a matching on the set of simplices, and to define various notions in terms of emerging combinatorics.

For example, a careful reader will see that the only simplices which are not matched in Figure 0.3 are the vertex 6, the edge 16, and the triangle 012. Discrete Morse theory (or, more specifically, Theorem 11.2) will allow us to immediately conclude that (the geometric realization of) our simplicial complex is homotopy equivalent to another space which is obtained by gluing a 2-disc onto a circle along some function on the boundary of that 2-disc.

This is of course, by itself, a great simplification of the initial space, and this is precisely how discrete Morse theory is often used. Since there are several functions along which the gluing may occur, there is more work needed for the complete understanding of the space. Still, this can be done by using a few more advanced topics of our theory, for example, by studying the associated Morse chain complex, and coupling this with the fact that the maps between circles are classified, up to homotopy, by their winding numbers.

In the end one can conclude that the topological space associated to our simplicial complex is homotopy equivalent to a circle and a 2-sphere, glued together at a single point; the standard "name" of this space is $S^2 \vee S^1$.

How to use this book

When writing this book, we have envisioned a number of various uses. To start with, it can certainly be adopted as a first text in algebraic topology, specifically as an introduction to homology. That being said, the author assumes the knowledge of fundamental groups, as would be the case at the University of Bremen, where fundamental groups are included in the undergraduate topology course. In a different system this has to be adjusted by either adding a crash course on the fundamental group, or skipping the topics which involve it. Parts 1 and 2 of this book may be taken to form a backbone of such an introductory course in homology theory.

Another target audience for this book consists of those readers who are interested in combinatorial topology, and specifically in the role played by discrete Morse theory. Such a reader should concentrate on Part 3, where the majority of examples are drawn from the vast pool of combinatorially defined simplicial, but not only simplicial, complexes. Many results of combinatorial topology are recovered there from the point of view of discrete Morse theory. The previous book by this author, [**Ko08**], may also be of benefit as a reference material here.

Finally, the author would be honoured if this text was found of interest by the dynamic and fast-growing community in applied topology. Certainly, a number of shortcuts can be done by an applied topologist interested only in simplicial or cellular models. A different, more computational, approach would essentially allow skipping Part 2, and also some of the examples. On the other hand, the algorithmic procedure from Chapter 12 for producing explicit homology generators from acyclic matchings would be of great interest, as would be Part 4, including the short Chapter 18 describing a relation to persistent homology.

Here is the summary of the contents of the four parts.

Part 1: Introduction to homology. We adopt the simplicial approach and gear the introduction towards advanced undergraduate or graduate students in mathematics, looking for their first exposure to homology theory, or computer science and engineering graduate students interested in applications of topology to their fields.

Part 2: More advanced topics in homology theory, including chain homotopy, long exact sequences, singular homology, and cellular homology. While invaluable for anyone learning algebraic topology, it may be skipped if applied topology is the primary focus.

Part 3: Basic discrete Morse theory. Graduate level introduction to the subject of discrete Morse theory. Formulation and proof of all the basic results which have so far been most useful. The emphasis here is on the approach via simple homotopy theory, using collapses and acyclic matchings. In the end a connection to the historical framework using discrete Morse functions and discrete vector fields is made.

Part 4: Collection of topics from advanced discrete Morse theory. Algebraic Morse theory and the change of bases. Discrete Morse theory via poset maps with small fibers. Connections to persistent homology.

Prerequisites

As prerequisites, we expect that the reader is familiar with linear algebra, group theory, and point-set topology. In particular, we expect the knowledge of the quotient group and the classification theorem for finitely generated abelian groups. We do not require detailed knowledge of finite fields, however we expect familiarity with the field with 2 elements, which we denote $\mathbb{Z}_2$, and vector spaces over that field.

Beyond group theory, we assume that the reader is familiar with parts of abstract algebra, including rings, modules, and tensor products, and that he has basic knowledge of the concepts from category theory.

Finally, the knowledge of the fundamental group would come in handy as the guiding principle for some of the intuition; that being said, it is not a strict prerequisite for most of the book.

Guide to the literature

Discrete Morse theory was introduced by Robin Forman in his seminal paper [**Fo98**]. Since then the subject has been treated in the textbook form by Knudson, [**Kn15**], and more recently by Scoville, [**Sc19**]. There have also been chapter-long treatments by Forman, [**Fo02a**], and by the author, [**Ko08**, Chapter 11]. Our approach here is closest to the last reference.

Furthermore, a large number of research articles related to this subject have appeared. This book consists of four parts, and we have decided to provide the reader with references and suggestions for further reading at the end of Parts 2, 3, and 4.

Part 1

Introduction to Homology

Chapter 1

The First Steps

1.1. Dimension 0: Counting points using vector spaces and free abelian groups

The simplest topological spaces imaginable are just collections of finitely many points, equipped with the usual discrete topology. The only information of interest would then be the number of points in such a space S. As a foretaste of things to come, let us see how this information can be extracted in an algebraic way.

Assume the space S has n points. We now describe how to retrieve n in a way which at a first glance would appear rather *round-about*, but which illustrates what will be done in general. Let us consider a vector space over the real numbers whose basis is indexed by the elements of S. We call it $V = \mathbb{R}\langle S\rangle$, and we can formally think about points from S as the actual basis vectors in V. Now, imagine that we do not know the set S; instead we are given the vector space V without any specified basis. The question is: *what can we say about the set* S*?*

Clearly, the vector space V will have plenty of bases, and we may not find the one corresponding to S. On the other hand, a basic course in linear algebra tells us that the dimension of V is well-defined, and of course it is equal to $|S|$. So, while being unable to recover the set S itself, without further information, we can easily recover the *cardinality* of S as the dimension of the vector space that was given to us. This situation is a precursor of *homology with coefficients in the field* $\mathbb{R}$.

As the next step, note, that we could have played the same trick taking free abelian groups instead of the vector spaces. Indeed, given S, we can consider the *free abelian group* $\mathbb{Z}\langle S\rangle$ generated by the elements of S. Recall that, by definition, the elements of $\mathbb{Z}\langle S\rangle$ are all possible linear combinations $c_1\alpha_1 + \cdots + c_t\alpha_t$, where $c_1, \ldots, c_t$ are integers and $\alpha_1, \ldots, \alpha_t$ are elements of S, and the addition operation is the one you expect:

$$(c_1\alpha_1 + \cdots + c_t\alpha_t) + (d_1\alpha_1 + \cdots + d_t\alpha_t) = (c_1 + d_1)\alpha_1 + \cdots + (c_t + d_t)\alpha_t.$$

Again, when we are given the abelian group $\mathbb{Z}\langle S\rangle$, but not told what the set S is, we can still read off the cardinality of S from that group. This is a corollary of the classification theorem of finitely generated abelian groups: the group $\mathbb{Z}\langle S\rangle$ is free, and $|S|$ is the dimension of that free part.

Finally, we could also consider the vector space $\mathbb{Z}_2\langle S\rangle$ instead of $\mathbb{R}\langle S\rangle$. Everything becomes even easier in this case, since that vector space has finitely many points, namely $2^{|S|}$ points, so it is very easy to read off the number $|S|$ from the vector space.

Can we allow the set S to be infinite? The answer is: yes, the cardinality of S can still be determined directly from $\mathbb{R}\langle S\rangle$ or from $\mathbb{Z}_2\langle S\rangle$. However, the details are slightly more involved, and we skip them here, as we do not want to get distracted by unnecessary deviations into the realm of set theory.

It turns out that there is a wide-reaching generalization of this "counting" method, and that we have just calculated our first instance of a *homology group*! Indeed, the space $\mathbb{R}\langle S\rangle$ is called the *0th homology group of* S *with coefficients in* $\mathbb{R}$, and it is denoted $H_0(S;\mathbb{R})$. Similarly, the space $\mathbb{Z}\langle S\rangle$ is called the *0th homology group of* S *with coefficients in* $\mathbb{Z}$ or, alternatively, *with integer coefficients*, and it is denoted $H_0(S;\mathbb{Z})$. The group $H_0(S;\mathbb{Z}_2)$ is defined the same way. Let us now see what happens for slightly less trivial spaces.

1.2. Dimension 1: Graphs

Let us now move up one in dimension and consider *graphs*, which are topological spaces obtained by taking a set of vertices and then connecting them by a number of edges. For a graph G, we write $G = (V, E)$, where V denotes the set of vertices of G, and E denotes the set of edges. In order to keep things simple we assume that

- the vertices of the graph G are labeled $v_1, \ldots, v_n$, with $n \geqslant 1$;
- G does not have edges glued on the same vertex with both ends (the so-called *loops*), and we also do not allow two edges to be glued on the same set of two vertices (multiple edges);
- for each edge $(v_i, v_j) \in E$ we require $i < j$.

The graphs without loops and without multiple edges are called *simple graphs*. Also our default choice is to consider graphs with only finitely many vertices and hence finitely many edges. We call these *finite graphs*.

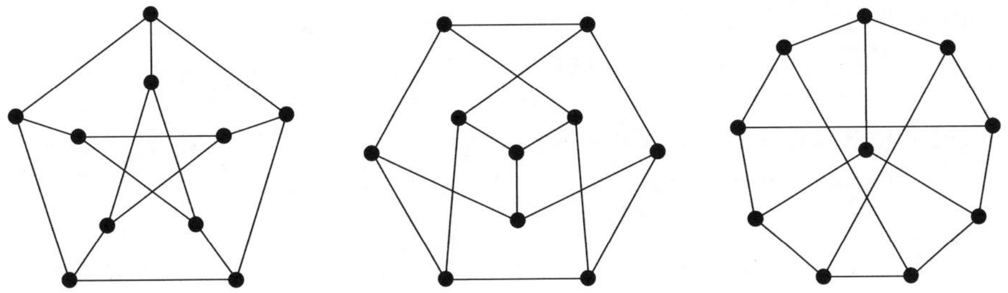

Figure 1.1. Three ways to draw the Petersen graph.

At times, graphs can confront us with surprisingly complicated problems. For example, it is hard to tell whether two graphs are isomorphic: the so-called *Graph Isomorphism Problem*; see [**KST**]. Figure 1.1 illustrates this fact by visually showing three rather different ways to draw the same graph, the so-called *Petersen graph*, whose vertices can be indexed by all 2-element subsets of a 5-element set and whose edges connect disjoint subsets.

The question of main interest in our present context is: what topological features of G can we "count", in analogy with what we did with the set S?

1.2.1. Counting connected components of a simple graph. Clearly, the first thing that we can count is the number of connected components of G. Here is how it can be done algebraically. Consider the vector space $\mathbb{R}\langle V\rangle$, with the chosen basis $v_1, \dots, v_n$. The basis vectors are in bijection with the vertices of G, and we use the same notation. For reasons which will become clear shortly, a consistent notation for that space will be $C_0(G;\mathbb{R})$, and the consistent name for this space will be the space of *0-dimensional chains of* G *with coefficients in* $\mathbb{R}$.

Let us define an equivalence relation on the set of vertices of G by saying that *two vertices connected by an edge are equivalent.* In other words, for any two vertices $v_i, v_j \in V$, which are connected by an edge in G, that is, $(v_i, v_j) \in E$, we want to have an algebraic way of saying "set the vertex v_i equal to the vertex v_j". The standard way to do that is to consider $v_j - v_i = 0$ as a relation or, equivalently, consider a relator $v_j - v_i$. Formally, let U be the subspace of $C_0(G;\mathbb{R})$ spanned by all such relators, corresponding to edges in E, and then consider the quotient vector space $C_0(G;\mathbb{R})/U$. This quotient is again a homology group! It is denoted by $H_0(G;\mathbb{R})$, and it is called, just as above, the *0th homology group of* G *with coefficients in* $\mathbb{R}$. We can formalize our verbal definition by writing

$$H_0(G;\mathbb{R}) := \mathbb{R}\big\langle V \,|\, v_j - v_i, \text{ for all } (v_i, v_j) \in E\big\rangle. \tag{1.1}$$

Let us make precise our choice of notations. Let R be some ring, let S be some set, and let T be some subset of $R\langle S\rangle$. We write $R\langle S \mid T\rangle$ to denote the quotient $R\langle S\rangle / R\langle T\rangle$. Here S is the set of generators, and T can be thought of as a set of relations. Taking the quotient is the algebraic way to say that we set certain expressions in $R\langle S\rangle$ to be equal to 0. When R is a field, the quotient $R\langle S\rangle / R\langle T\rangle$ is a vector space over R. When $R = \mathbb{Z}$, the quotient $R\langle S\rangle / R\langle T\rangle$ is an abelian group. Typically, it will not be free.

In general, the vector subspace U, defined above, is denoted by $B_0(G;\mathbb{R})$ and is called the space of *0-dimensional boundaries of* G *with coefficients in* $\mathbb{R}$. We leave it as an exercise, see Exercise (2)(a), to show that the dimension of the vector space $H_0(G;\mathbb{R})$ is equal to the number of connected components of G. This number is also called the *0th Betti number* of G, and it is denoted by $\beta_0(G)$.

Switching from $\mathbb{R}$ to $\mathbb{Z}_2$, the vector space $\mathbb{Z}_2\langle V\rangle$ is denoted by $C_0(G;\mathbb{Z}_2)$ and everything can be done in much the same way. We let the sums $v+w$ (which over $\mathbb{Z}_2$ is the same as $v-w$) span a vector subspace U of $C_0(G;\mathbb{Z}_2)$, and let the quotient $C_0(G;\mathbb{Z}_2)/U$ be denoted $H_0(G;\mathbb{Z}_2)$, which is then called the *0th homology group of* G *with coefficients in* $\mathbb{Z}_2$. In fact, taking an arbitrary field $\mathbf{k}$ we can define

$$H_0(G;\mathbf{k}) := \mathbf{k}\big\langle V \,|\, v_j - v_i, \text{ for all } (v_i, v_j) \in E\big\rangle .$$

Again, we leave it as an exercise, see Exercise (2b), to show that

$$\dim H_0(G;\mathbf{k}) = \beta_0(G),$$

which does not depend on the choice of the field $\mathbf{k}$.

Let us now go through the above procedure again, this time replacing the vector space $\mathbb{R}\langle V\rangle$ with the free abelian group $\mathbb{Z}\langle V\rangle$, which we denote $C_0(G;\mathbb{Z})$. We can again form a subgroup H generated by all the differences $v_j - v_i$, whenever $(v_i, v_j) \in E$. As above, consider the quotient $C_0(G;\mathbb{Z})/H$:

$$H_0(G;\mathbb{Z}) := \mathbb{Z}\big\langle V \,|\, v_j - v_i, \text{ for all } (v_i, v_j) \in E\big\rangle . \tag{1.2}$$

Remember that, in principle, a quotient of free abelian groups does not have to be free (though it certainly has to be abelian). Fortunately, nothing of the sort happens on the right-hand side of Equation (1.2). Exercise (2)(c) asks the reader to show that $H_0(G;\mathbb{Z})$ is free abelian, and that its dimension is equal to the Betti number $\beta_0(G)$.

Remark 1.1. When the graph G is not simple, everything can be done in almost the same way. Indeed, the space $C_0(G;\mathbb{R})$ is just the same. The loops will have no influence, since a loop based at a vertex v_i will simply give the relation $v_i - v_i = 0$ or, equivalently, will ask the vertex to be equivalent to itself. The multiple edges will also not change anything since repeating edges will just repeat the relations $v_j - v_i = 0$, which are there anyway. In other words, we can simply adopt Equation (1.1) directly.

1.2.2. Counting 1-dimensional holes in simple graphs. We would now like to understand what is going on in the context above in dimension 1. If the finite graph G is *planar*, that is, there is a way to draw it in the plane without self-intersections, then it will divide the plane into regions, with exactly one infinitely large region surrounding the graph. We could then count the number of bounded regions, and say that their number is the number of "1-dimensional holes" in the graph G. That would actually be fine, and we could let the 1*st Betti number* $\beta_1(G)$ denote that number. There is still an issue, though, with the question of whether or not this number will depend on the actual way we drew the graph, but that can be settled by a simple induction argument. In fact, it is not difficult to show, for example using induction on $|V|+|E|$, that we will have $\beta_1(G) = |E| - |V| + \beta_0(G)$, for all planar graphs G, even the non-simple ones.

A much bigger problem is that not all graphs are planar; in fact, most of them are not. If the graph is not planar, it can actually be rather confusing to talk about the number of 1-dimensional holes, or even to try to say what such a hole would actually be. In fact, it might be the sort of "intuition", which can make the understanding of what is going on harder, not easier. For example, how many holes should the complete graph on 5 vertices K_5 have? We want to say that "K_5 has 6 holes", but how can we formalize, or even visualize, that? (See Figure 1.2.)

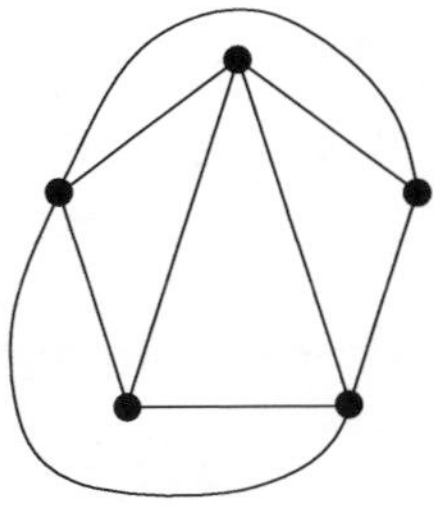

Figure 1.2. The graph K_5 without an edge has 5 holes, adding one more edge should create the 6th one.

We shall not talk about 1-dimensional holes of a graph for a simple reason: *we do not know what it means.* Instead, to draw an analogy to the previous section, we can learn how to add cycles and then measure the dimensions of the obtained groups.

Let us now describe the formal framework. Recall that the vertices of the simple graph G are labeled by $v_1, \dots, v_n$. In complete analogy to the 0-dimensional case, let $C_1(G;\mathbb{R})$ denote the vector space $\mathbb{R}\langle E\rangle$, whose basis is indexed by the edges of E. In other words, for $1 \leqslant i < j \leqslant n$, such that $(v_i, v_j) \in E$, we let e_{ij} denote the corresponding basis vector; for convenience, we shall also set $e_{ji} := -e_{ij}$, for all $1 \leqslant j < i \leqslant n$, and set $e_{ii} := 0$, for all $1 \leqslant i \leqslant n$. By construction, a vector $c \in C_1(G;\mathbb{R})$ is a linear combination $\sum_{i<j,(v_i,v_j)\in E} \alpha_{ij} e_{ij}$, where $\alpha_{ij} \in \mathbb{R}$, for all $i < j$, $(v_i, v_j) \in E$. We shall say that c is a *cycle* if for every $1 \leqslant k \leqslant n$ we have

$$\alpha_{1k} + \alpha_{2k} + \cdots + \alpha_{k-1,k} + \alpha_{k+1,k} + \cdots + \alpha_{nk} = 0, \tag{1.3}$$

where we use the handy notation $\alpha_{ji} := -\alpha_{ij}$, for $i < j$. One can see that the "old-fashioned" graph cycles are reflected in this construction as follows: a cycle $v_{w_1}, v_{w_2}, \dots, v_{w_t}$ corresponds to the vector

$$e_{w_1 w_2} + e_{w_2 w_3} + \cdots + e_{w_{t-1} w_t} + e_{w_t w_1}.$$

One can furthermore see that all cycles actually form a vector subspace. This can be either seen via an ad hoc computation or, more structurally, by viewing it as the kernel of a certain linear map; see the next subsection. We denote this vector space by $Z_1(G;\mathbb{R})$ and call it the *group of* 1*-cycles of* G *with real coefficients.* We shall also denote the same space $H_1(G;\mathbb{R})$ and call it the *first homology group of* G *with real coefficients.* For higher-dimensional spaces, these two groups do not have to coincide, but for graphs they do. We set the first Betti number $\beta_1(G)$ to be the dimension $\dim H_1(G;\mathbb{R})$.

As an example, let G be the complete graph on 3 vertices: $V = \{v_1, v_2, v_3\}$ and $E = \{(v_1, v_2), (v_1, v_3), (v_2, v_3)\}$. A cycle is a linear combination $\alpha_{12}e_{12} + \alpha_{13}e_{13} + \alpha_{23}e_{23}$ satisfying

$$\begin{cases} \alpha_{12} + \alpha_{13} = 0, \\ \alpha_{12} - \alpha_{23} = 0, \\ \alpha_{13} + \alpha_{23} = 0. \end{cases}$$

The solutions to this system form a line in $\mathbb{R}^3$ generated by the vector $(1, -1, 1)$, where the ordered basis is taken to be $\{e_{12}, e_{13}, e_{23}\}$. So as the homology group we get $H_1(G;\mathbb{R}) = \mathbb{R}\langle(1,-1,1)\rangle \approx \mathbb{R}$. It makes sense to think about $e_{12} - e_{13} + e_{23}$ as a *generating cycle.*

The reader who is familiar with the fundamental group will appreciate how much easier it is to compute the first homology group of this graph as opposed to the fundamental group of the circle. On the other hand, it is not a priori clear, although it is true and easy to see in this particular case that different graph representations of the same topological space will yield isomorphic homology groups. In general, this is known as the question of *invariance under the simplicial subdivision.*

1.2.3. The boundary operator. It is useful to view what we did so far through the lens of a certain linear map

$$\partial_1 : C_1(G;\mathbb{R}) \longrightarrow C_0(G;\mathbb{R}), \tag{1.4}$$

with which we now proceed. Define the linear map ∂_1 by setting

$$\partial_1(e_{ij}) := v_j - v_i, \text{ for all } 1 \leqslant i < j \leqslant n, \tag{1.5}$$

on the basis vectors, and then extending this linearly. This map is called the *boundary operator*. We leave it as Exercise (3) to show that $B_0(G;\mathbb{R})$ is the image of ∂_1 and that $Z_1(G;\mathbb{R})$ is the kernel of this map. This yields alternative definitions for both of these groups.

The whole context can be replicated nearly verbatim, with the real coefficients replaced by integers. The kernel of the group homomorphism $\partial_1 : C_1(G;\mathbb{Z}) \longrightarrow C_0(G;\mathbb{Z})$ must itself be a free abelian group and is denoted by $H_1(G;\mathbb{Z})$.

We can also use $\mathbb{Z}_2$-coefficients instead. The kernel of the linear map $\partial_1 : C_1(G;\mathbb{Z}_2) \longrightarrow C_0(G;\mathbb{Z}_2)$ is clearly a vector space over $\mathbb{Z}_2$; it is denoted by $H_1(G;\mathbb{Z}_2)$. In fact, the case of $\mathbb{Z}_2$-coefficients is in some sense easier to deal with. In this situation, the elements of $C_1(G;\mathbb{Z}_2)$ simply correspond to graphs on n vertices. Such a graph corresponds to a cycle if and only if the valencies[1] of all vertices are even. The reader is invited to see how adding such graphs with $\mathbb{Z}_2$-arithmetic works in practice.

We remark that the identity

$$\beta_1(G) - \beta_0(G) = |E| - |V| \tag{1.6}$$

holds for all finite graphs G, not just for the planar ones. Indeed, we have

$$|E| = \dim C_1(G;\mathbb{R}) = \dim \operatorname{Ker} \partial_1 + \dim(C_1(G;\mathbb{R})/\operatorname{Ker} \partial_1), \tag{1.7}$$

$$|V| = \dim C_0(G;\mathbb{R}) = \dim \operatorname{Im} \partial_1 + \dim(C_0(G;\mathbb{R})/\operatorname{Im} \partial_1), \tag{1.8}$$

and clearly

$$\dim(C_1(G;\mathbb{R})/\operatorname{Ker} \partial_1) = \dim \operatorname{Im} \partial_1,$$

since $\partial_1 : C_1(G;\mathbb{R})/\operatorname{Ker} \partial_1 \to \operatorname{Im} \partial_1$ is an isomorphism of vector spaces. We then obtain Equation (1.6) by subtracting Equation (1.8) from Equation (1.7) and recalling that $\dim \operatorname{Ker} \partial_1 = \beta_1(G)$ and $\dim(C_0(G;\mathbb{R})/\operatorname{Im} \partial_1) = \beta_0(G)$.

1.2.4. Non-simple graphs. Again, passing on to non-simple graphs will not present much difficulty. When G is non-simple, the edges are no longer uniquely determined by their vertices. Instead, we have a set E of edges and two functions

$$\partial^\circ, \partial_\circ : E \to V,$$

where $\partial^\circ(e)$ is the initial vertex of e, and $\partial_\circ(e)$ is the terminal one. If $\partial^\circ(e) = v_i$ and $\partial_\circ(e) = v_j$, we require $i \leqslant j$. For loops we will have $\partial^\circ(e) = \partial_\circ(e)$, and for multiple edges e_1 and e_2, we will have $\partial^\circ(e_1) = \partial^\circ(e_2)$ and $\partial_\circ(e_1) = \partial_\circ(e_2)$. The vector spaces $C_1(G;\mathbb{R})$ and $C_0(G;\mathbb{R})$ are defined in the

[1]Recall that the valency of a vertex is also alternatively called the *degree* of a vertex.

same way as for the simple graphs, and we define the boundary operator $\partial_1 : C_1(G;\mathbb{R}) \to C_0(G;\mathbb{R})$ by setting

$$\partial_1(e) := \partial_\circ(e) - \partial^\circ(e), \text{ for all } e \in E.$$

Then we set $H_1(G;\mathbb{R}) := \operatorname{Ker}\partial_1$. Of course, when G is simple, this coincides with our previous definition.

1.2.5. Infinite graphs. When we have a graph $G = (V, E)$ where V or E can be infinite, everything is still the same except for one point where one has to be somewhat careful. For this, recall that elements of a vector space are *finite* linear combinations of basis vectors, even when the basis itself is allowed to be infinite. Similarly, an element of a free abelian group generated by a set X is a *finite* linear combination of the generators.

Keeping this important technical detail in mind, we can still define the boundary operator ∂_1 by taking the linear extension of Equation (1.5). Once we have the boundary operator, we simply set $H_1(G;\mathbb{R}) := \operatorname{Ker}\partial_1$ and $H_0(G;\mathbb{R}) := C_0(G;\mathbb{R})/\operatorname{Im}\partial_1$, just as before. This will extend the definition of homology to infinite graphs. In particular, the cycles will be *finite* linear combinations of edges satisfying that the *sum is* 0 *at each vertex* condition; cf. Equation (1.3).

As an example consider the infinite graph $G = (V, E)$ given by the following:

$$V := \{v_m \mid m \in \mathbb{Z}\}, \quad E := \{(v_m, v_{m+1}) \mid m \in \mathbb{Z}\}.$$

Clearly, there is no finite linear combination of edges having boundary 0, so $H_1(G;\mathbb{R}) = 0$. However, there exists an infinite linear combination of edges having boundary 0, namely take the sum of *all* edges $\sum_m e_{m,m+1}$. Following up on this innocent looking example will eventually lead to *Borel-Moore homology*; see [**BM60, Br97**].

1.3. Dimension 2: Losing the freedom

1.3.1. Simplicial complexes of dimension 2. To proceed with dimension 2 we need a slightly more formal definition than the one we have had for graphs. The 2-dimensional simplicial complexes can be obtained from simple graphs by filling out some of the triangles. In order to keep technicalities as simple as possible, we restrict our framework a little bit further by considering the so-called plain complexes.

Definition 1.2. A *plain 2-dimensional simplicial complex* K consists of a finite simple graph $G = (V, E)$, together with a set of triangles T, where

(1) each triangle is a triple (v_i, v_j, v_k), for some $v_i, v_j, v_k \in V$, such that $i < j < k$;

(2) if $(v_i, v_j, v_k) \in T$, then all the 3 tuples (one should think of them as edges) (v_i, v_j), (v_i, v_k), and (v_j, v_k) must also lie in E;

(3) all triples in T are distinct.

We shall set $K(0) := V$, $K(1) := E$, and $K(2) := T$.

1.3.2. Homology groups in dimensions 0 and 2. Let us set

$$C_0(K;\mathbb{R}) := \mathbb{R}\langle V\rangle\,, \quad C_1(K;\mathbb{R}) := \mathbb{R}\langle E\rangle\,, \text{ and } C_2(K;\mathbb{R}) := \mathbb{R}\langle T\rangle\,.$$

The 0th homology group $H_0(K;\mathbb{R})$ is the same as $H_0(G;\mathbb{R})$; to define it, we simply ignore that we have added triangles.

Let us describe the second homology group $H_2(K;\mathbb{R})$. First, for all $1 \leqslant i < j < k \leqslant n$, such that $(v_i, v_j, v_k) \in T$, we let t_{ijk} denote the corresponding generator of $C_2(K;\mathbb{R})$. For convenience, we set

$$\begin{aligned} &t_{jki} := t_{kij} := t_{ijk} \text{ and} \\ &t_{jik} := t_{ikj} := t_{kji} := -t_{ijk}. \end{aligned} \tag{1.9}$$

An easy way to remember this sign rule is to say that each time some two neighboring indices are swapped, the generator changes its sign.

A *2-chain* is an expression of the type $\sum_{i,j,k} \alpha_{ijk} t_{ijk}$, where $\alpha_{ijk} \in \mathbb{R}$, and the summation is taken over all triples (i, j, k), such that $i < j < k$, and $(v_i, v_j, v_k) \in T$. We say that a 2-chain is a *2-cycle* if for any $(v_i, v_j) \in E$ we have

$$\sum_{k \neq i,j} \alpha_{ijk} = 0, \tag{1.10}$$

where, in analogy to Equations (1.3) and (1.9) we use the notation $\alpha_{jki} := \alpha_{kij} := \alpha_{ijk}$ and $\alpha_{jik} := \alpha_{ikj} := \alpha_{kji} := -\alpha_{ijk}$. Note that over $\mathbb{Z}_2$, Equation (1.10) just says that we have selected a set of triangles such that each edge belongs to an even number of these triangles.

Now the groups $Z_2(K;\mathbb{R})$ and $H_2(K;\mathbb{R})$ are both set to be the group of all 2-cycles. Again, one can show that the latter is actually a vector subspace. This can be done either by an ad hoc computation or by viewing it as the kernel of the linear map defined in the next subsection.

Completely analogously, one can define $H_2(K;\mathbb{Z})$ and $H_2(K;\mathbb{Z}_2)$. In Exercise (4) the reader is asked to show that $H_2(K;\mathbb{Z})$ is a free abelian group.

1.3.3. Homology group in dimension 1. To start with, the group of 1-cycles $Z_1(K;\mathbb{R})$ is the same as $H_1(G;\mathbb{R})$. As the second ingredient for defining the first homology group, for each $i < j < k$ such that $(v_i, v_j, v_k) \in T$ we want to introduce a relation

$$e_{ij} + e_{jk} = e_{ik}.$$

The way to do it is to span the subspace, which we call $B_1(K;\mathbb{R})$, by all the elements $e_{ij} - e_{ik} + e_{jk}$, for $i < j < k$, $(v_i, v_j, v_k) \in T$; note that each such element can alternatively be written in the cyclic fashion as $e_{ij} + e_{jk} + e_{ki}$. Then take the quotient $Z_1(K;\mathbb{R})/B_1(K;\mathbb{R})$. The quotient is well-defined, since any element $e_{ij} - e_{ik} + e_{jk}$ is obviously a cycle. Taking this quotient is an algebraic way of saying that we allow the cycles to be deformed across triangles, thus modeling the continuous notion of homotopy. Per definition, we now set $H_1(K;\mathbb{R}) := Z_1(K;\mathbb{R})/B_1(K;\mathbb{R})$.

Again, it is rather useful to phrase everything we are doing using linear maps as the so-called *boundary operators*. In fact, here we have two such maps: one map in dimension 1,

$$\partial_1 : C_1(K;\mathbb{R}) \longrightarrow C_0(K;\mathbb{R}),$$

defined by $\partial_1(e_{ij}) = v_j - v_i$, for all $i < j$; and one map in dimension 2,

$$\partial_2 : C_2(K;\mathbb{R}) \longrightarrow C_1(K;\mathbb{R}),$$

defined by $\partial_1(t_{ijk}) = e_{ij} - e_{ik} + e_{jk}$, for all $i < j < k$. We can then set

$$Z_1(K;\mathbb{R}) := \operatorname{Ker} \partial_1, \quad Z_2(K;\mathbb{R}) := \operatorname{Ker} \partial_2,$$

$$B_0(K;\mathbb{R}) := \operatorname{Im} \partial_1, \text{ and } B_1(K;\mathbb{R}) := \operatorname{Im} \partial_2.$$

To make notations uniform, we furthermore set

$$Z_0(K;\mathbb{R}) := C_0(K;\mathbb{R}) \text{ and } B_2(K;\mathbb{R}) := 0.$$

Then we can summarize what we have defined so far as

$$H_0(K;\mathbb{R}) = Z_0(K;\mathbb{R})/B_0(K;\mathbb{R}),$$
$$H_1(K;\mathbb{R}) = Z_1(K;\mathbb{R})/B_1(K;\mathbb{R}),$$
$$H_2(K;\mathbb{R}) = Z_2(K;\mathbb{R})/B_2(K;\mathbb{R}).$$

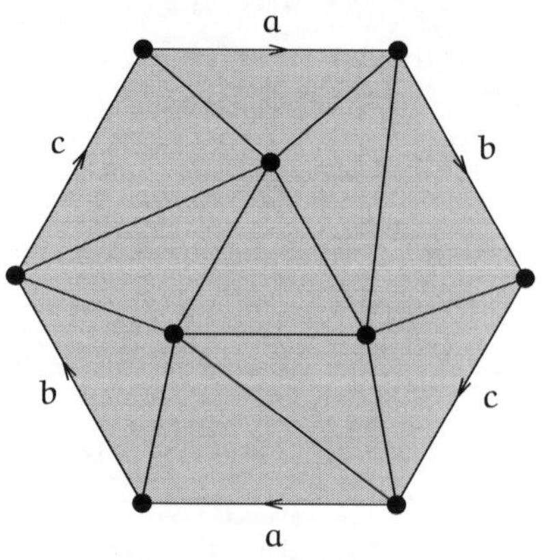

Figure 1.3. Simplicial complex X with torsion in $H_1(X;\mathbb{Z})$. This is a triangulation of the real projective plane.

Let us now see what happens here when we use integer coefficients instead. Clearly, $Z_1(K;\mathbb{Z})$ is a free abelian group, since it is the kernel of a group homomorphism from a free abelian group, and $B_1(K,\mathbb{Z})$ is a free abelian group, since it is the image of a group homomorphism into a free abelian group. However, as we mentioned before, when one takes a quotient of two free abelian groups, it can happen that the quotient is not free. We have said it already, but here it is the first time that we have the situation where this actually might happen. In this case, one speaks of the existence of *torsion* in the corresponding homology group. For torsion to occur, we need to have a 1-cycle c which is not a 1-boundary, but for which there exists a positive integer m such that $m \cdot c$ is a 1-boundary. Figure 1.3 shows an example of such a situation.

Exercises

(1) The maximal connected subgraphs of G are called *the connected components*. Show by elementary methods that for any graph G without self-crossings on the 2-dimensional sphere we have the formula

$$v + r = e + c + 1,$$

where v is the number of vertices, e is the number of edges, c is the number of connected components of G, and r is the number of regions into which the sphere is divided by our graph.

(2) Let G be a finite simple graph. Let c denote the number of connected components of G.
   (a) Show that $H_0(G;\mathbb{R}) \approx \mathbb{R}^c$.
   (b) Show that $H_0(G;\mathbf{k}) \approx \mathbf{k}^c$, where $\mathbf{k}$ is an arbitrary field.
   (c) Show that $H_0(G;\mathbb{Z})$ is a free abelian group and that furthermore we have an isomorphism $H_0(G;\mathbb{Z}) \approx \mathbb{Z}^c$.

(3) Let G be a finite simple graph. Show that $B_0(G;\mathbb{R})$ is the image of ∂_1 and that $Z_1(G;\mathbb{R})$ is the kernel of the boundary map defined by Equation (1.5).

(4) Assume K is a plain 2-dimensional simplicial complex. Show that $H_2(K;\mathbb{Z})$ is a free abelian group.

(5) Construct a plain connected[2] 2-dimensional simplicial complex K such that
   (a) $H_1(K;\mathbb{Z}) \approx \mathbb{Z} \oplus \mathbb{Z}_2$;
   (b) $H_1(K;\mathbb{Z}) \approx \mathbb{Z}_3$.

[2]Such a complex is called connected if the underlying edge graph is connected.

(6) If you are familiar with the concept of simplicial subdivision, construct a plain 2-dimensional simplicial complex K such that its second homology group is non-trivial, i.e., $\mathsf{H}_2(\mathsf{K};\mathbb{R}) \neq 0$, yet it does not contain a simplicial subdivision of a 2-dimensional sphere. What is the minimal number of triangles that one needs?

Chapter 2

Simplicial Homology

In the previous chapter we have gotten a low-dimensional glimpse of the general idea of how we are going to tie algebraic structures to combinatorially defined topological spaces. Let us now set up the formal framework.

There are many different homology theories defined for various sets of mathematical objects. We do not make any attempt to reach the highest possible generality. On the contrary, we start in the elementary setting of plain simplicial complexes and go for the direct hands-on definition of their homology groups. We can then compute homology groups of sample spaces and spend some time contemplating the general properties.

Once we feel comfortable in this restricted setting, we shall proceed to expand the universe of objects which we consider and to gradually deal with the additional complications as they arise.

The general intuitive idea of homology would be to use algebraic structures for encoding certain numbers. However, we shall see that the actual situation will turn out to be quite a bit more complicated.

2.1. Plain simplicial complexes

As mentioned above, while defining homology we start by looking at the simplest possible case: the so-called *plain* simplicial complexes. Though stripped down to bare necessities, these will already be sufficient to give us the first taste and to demonstrate most of the interesting features of simplicial homology.

2.1.1. Simplices and complexes. When working in the simplicial context, we like to start counting from 0. The reasons for this will become apparent as we move along. Accordingly, we introduce the following handy notation: for all integers t, such that $t \geqslant 0$, we set $[t] := \{0, 1, \ldots, t\}$.

Definition 2.1. Assume we are given an integer $t \geqslant 0$, and let $\mathcal{K}$ be some collection of subsets of $[t]$. Then $\mathcal{K}$ is called a *plain simplicial complex*[1] if the following two conditions are satisfied:

(1) for each $x \in [t]$, we have $\{x\} \in \mathcal{K}$;

(2) if $\mathcal{K}$ contains a subset σ, then it also contains all the subsets of σ.

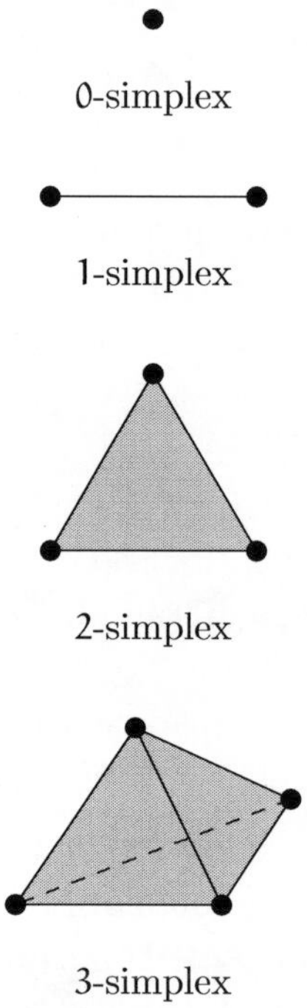

Figure 2.1. Geometric intuition behind simplices.

Elements of $\mathcal{K}$ are called *simplices*, see Figure 2.1.

The *dimension* of such a simplex is one less than its cardinality, so the minimal possible dimension of a non-empty simplex is 0, and the maximal possible dimension is t. This number is used so frequently, that we want to have a separate notation for it: for $\sigma \in \mathcal{K}$, we set $\dim(\sigma) := |\sigma| - 1$.

We call a simplex of dimension n simply an n-*simplex*. The set of n-simplices of a plain simplicial complex $\mathcal{K}$ is denoted by $\mathcal{K}(n)$. For reasons which will become apparent later, it is handy to consider the empty set to be the unique (-1)-simplex of $\mathcal{K}$. Furthermore, it is practical to have $\mathcal{K}(n)$

[1] An alternative 'full' name for such an object is a 'standard finite abstract simplicial complex'.

defined for all integers n, so we agree on the convention that $\mathcal{K}(n)$ is the empty set, unless $-1 \leqslant n \leqslant t$.

Following that terminology, the one-element sets contained in $\mathcal{K}$ are the 0-simplices, and they are also called *vertices*. The 1-simplices are also called *edges*, though this is a bit less frequent.

Let $\dim(\mathcal{K})$ denote the maximal dimension achieved by a simplex in $\mathcal{K}$, in other words, we set

$$\dim(\mathcal{K}) := \max_{\sigma \in \mathcal{K}} \dim(\sigma).$$

This number is well-defined as we do not allow $\mathcal{K}$ to be empty, so it must contain some simplices. We call this number the *dimension* of $\mathcal{K}$. Of course, we have $0 \leqslant \dim \mathcal{K} \leqslant t$.

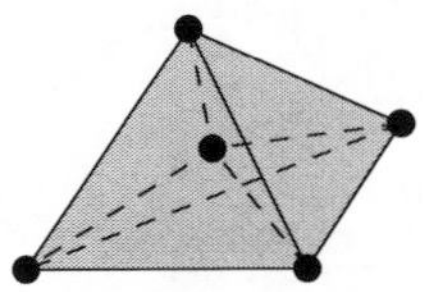

Figure 2.2. A visualization of the 4-simplex. The reader familiar with convex geometry will recognize the Schlegel diagram of the corresponding polytope.

An n-simplex has $n+1$ vertices, these vertices can be re-indexed by the set $[n]$, and there is a unique such re-indexing which also preserves the natural order of the vertices. We shall think about an n-simplex σ as an *ordered* sequence $(v_0, \dots, v_n)$ of elements of $[t]$. Such a sequence is also called an $[n]$*-tuple* or, if only the number of the elements is to be emphasized, an $(n+1)$*-tuple*. The elements of this ordered sequence are called *vertices of* σ. Because subsets of simplices are simplices again, vertices of any simplex are also vertices of the underlying simplicial complex.

Given an $[n]$-tuple $(v_0, \dots, v_n)$, and any index $0 \leqslant i \leqslant n$, it is customary to write $(v_0, \dots, \widehat{v}_i, \dots, v_n)$ to denote the tuple obtained by *omitting* the vertex v_i. Even though the notation may suggest otherwise, we make no assumption here that $i \neq 0$ or that $i \neq n$. On the contrary, deleting the first or the last vertex is allowed, and we get $(v_0, \dots, \widehat{v}_i, \dots, v_n) = (v_1, \dots, v_n)$, for $i = 0$, and $(v_0, \dots, \widehat{v}_i, \dots, v_n) = (v_0, \dots, v_{n-1})$, for $i = n$. This notation can easily be extended to cover the case when we omit more than one vertex, so, for instance, we can write $(n-1)$-tuples as $(v_0, \dots, \widehat{v}_i, \dots, \widehat{v}_j, \dots, v_n)$, where $i < j$. Furthermore, when $n = 0$, we shall mostly drop the round brackets and write, for instance, v_0 instead of (v_0).

It can be handy to describe the plain simplicial complex $\mathcal{K}$ by giving a list of the maximal sets which it contains. For brevity, we often skip commas and curly brackets from the set notation, especially when dealing with sets

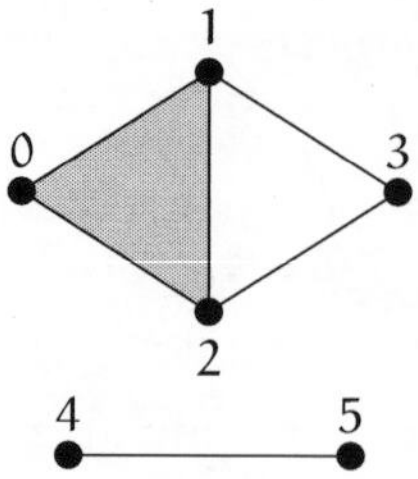

Figure 2.3. The plain simplicial complex $\mathcal{X}$.

of sets, so that $\{0, 1, 2\}$ becomes 012. For example, assume $t = 5$, and consider the simplicial complex $\mathcal{X}$ whose set of maximal simplices is $\{012, 13, 23, 45\}$. This simplicial complex has 6 vertices, 6 edges, and 1 simplex of dimension 2. We also have $\dim \mathcal{X} = 2$. There is a geometric way of thinking about $\mathcal{X}$, shown in Figure 2.3; more on this will be said in Section 2.4.

2.1.2. Chain groups.

Let us fix some dimension n. What we want is to set up a framework in which we can add and subtract simplices of that dimension. If we allow these operations, then we also need to allow multiplying simplices by integers, since multiplying by a positive integer is a result of repeated addition of the simplex to itself, while multiplying by a negative integer is a result of repeated subtraction of that simplex. In fact, we need to allow all possible linear combinations $c_1\alpha_1 + \cdots + c_t\alpha_t$, where $c_1, \dots, c_t$ are integers and $\alpha_1, \dots, \alpha_t$ are elements of $\mathcal{K}(n)$. On the other hand, adding and subtracting such linear combinations from each other does not give anything new anymore: we simply get some other linear combinations of this type.

Traditionally, such linear combinations are called *n-chains,* or simply *chains.* In fact, the set of all n-chains forms an abelian group under addition. More specifically, we arrive at a standard construction in algebra, which is called the *free abelian group generated by* $\mathcal{K}(n)$. We give a formal summary in the following definition.

Definition 2.2. Assume $\mathcal{K}$ is a plain simplicial complex, and let n be an arbitrary integer.

- A linear combination $c_1\alpha_1 + \cdots + c_t\alpha_t$, where $c_1, \dots, c_t$ are integers and $\alpha_1, \dots, \alpha_t$ are elements of $\mathcal{K}(n)$, is called an *n-chain* of $\mathcal{K}$.
- The free abelian group generated by $\mathcal{K}(n)$ is called the *nth chain group* of $\mathcal{K}$.[2] It will be denoted $C_n(\mathcal{K}; \mathbb{Z})$, or simply $C_n(\mathcal{K})$.

To distinguish between the actual subsets of $[t]$ and the corresponding generators of the chain groups, we shall use round brackets. So the generator

[2]Actually the full name would be the *nth chain group with integer coefficients.*

$(0) + (4)$	$\in$	$C_0(\mathcal{X})$
$(12) - 3 \cdot (45)$	$\in$	$C_1(\mathcal{X})$
$-7 \cdot (012)$	$\in$	$C_2(\mathcal{X})$

Table 2.1. Examples of chains of the sample complex $\mathcal{X}$.

corresponding to the set $\{0, 1, 2\} = 012$ will be denoted by (012), for a few examples, see Table 2.1.

Recall that the empty set is not a group, since any group must contain the neutral element. Instead, the free abelian group generated by the empty set is the so-called *trivial group*, that is, a group which consists only of the neutral element. When no confusion arises, we shall denote both the group and the neutral element by 0. For any integer n outside of the interval $[-1, \dim \mathcal{K}]$, we have seen that $\mathcal{K}(n)$ was an empty set. Accordingly, for these values of n we get $C_n(\mathcal{K}) = 0$.

The question remains as to what to do about $C_{-1}(\mathcal{K})$. There are two valid options: either we set $C_{-1}(\mathcal{K}) := 0$ or, following the logic above, we let it be the free abelian group generated by the unique (-1)-simplex, in which case it would be isomorphic to $\mathbb{Z}$. For now, we go with the first option, and set $C_{-1}(\mathcal{K}) := 0$, while noting that the alternative choice will later lead to the notion of *reduced homology*.

For the sample complex $\mathcal{X}$ in Figure 2.3 we get $C_0(\mathcal{X}) \approx \mathbb{Z}^6$, $C_1(\mathcal{X}) \approx \mathbb{Z}^6$, $C_2(\mathcal{X}) \approx \mathbb{Z}$, and all other chain groups are trivial.

2.2. The boundary operator

Our next goal is to produce an algebraic framework associated to plain simplicial complexes. This framework will consist of free abelian groups and maps between them. To do this, we shall now connect the chain groups using a family of special group homomorphisms.

2.2.1. Cycles and boundaries. Recall that if G and H are two abelian groups, and G is generated by some set S, then we can uniquely specify a group homomorphism φ from G to H by fixing the values of φ on the elements of S. Usually, not every choice of values is allowed, but if G is the free abelian group generated by S, and H is abelian, then there are *no restrictions.* This is because the only possible restriction would be to require that any relation satisfied by elements of S within G also needs to be satisfied by their images under φ within the group H. However, since G is generated freely, there would be no such relations, except for the commutators. This observation can be applied in our situation, where we define a group homomorphism from $C_n(\mathcal{K})$ to $C_{n-1}(\mathcal{K})$ by simply specifying its values on simplices.

Definition 2.3. Let $\mathcal{K}$ be a plain simplicial complex. For all integers n, $n \geqslant 1$, we define a *boundary operator*

$$\partial_n : C_n(\mathcal{K}) \longrightarrow C_{n-1}(\mathcal{K})$$

as follows: for any simplex $\alpha \in \mathcal{K}(n)$, say $\alpha = (v_0, \dots, v_n)$, where $v_0 < \cdots < v_n$, we set

$$\partial_n \alpha := \sum_{i=0}^{n} (-1)^i \,(v_0, \dots, \widehat{v}_i, \dots, v_n)\,, \tag{2.1}$$

and then extend the definition to the whole chain group $C_n(\mathcal{K})$ by means of linearity.

When $n \leqslant 0$ or $n \geqslant \dim \mathcal{K} + 1$ we simply set ∂_n to be the 0-map.

The chain $\partial_n \alpha$ is then called the *boundary* of α. We have

$$\partial_0(v_0) = 0, \quad \partial_1(v_0, v_1) = v_1 - v_0,$$

$$\partial_2(v_0, v_1, v_2) = (v_1, v_2) - (v_0, v_2) + (v_0, v_1),$$

$$\partial_3(v_0, v_1, v_2, v_3) = (v_1, v_2, v_3) - (v_0, v_2, v_3) + (v_0, v_1, v_3) - (v_0, v_1, v_2),$$

and so on. When we need to state things more precisely we shall also write $\partial_n^{\mathcal{K}}$.

Definition 2.4. The *nth cycle group* of a plain simplicial complex $\mathcal{K}$ is defined to be the kernel of the boundary operator $\partial_n : C_n(\mathcal{K}) \to C_{n-1}(\mathcal{K})$. This is a free abelian subgroup of $C_n(\mathcal{K})$, and we denote it by $Z_n(\mathcal{K})$.

The elements of $Z_n(\mathcal{K})$ are called *n-cycles* or simply *cycles.*

Definition 2.5. The *nth boundary group* of a plain simplicial complex $\mathcal{K}$ is the image of the boundary operator $\partial_{n+1} : C_{n+1}(\mathcal{K}) \to C_n(\mathcal{K})$. This is a free abelian subgroup of $C_n(\mathcal{K})$, and it is denoted by $B_n(\mathcal{K})$.

The elements of $B_n(\mathcal{K})$ are called *n-boundaries* or simply *boundaries.*

2.2.2. Boundary of a boundary. The crucial fact about the boundary operator is that its second iteration will always be 0. This follows from the next proposition.

Proposition 2.6. *The boundary of any simplex is itself a cycle. Another way to say the same thing is: taking the boundary of the boundary of a simplex yields* 0.

Proof. The proposition can be shown by the following direct calculation of taking the boundary twice:

$$\begin{aligned}\partial_{n-1}(\partial_n(v_0,\dots,v_n)) &= \partial_{n-1}\Big(\sum_{i=0}^{n}(-1)^i(v_0,\dots,\widehat{v}_i,\dots,v_n)\Big)\\ &= \sum_{i=0}^{n}(-1)^i\partial_{n-1}(v_0,\dots,\widehat{v}_i,\dots,v_n)\\ &= \sum_{i=0}^{n}(-1)^i\Big(\sum_{j=0}^{i-1}(-1)^j(v_0,\dots,\widehat{v}_j,\dots,\widehat{v}_i,\dots,v_n)\\ &\qquad + \sum_{j=i+1}^{n}(-1)^{j-1}(v_0,\dots,\widehat{v}_i,\dots,\widehat{v}_j,\dots,v_n)\Big)\\ &= \sum_{0\leqslant k<l\leqslant n}((-1)^{k+l}+(-1)^{k+l-1})(v_0,\dots,\widehat{v}_k,\dots,\widehat{v}_l,\dots,v_n)\\ &= 0.\end{aligned}$$

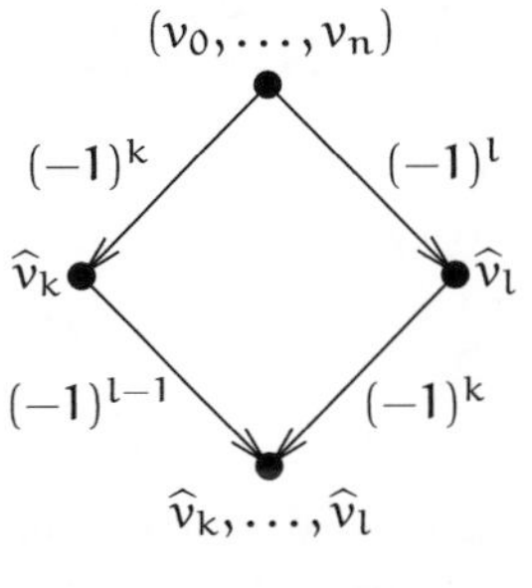

Figure 2.4. Cancelling terms when $k < l$.

A verbal summary might be instructive. It is clear even before calculating $\partial_{n-1}(\partial_n(v_0,\dots,v_n))$ that the result will be a linear combination of $(n-2)$-simplices obtained from $(v_0,\dots,v_n)$ by deleting two vertices. Surely, to show that this linear combination is equal to 0 all we need to do is to choose arbitrary indices $0 \leqslant k < l \leqslant n$, and then show that the coefficient of the term $(v_0,\dots,\widehat{v}_k,\dots,\widehat{v}_l,\dots,v_n)$ is equal to 0. The crucial observation now is that this term will appear exactly twice in the double boundary calculation: once when we *first* delete v_k, and *then* delete v_l, and once, when we first delete v_l, and then delete v_k. These two will each contribute a coefficient from the set $\{1,-1\}$, and these coefficients will have opposite signs; see Figure 2.4. □

Since n-chains are finite linear combinations of n-simplices, Proposition 2.6 actually implies that the boundary of *any* chain is a cycle. Here are some equivalent ways to express that relation:

- in the set-theoretic language: $B_n(\mathcal{K})$ is contained in $Z_n(\mathcal{K})$, for all n;
- in the functorial language: $\partial_{n-1} \circ \partial_n = 0$, for all n.

The equality $\partial_{n-1} \circ \partial_n = 0$ is often simplified to $\partial^2 = 0$, and one says that *the square of the boundary operator is zero.*

2.2.3. An example. Let us see what all these maps and groups are in our sample complex $\mathcal{X}$. To start with, we see that all the groups $Z_n(\mathcal{X})$, $B_n(\mathcal{X})$, and $C_n(\mathcal{X})$, are trivial, whenever $n \neq 0, 1, 2$.

Now let $n = 0$. Since $\partial_0 = 0$, we have $Z_0(\mathcal{X}) = C_0(\mathcal{X}) \approx \mathbb{Z}^6$. To compute $B_0(\mathcal{X})$ we need to understand the boundary operator $\partial_1 : C_1(\mathcal{X}) \to C_0(\mathcal{X})$. Since $\partial_1(i, j) = j - i$, whenever (i, j) is an edge of $\mathcal{K}$, we have

$$\operatorname{Im} \partial_1 = \langle (1) - (0), (2) - (0), (2) - (1), (3) - (1), (3) - (2), (5) - (4) \rangle,$$

where we note that we use the shorthand notation $\langle \rangle$ or $\langle \mid \rangle$ to denote a group presentation when using integer coefficients.

These generators are dependent. For example, we have $((2) - (1)) + ((1) - (0)) = (2) - (0)$, so any of these three generators can be expressed using the other two. We can thus just drop one of them. It is by no means predetermined which one we should drop and there are usually many choices which we need to make. We choose to drop $(2) - (1)$ and $(3) - (2)$, both of which can be expressed through the remaining four generators. On the other hand, the four generators which are left are clearly independent and generate the free abelian subgroup

$$B_0(\mathcal{X}) = \operatorname{Im} \partial_1 = \langle (1) - (0), (2) - (0), (3) - (1), (5) - (4) \rangle \approx \mathbb{Z}^4.$$

Let $n = 1$. One can see that $\operatorname{Ker} \partial_1$ is freely generated by $(01) + (12) - (02)$ and $(12) + (23) - (13)$, so

$$Z_1(\mathcal{X}) = \operatorname{Ker} \partial_1 = \langle (01) + (12) - (02), (12) + (23) - (13) \rangle \approx \mathbb{Z}^2.$$

The boundary operator $\partial_2 : C_2(\mathcal{X}) \to C_1(\mathcal{X})$ takes (012) to $(12) - (02) + (01)$. We conclude that

$$B_1(\mathcal{X}) = \operatorname{Im} \partial_2 = \langle (12) - (02) + (01) \rangle \approx \mathbb{Z}.$$

Finally, let $n = 2$. Since $\partial_2(012) \neq 0$, we have $Z_2(\mathcal{X}) = \operatorname{Ker} \partial_2 = 0$. On the other hand, we also have $\partial_3 = 0$, so $B_2(\mathcal{X}) = \operatorname{Im} \partial_3 = 0$ as well. The final answer is shown in Table 2.2.

	$C_n(\mathcal{X})$	$Z_n(\mathcal{X})$	$B_n(\mathcal{X})$
$n = 0$	$\mathbb{Z}^6$	$\mathbb{Z}^6$	$\mathbb{Z}^4$
$n = 1$	$\mathbb{Z}^6$	$\mathbb{Z}^2$	$\mathbb{Z}$
$n = 2$	$\mathbb{Z}$	0	0

Table 2.2. Chain, cycle, and boundary groups of $\mathcal{X}$.

2.3. Homology of a plain simplicial complex

We can now associate the so-called homology groups to any plain simplicial complex. Before we do this, we need to review some basic algebraic notions.

2.3.1. Cycles modulo boundaries. Recall from your course in abstract algebra that given an abelian group G and a subgroup H, we can define a quotient group G/H. Actually, the quotient can be defined for any groups G and H, as long as H is a *normal* subgroup of G; and, of course, all the subgroups of an abelian group are normal. The elements of this quotient group are the so-called *cosets of* H. For non-abelian groups one would need to distinguish between left and right cosets. Since we assume that G is abelian, we do not need to do that here.

Each coset of H is obtained by choosing an element $g \in G$ and then taking the set $H_g = \{g + h \,|\, h \in H\}$. An alternative notation for this set is $g + H$. In particular, we have $H_e = H + e = H$. These cosets produce a disjoint partition of G, see Figure 2.5. Different choices of g may yield the same coset, in fact, we recall from abstract algebra that $H_g = H_k$ if and only if $g - k \in H$. The set of cosets, which we denote by G/H, can then be turned into an abelian group by defining the addition operation using the formula $H_g + H_k := H_{g+k}$. We can now adapt this general algebraic construction to our special case.

Definition 2.7. Let $\mathcal{K}$ be a plain simplicial complex, and let n be an arbitrary integer. We set

$$H_n(\mathcal{K}) := Z_n(\mathcal{K})/B_n(\mathcal{K}), \tag{2.2}$$

and call this group the *nth homology group* of $\mathcal{K}$.[3]

Expressed verbally:

> *the nth homology group is the quotient of the group of all n-cycles by the group of all n-boundaries.*

[3]The full name is actually the *nth homology group of $\mathcal{K}$ with integer coefficients*; cf. Subsection 2.3.6.

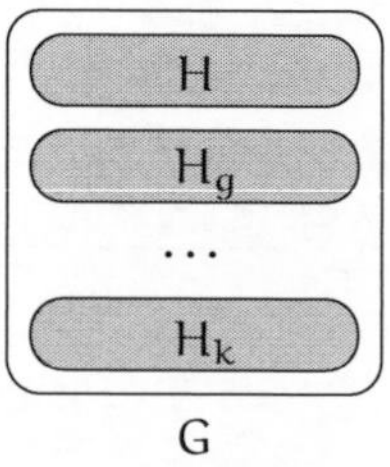

Figure 2.5. A decomposition of a group into cosets.

The etymology of Definition 2.7 is clear: *homologous* should encode *similar*. Colloquially one often talks about *looking at the cycles which are not boundaries.* What one is attempting to measure here are the *essential* cycles, i.e., those which are not boundaries, and consequently one also equates two cycles which differ by a boundary.

2.3.2. A presentation of the homology group. A classical algebraic situation in which one uses the quotient construction for abelian groups is when an abelian group is defined by a *presentation*, that is, by listing its generators and by providing a set of relations which these generators need to satisfy. Formally, the group itself is then a quotient of the free abelian group by the subgroup which is generated by these relations.

Accordingly, we can view the group $H_n(\mathcal{K})$ as being obtained from the nth cycle group $Z_n(\mathcal{K})$ by adding more relations: one for each $(n+1)$-simplex of $\mathcal{K}$. Specifically, each such new relation says that the boundary of a certain simplex is set to be 0. As already mentioned, the nth cycle group $Z_n(\mathcal{K})$ is free. Combining any set of generators for this group with the relations, which we have just described, will give an explicit presentation of $H_n(\mathcal{K})$.

Clearly, the group $H_n(\mathcal{K})$ is still abelian. However, it may no longer be free, which is hardly surprising as we have added some relations.

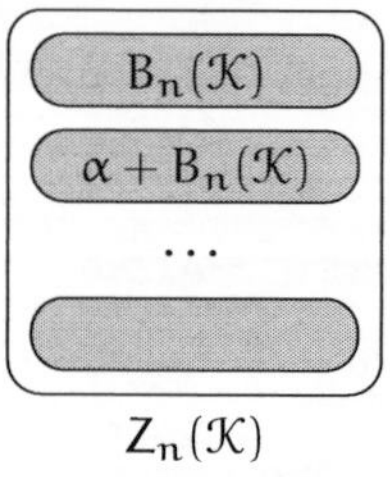

Figure 2.6. Homology classes.

2.3.3. Homology classes. Let us now turn our attention to the single elements of the homology group $H_n(\mathcal{K})$. Since $H_n(\mathcal{K})$ is defined as a quotient group, its elements are de facto *subsets of elements* of the group $Z_n(\mathcal{K}) \subseteq C_n(\mathcal{K})$. Each such set is called a *homology class.* Choosing an arbitrary cycle $\alpha \in Z_n(\mathcal{K})$ will give a homology class $\alpha + B_n(\mathcal{K})$, see Figure 2.6, which is then denoted by $[\alpha]$. In this situation, the cycle α is said to *represent* the homology class $[\alpha]$.

Different cycles may yield the same homology class. In fact, we have $[\alpha] = [\beta]$ if and only if $\alpha - \beta \in B_n(\mathcal{K})$. The rules of arithmetic of the homology classes are straightforward: we have $[\alpha] + [\beta] = [\alpha + \beta]$, and $[c\alpha] = c[\alpha]$, whenever c is an integer, and $\alpha, \beta \in Z_n(\mathcal{K})$.

In the future, when we say *let* $[\alpha] \in H_n(\mathcal{K})$, we mean *pick an* n*-cycle* α *and take the corresponding homology class.*

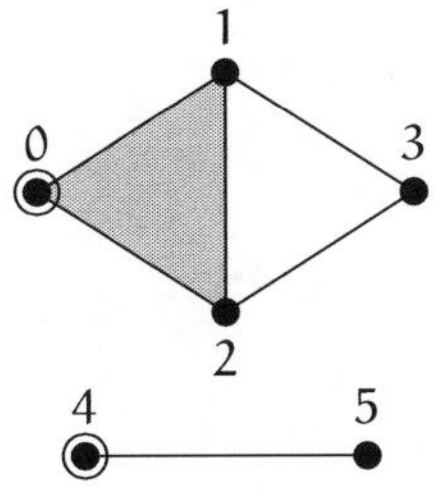

Figure 2.7. Generators of $H_0(\mathcal{X})$.

2.3.4. Homology groups of $\mathcal{X}$. Let us calculate the homology groups of our sample complex $\mathcal{X}$. If $Z_n(\mathcal{X}) = 0$, then clearly $H_n(\mathcal{X}) = 0$, so we immediately have $H_n(\mathcal{X}) = 0$ for all $n \neq 0, 1$.

For $n = 0$ we have $H_0(\mathcal{X}) = C_0(\mathcal{X})/B_0(\mathcal{X})$. Therefore we have

$$H_0(\mathcal{X}) = \langle (0), (1), (2), (3), (4), (5) \mid (1) - (0), (2) - (0), (2) - (1), (3) - (1), (3) - (2), (5) - (4) \rangle .$$

A relation $a - b = 0$ is the same as saying that $a = b$, so, slightly abusing our notations, we can write

$$H_0(\mathcal{X}) = \langle (0), (1), (2), (3), (4), (5) \mid (0) = (1) = (2) = (3),\ (4) = (5) \rangle .$$

Clearly this means that $H_0(\mathcal{X}) \approx \mathbb{Z}^2$, and we can for example choose $[(0)]$ and $[(4)]$ as generators for that group, so $H_0(\mathcal{X}) = \langle [(0)], [(4)] \rangle$.[4] see Figure 2.7.

For $n = 1$, we have

$$H_1(\mathcal{X}) = \langle (01) + (12) - (02), (12) + (23) - (13) \mid (01) + (12) - (02) \rangle ,$$

so $H_1(\mathcal{X}) = \langle [(12) + (23) - (13)] \rangle \approx \mathbb{Z}$. Note that there are infinitely many possible choices of cycles which will generate $H_1(X)$. We have taken $(12) +$

[4]The reader is invited to unwind the three types of brackets in the expression $\langle [(0)], [(4)] \rangle$

$(23) - (13)$, but we might have as well taken $(01) + (13) - (23) - (02)$ or $2 \cdot (01) + 3 \cdot (12) + (23) - (13) - 2 \cdot (02)$; cf. Figure 2.8.

2.3.5. The 0th homology group. Let us look at the meaning of the 0th homology group of a plain simplicial complex $\mathcal{K}$. The simplest possible case, which we already considered in the previous chapter, is when $\mathcal{K}$ has dimension 0. In other words, $\mathcal{K}$ is just a collection of vertices $\mathcal{K}(0)$. In this situation, we have $H_0(\mathcal{K}) = Z_0(\mathcal{K}) = C_0(\mathcal{K}) \approx \mathbb{Z}^{\mathcal{K}(0)}$. So, if we are just given the free abelian group $H_0(\mathcal{K})$, taking its *dimension* provides a way, albeit admittedly a rather roundabout way, to *count* the vertices of $\mathcal{K}$.[5]

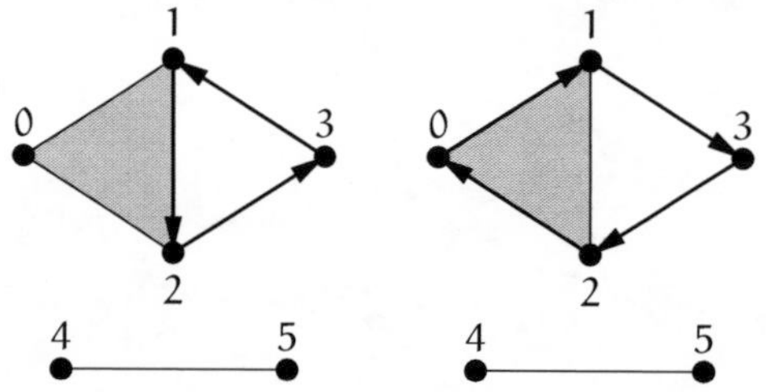

Figure 2.8. Choices of cycles generating $H_1(\mathcal{X})$.

In the general case, we have $H_0(\mathcal{K}) = Z_0(\mathcal{K})/B_0(\mathcal{K}) = C_0(\mathcal{K})/B_0(\mathcal{K})$. The free abelian group $B_0(\mathcal{K})$ is generated by the differences $i - j$, where (i, j) is an edge of $\mathcal{K}$. As mentioned above in the computation of the homology of $\mathcal{X}$, to have such a difference as a relation is the same as to simply equate $i = j$. So, we obtain $H_0(\mathcal{K})$ from $C_0(\mathcal{K})$ by equating (the generators corresponding to) any two vertices which are connected by an edge. One way to re-phrase this is to consider an equivalence relation on the set $\mathcal{K}(0)$, by requesting that any two vertices which are connected by an edge must be equivalent. We then immediately see that $H_0(\mathcal{K})$ is again a free abelian group, and that its generating set can be indexed by these equivalence classes. These deliberations can be formalized as follows.

Definition 2.8. We say that a plain simplicial complex is *connected* if any two vertices $v, w \in \mathcal{K}(0)$ can be connected by a path $v = v_1, v_2, \ldots, v_k = w$, all of whose edges are in $\mathcal{K}(1)$, that is, $\{v_1, v_2\}, \ldots, \{v_{k-1}, v_k\} \in \mathcal{K}(1)$.

In other words, a plain simplicial complex $\mathcal{K}$ is connected if and only if the underlying graph, whose vertex set is $\mathcal{K}(0)$ and whose edge set is $\mathcal{K}(1)$, is connected. This graph is also called the 1-*skeleton* of $\mathcal{K}$, and is denoted by $\mathrm{sk}_1 \mathcal{K}$.

[5]The fact that this dimension is well-defined is a standard one in abstract algebra.

The vertex sets of connected components of the graph $\mathrm{sk}_1 \mathcal{K}$ are precisely the equivalence classes which we just talked about. We can now state a theorem, which we essentially have already proven in the discussion above.

Theorem 2.9. *Assume $\mathcal{K}$ is a non-empty plain simplicial complex, and let q be the number of the connected components of $\mathrm{sk}_1 \mathcal{K}$. Then we have $H_0(\mathcal{K}) \approx \mathbb{Z}^q$.*

More precisely, assume $V_1, \dots, V_q$ are the vertex sets of the connected components of $\mathrm{sk}_1 \mathcal{K}$. Any choice $v_1 \in V_1, \dots, v_q \in V_q$ will give a basis for the 0th homology group: we have $H_0(\mathcal{K}) = \langle [v_1], \dots, [v_q] \rangle$.

For our sample complex $\mathcal{X}$, the graph $\mathrm{sk}_1 \mathcal{X}$ has 2 connected components, so our calculation $H_0(\mathcal{X}) = \langle [0], [4] \rangle \approx \mathbb{Z}^2$ fits well with the statement of Theorem 2.9.

In a certain sense, Theorem 2.9 can be extended to all dimensions; see Theorem 2.29.

2.3.6. Homology with field coefficients. As mentioned earlier, what we have defined so far is known as homology groups *with integer coefficients*. This is a very standard choice of coefficients. Another widely used option is the use of so-called *field coefficients*.

Let $\mathbf{k}$ be an arbitrary field, and let $\mathcal{K}$ be a plain simplicial complex. For a non-negative integer n, let $C_n(\mathcal{K}; \mathbf{k})$ denote the vector space over $\mathbf{k}$ with basis $\mathcal{K}(n)$. The boundary operator $\partial_n : C_n(\mathcal{K}; \mathbf{k}) \to C_{n-1}(\mathcal{K}; \mathbf{k})$ is again defined by formula (2.1). We can then consider the groups of cycles $Z_n(\mathcal{K}; \mathbf{k}) := \operatorname{Ker} \partial_n$ and the groups of boundaries $B_n(\mathcal{K}; \mathbf{k}) := \operatorname{Im} \partial_n$.

Definition 2.10. Assume, as above, that $\mathcal{K}$ is a plain simplicial complex, n is an arbitrary integer, and $\mathbf{k}$ is an arbitrary field. We set

$$H_n(\mathcal{K}; \mathbf{k}) := Z_n(\mathcal{K}; \mathbf{k}) / B_n(\mathcal{K}; \mathbf{k}) \tag{2.3}$$

and call this group the n*th homology group* of $\mathcal{K}$ with coefficients in $\mathbf{k}$.

Admittedly, the terminology is somewhat confusing, since the $H_n(\mathcal{K}; \mathbf{k})$ is not just a group, it is actually a vector space over $\mathbf{k}$.

The typical choices for $\mathbf{k}$ are the fields $\mathbb{Z}_2$ and $\mathbb{Q}$.

2.3.7. Betti numbers and torsion coefficients. Before moving on to a higher dimension, let us stop and contemplate what possible structure a homology group might have. We know that $H_n(\mathcal{K})$ is abelian, and we know that it is finitely generated; see Subsection 2.3.2. We can therefore apply one of the main theorems of group theory: *the fundamental theorem of finitely generated abelian groups.* Recall that this theorem says that any finitely generated abelian group G is isomorphic to a direct sum of infinite cyclic groups and finite cyclic groups whose orders divide each other. In other words, we can always write

$$G \approx \mathbb{Z}^r \oplus \mathbb{Z}_{m_1} \oplus \cdots \oplus \mathbb{Z}_{m_t}, \tag{2.4}$$

such that $m_1|m_2|\ldots|m_t$. The group $\mathbb{Z}^r$ in Equation (2.4) is called the *free part* of G, and the group $\mathbb{Z}_{m_1} \oplus \cdots \oplus \mathbb{Z}_{m_t}$ is called its *torsion part*; see Table 2.3. The numbers r and $m_1, \ldots, m_t$ are uniquely determined by G.

$$\mathbb{Z}_6 \oplus \mathbb{Z}_{10} \approx \mathbb{Z}_2 \oplus \mathbb{Z}_{30}$$
$$\mathbb{Z}_6 \oplus \mathbb{Z}_{10} \oplus \mathbb{Z}_{14} \approx \mathbb{Z}_2 \oplus \mathbb{Z}_2 \oplus \mathbb{Z}_{210}$$

Table 2.3. Examples of decomposition in Equation (2.4).

Definition 2.11. Assume $H_n(\mathcal{K}) \approx \mathbb{Z}^r \oplus \mathbb{Z}_{m_1} \oplus \cdots \oplus \mathbb{Z}_{m_t}$, such that $m_1|m_2|\ldots|m_t$. The number r is called the *nth Betti number of $\mathcal{K}$* and is denoted by $\beta_n(\mathcal{K})$. The numbers $m_1, \ldots, m_t$ are called the *torsion coefficients* of $H_n(\mathcal{K})$.

For our sample complex $\mathcal{X}$ we have $\beta_0(\mathcal{X}) = 2$, $\beta_1(\mathcal{X}) = 1$, and $\beta_n(\mathcal{X}) = 0$, for all $n \neq 0, 1$. There is no torsion in the homology of $\mathcal{X}$ in any dimension.

In analogy to Definition 2.11 one can define Betti numbers with respect to any field.

Definition 2.12. Assume $\mathbf{k}$ is an arbitrary field, and $H_n(\mathcal{K}; \mathbf{k}) \approx \mathbf{k}^n$. The number n is called the *nth Betti number of $\mathcal{K}$ with coefficients in* $\mathbf{k}$ and is denoted by $\beta_n(\mathcal{K}; \mathbf{k})$.

It is possible to show that $\beta_i(\mathcal{K}) = \beta_i(\mathcal{K}; \mathbb{Q})$ and that the Betti number $\beta_i(\mathcal{K}; \mathbf{k})$ for each i only depends on the characteristic of $\mathbf{k}$. This is best shown within the context of the universal coefficient theorem for homology, and we shall not do this here.

2.3.8. Reduced homology. When a plain simplicial complex $\mathcal{K}$ consists of a single vertex, it has exactly one non-trivial homology group, namely $H_0(\mathcal{K}) \approx \mathbb{Z}$. From a certain point of view, one would like to consider this one-point complex $\mathcal{K}$ as the most trivial case, and accordingly, have a homology theory where *all* homology groups of this complex would be trivial. This is realized in the concept of *reduced homology*, which is defined as follows.

Definition 2.13. Let $\mathcal{K}$ be a plain simplicial complex. The *reduced homology* groups of $\mathcal{K}$ are given by: $\widetilde{H}_n(\mathcal{K}) := H_n(\mathcal{K})$, if $n \geqslant 1$, and

$$\widetilde{H}_0(\mathcal{K}) := \begin{cases} 0, & \text{if } \mathcal{K} \text{ is connected;} \\ \mathbb{Z}^{q-1}, & \text{if } \mathcal{K} \text{ is disconnected,} \end{cases}$$

where q is the number of connected components of $\mathcal{K}$.

The reduced homology with field coefficients is defined in the same way. When $\mathbf{k}$ is an arbitrary field, we set $\widetilde{H}_n(\mathcal{K};\mathbf{k}) := H_n(\mathcal{K};\mathbf{k})$, if $n \geqslant 1$, and

$$\widetilde{H}_0(\mathcal{K};\mathbf{k}) := \begin{cases} 0, & \text{if } \mathcal{K} \text{ is connected;} \\ \mathbf{k}^{t-1}, & \text{if } \mathcal{K} \text{ is disconnected.} \end{cases}$$

2.3.9. Euler-Poincaré formula for plain simplicial complexes. The famous Descartes-Euler polyhedral formula says that for a simply connected polyhedron the number of faces plus the number of vertices is 2 more than the number of edges. The next theorem states a very closely related statement for the plain simplicial complexes.

Theorem 2.14 (Euler-Poincaré). *Assume $\mathcal{K}$ is a plain simplicial complex of dimension n, and $\mathbf{k}$ is an arbitrary field. Then we have the following equality of alternating sums:*

$$\begin{aligned}(2.5)\quad & |\mathcal{K}(0)| - |\mathcal{K}(1)| + |\mathcal{K}(2)| - \dots + (-1)^n|\mathcal{K}(n)| \\ & = \beta_0(\mathcal{K};\mathbf{k}) - \beta_1(\mathcal{K};\mathbf{k}) + \beta_2(\mathcal{K};\mathbf{k}) - \dots + (-1)^n\beta_n(\mathcal{K};\mathbf{k}).\end{aligned}$$

Proof. First, a standard fact from linear algebra tells us that for all i we have a linear isomorphism

$$C_i(\mathcal{K};\mathbf{k})/\operatorname{Ker}\partial_i \approx \operatorname{Im}\partial_i.$$

Hence, for all i, we have

$$|\mathcal{K}(i)| = \dim C_i(\mathcal{K};\mathbf{k}) = \dim\operatorname{Ker}\partial_i + \dim\operatorname{Im}\partial_i. \tag{2.6}$$

Summing Equation (2.6) over all i with alternating coefficients $(-1)^i$ will yield

$$\begin{aligned}\sum_i (-1)^i|\mathcal{K}(i)| &= \sum_i (-1)^i(\dim\operatorname{Ker}\partial_i + \dim\operatorname{Im}\partial_i) \\ &= \sum_i (-1)^i \dim\operatorname{Ker}\partial_i + \sum_i (-1)^i \dim\operatorname{Im}\partial_i.\end{aligned} \tag{2.7}$$

Furthermore, by the definition of Betti numbers and homology groups, for all i we have

$$\begin{aligned}\beta_i(\mathcal{K};\mathbf{k}) = \dim H_i(\mathcal{K};\mathbf{k}) &= \dim Z_i(\mathcal{K};\mathbf{k}) - \dim B_i(\mathcal{K};\mathbf{k}) \\ &= \dim\operatorname{Ker}\partial_i - \dim\operatorname{Im}\partial_{i+1}.\end{aligned} \tag{2.8}$$

Again, summing Equation (2.8) over all i with alternating coefficients $(-1)^i$ will yield

$$
\begin{aligned}
\sum_i (-1)^i \beta_i(\mathcal{K};\mathbf{k}) &= \sum_i (-1)^i (\dim \operatorname{Ker} \partial_i - \dim \operatorname{Im} \partial_{i+1}) \\
&= \sum_i (-1)^i \dim \operatorname{Ker} \partial_i + \sum_i (-1)^i \dim \operatorname{Im} \partial_i.
\end{aligned} \tag{2.9}
$$

Comparing Equations (2.7) and (2.9) yields Equation (2.5). □

At this point it is curious to note that the left-hand side of Equation (2.5) does not depend on the field $\mathbf{k}$. Therefore, even though the Betti numbers themselves may very well vary when the field changes, their alternating sum will remain constant.

The uses of Theorem 2.14 are manifold. For example, if we are considering the homology with coefficients in a field $\mathbf{k}$ of a two-dimensional plain simplicial complex $\mathcal{K}$, and we know the 1st and the 0th Betti number of $\mathcal{K}$, then we can determine the 2nd Betti number, and therefore the whole homology group $H_2(\mathcal{K};\mathbf{k})$.

Finally we remark that Theorem 2.14 holds for integers as well. To see this one can either essentially repeat the proof above or refer to the fact that $\beta_n(\mathcal{K}) = \beta_n(\mathcal{K};\mathbb{Q})$, for all n.

2.4. Geometric realization

A certain geometric picture can be associated to each plain simplicial complex. This picture is now useful in supplying us with the geometric intuition for the algebraic constructions, and it will be useful later in connecting our formal algebraic framework to the world of topology.

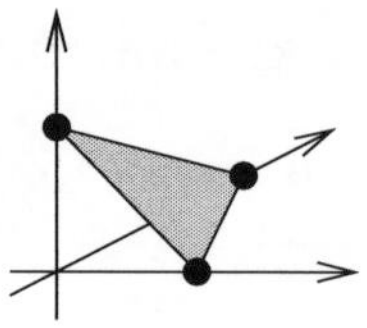

Figure 2.9. The standard 2-simplex.

2.4.1. Finite geometric simplicial complexes. A *geometric simplex* is a convex hull of a set of affinely independent points in a Euclidean space. Taking convex hulls of various subsets of this set yields all of its geometric subsimplices.

For later gluing constructions it is useful to distinguish one generic geometric simplex in every dimension.

Definition 2.15. Let n be a positive integer. The *standard n-simplex*, denoted Δ^n, is the convex hull of $n+1$ points in $\mathbb{R}^{n+1}$, whose coordinates are $(1,0,\dots,0)$, $(0,1,\dots,0)$, $\dots$, $(0,0,\dots,1)$.

The points of the standard n-simplex have natural coordinates inherited from the imbedding in $\mathbb{R}^{n+1}$. These are the so-called *barycentric coordinates.* Another way to describe them is to say that we consider all $(n+1)$-tuples of non-negative real numbers, whose sum is equal to 1, see Figure 2.9.

The geometric simplices can be glued together to form more complicated structures.

Definition 2.16. A *finite geometric simplicial complex* is a union of finitely many geometric simplices, such that for any two simplices σ and τ their intersection $\sigma \cap \tau$ is either empty or is a (not necessarily proper) subsimplex of each of them, see Figure 2.10.

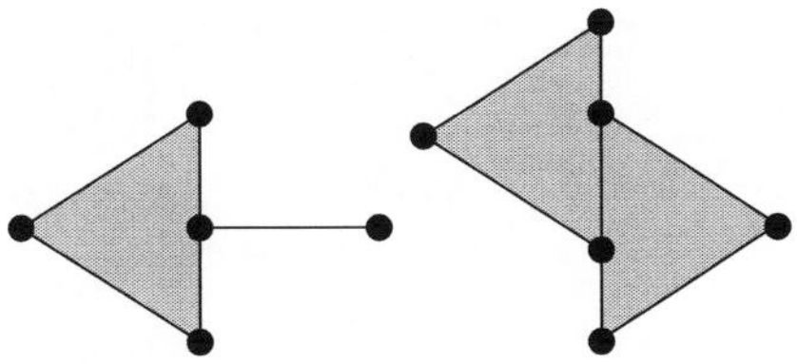

Figure 2.10. Constructions which are not geometric simplicial complexes.

2.4.2. The plain geometric realization.

Definition 2.17. Let $t \geqslant 0$ be an integer, and let $\mathcal{K}$ be a collection of non-empty subsets of $[t]$ which is a plain simplicial complex. Consider the standard simplex Δ^t in $\mathbb{R}^{t+1}$, and let $|\mathcal{K}|$ denote the union of those boundary simplices in Δ^t, which correspond to the sets in $\mathcal{K}$.

The set $|\mathcal{K}|$ is called the *plain geometric realization* of $\mathcal{K}$. It has a natural topology inherited from the Euclidean space $\mathbb{R}^{t+1}$.

As an example, our Figure 2.3 could be thought of as showing parts of the boundary of the simplex with 6 vertices. Clearly, a plain geometric realization of a plain simplicial complex is a finite geometric simplicial complex.

It might be instructive to go through our algebraic inventory and see the geometric counterparts. Clearly, what we call vertices and edges of the plain simplicial complex are precisely the vertices and edges of its plain geometric realization. In general the n-simplices correspond to the geometric simplices with $n+1$ vertices and the dimension coincides with the geometric

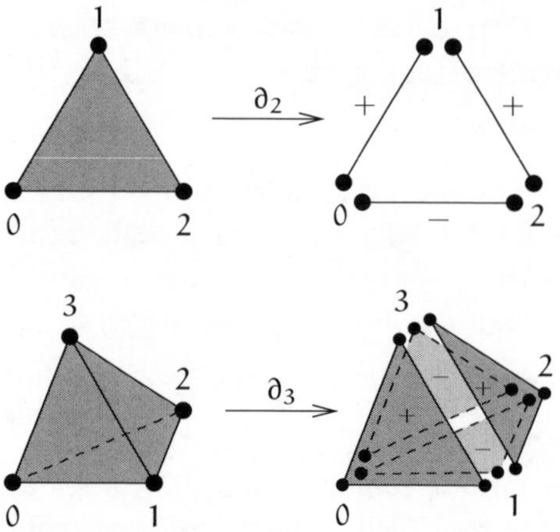

Figure 2.11. Geometric view of the boundary map evaluated on a 2-simplex and on a 3-simplex.

dimension. The subcomplex corresponds to taking the convex closure of a subset of simplices.

Finally, we note that the boundary map corresponds to taking the geometric boundary, at least as long as one forgets about the signs, see Figure 2.11. This explains the etymology of our notation.

It would be both tempting and correct to say that when computing the (simplicial) homology of the plain simplicial complex, we are actually computing the (singular) homology of the geometric realization, viewed as a topological space. The subtle point which is preventing us from doing that, is that it is not clear a priori why two plain simplicial complexes whose plain geometric realizations are homeomorphic should have the same homology. Phrased equivalently, a topological space has many possible presentations as a geometric realization of a plain simplicial complex[6], and it is not clear why all of them should yield the same homology. In fact, it is well known that relating two different triangulations of the same space can be a notoriously difficult question. We avoid these complications by steering clear of topology altogether. Instead, we develop the pure algebraic point of view, connecting back to topology here and there, but never needing topology for developing our theory.

---

[6]These are called *triangulations*.

2.5. Finite abstract simplicial complexes and standard constructions

2.5.1. The general setting. Although the plain simplicial complexes are sufficient to demonstrate many important aspects of homology, several features of the arising theory remain unsatisfactory. Fortunately, restricting ourselves to the sets $[t]$ as indexing sets of the vertices of the complex turns out to be unnecessary, and the first thing which one can do in order to relax the conditions of Definition 2.1 is to allow any finite set to be a set of vertices of $\mathcal{K}$.

Definition 2.18. Assume S is a finite set, and let $\mathcal{K}$ be a family of subsets of S. Then, $\mathcal{K}$ is called an *abstract simplicial complex* on the set S if the following two conditions are satisfied:

(1) for all $v \in S$, we have $\{v\} \in \mathcal{K}$;

(2) if $\sigma \in \mathcal{K}$ and $\tau \subset \sigma$, then $\tau \in \mathcal{K}$.

Let us make a couple of remarks concerning Definition 2.18. First, we did not specify at this point any particular order on the set of the vertices of the abstract simplicial complex, making it impossible to now define the boundary operator, at least over the integers. This issue will be addressed later.

Second, we do not require that the subsets in $\mathcal{K}$ are non-empty. In fact, quite the opposite: if S contains an element v, then by Definition 2.18(1) we have $\{v\} \in \mathcal{K}$, but $\emptyset \subseteq \{v\}$, so by Definition 2.18(2) we get $\emptyset \in \mathcal{K}$.

To be fair, we need to remark that we also allow S itself to be the empty set. If this is the case, then both conditions of Definition 2.18 are trivially satisfied. There are then two possibilities for the family $\mathcal{K}$. Either this family is empty or it consists of the empty set. To distinguish the two, in the first case we say that the abstract simplicial complex is *void*, and in the second case we call it the *empty* simplicial complex.

Definition 2.19. Given an abstract simplicial complex $\mathcal{K}$, and a subfamily $\mathcal{L} \subseteq \mathcal{K}$, we say that $\mathcal{L}$ is a *subcomplex* of $\mathcal{K}$ if $\mathcal{L}$ itself is an abstract simplicial complex on the set of its vertices.

As before, we set $\dim \sigma := |\sigma| - 1$, for all $\sigma \in \mathcal{K}$, we set $\dim \mathcal{K} := \max_{\sigma \in \mathcal{K}} \dim \sigma$, and we call these numbers the dimension of the simplex σ and the dimension of the abstract simplicial complex $\mathcal{K}$, respectively.

Finally, we give a name to the quantity which appeared previously in the Euler-Poincaré formula (2.5).

Definition 2.20. Let $\mathcal{K}$ be a finite abstract simplicial complex, such that $\mathcal{K}(0)$ is non-empty. We set

$$\chi(\mathcal{K}) := |\mathcal{K}(0)| - |\mathcal{K}(1)| + \cdots + (-1)^n |\mathcal{K}(n)|,$$

where $n = \dim \mathcal{K}$. The number $\chi(\mathcal{K})$ is called the *Euler characteristic* of $\mathcal{K}$.

If $\mathcal{K}$ is empty, we set $\chi(\mathcal{K}) := 0$, and when it is void, we set $\chi(\mathcal{K}) := 1$.

Furthermore, we set $\widetilde{\chi}(\mathcal{K}) := \chi(\mathcal{K}) - 1$, and call this the *reduced Euler characteristic* of $\mathcal{K}$. In particular, the reduced Euler characteristic of the void simplicial complex is equal to 0.

2.5.2. Deletion. We shall now proceed with defining various standard constructions for abstract simplicial complexes.

The easiest operation on a simplicial complex is the deletion of one of its simplices α. In order to preserve the simplicial structure we are bound to delete not just α, but all the simplices which contain α as well.

Definition 2.21. Let $\mathcal{K}$ be an abstract simplicial complex, and let α be a simplex of $\mathcal{K}$. The *deletion* of α is the abstract simplicial subcomplex of $\mathcal{K}$, denoted $\mathrm{dl}_{\mathcal{K}}(\alpha)$ and defined by

$$\mathrm{dl}_{\mathcal{K}}(\alpha) := \{\sigma \in \mathcal{K} \mid \sigma \not\supseteq \alpha\}.$$

Note that in particular, the deletion of an arbitrary simplex can be defined using deletions of vertices only, and we have

$$\mathrm{dl}_{\mathcal{K}}(\alpha) = \bigcup_{v \in \alpha} \mathrm{dl}_{\mathcal{K}}(v) = \bigcup_{v \in \alpha} \{\sigma \in \mathcal{K} \mid v \notin \sigma\}.$$

Geometrically, the deletion of a vertex corresponds to deleting a small neighborhood of the vertex, and then all the simplices which are affected by that. For higher-dimensional simplices, in order to interpret the deletion geometrically, we need to choose a generic point in the interior of that simplex, delete a small neighborhood around that point, and then delete all the simplices which are affected by that.

2.5.3. Closed star. The next definition gives a simplicial way to describe the neighborhood of a simplex.

Definition 2.22. Let $\mathcal{K}$ be an abstract simplicial complex, and let α be a simplex of $\mathcal{K}$. The *star* of α is the abstract simplicial subcomplex of $\mathcal{K}$, denoted $\mathrm{st}_{\mathcal{K}}(\alpha)$, defined by

$$\mathrm{st}_{\mathcal{K}}(\alpha) := \{\sigma \in \mathcal{K} \mid \sigma \cup \alpha \in \mathcal{K}\}.$$

For example, the star of the simplex α which has the maximal dimension consists of α itself and all the simplices it contains, whereas the star of a vertex v consists of all the simplices which contain v together with all the simplices which are contained in one of them.

The star is sometimes called the *closed star* in order to distinguish the above construction from the so-called *open star*.

Definition 2.23. Let $\mathcal{K}$ be an abstract simplicial complex, and let α be a simplex of $\mathcal{K}$. The *open star* of α is a subset of the set of simplices of $\mathcal{K}$, denoted $\mathrm{st}^{\circ}_{\mathcal{K}}(\alpha)$ defined by

$$\mathrm{st}^{\circ}_{\mathcal{K}}(\alpha) := \{\sigma \in \mathcal{K} \mid \sigma \supseteq \alpha\}.$$

Note, that unlike the closed star, the open star does not in general form an abstract simplicial complex. Of course we have

$$\mathrm{dl}_{\mathcal{K}}(\alpha) = \mathcal{K} \setminus \mathrm{st}^{\circ}_{\mathcal{K}}(\alpha).$$

2.5.4. Link. The link of a simplex α is a slightly trickier concept. Formally we have the following definition.

Definition 2.24. Let $\mathcal{K}$ be an abstract simplicial complex, and let α be a simplex of $\mathcal{K}$. The *link* of α is the abstract simplicial subcomplex of $\mathcal{K}$, denoted $\mathrm{lk}_{\mathcal{K}}(\alpha)$ and defined by

$$\mathrm{lk}_{\mathcal{K}}(\alpha) := \{\sigma \in \mathcal{K} \mid \sigma \cap \alpha = \emptyset, \text{ and } \sigma \cup \alpha \in \mathcal{K}\}.$$

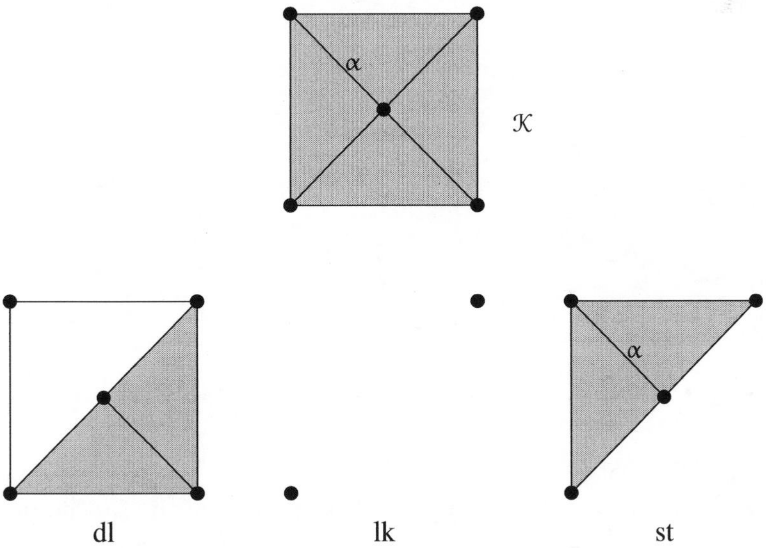

Figure 2.12. Deletion, star, and link of the simplex α.

For example, if $\mathcal{K}$ is the boundary of a tetrahedron, then the link of an edge consists of the two other vertices of $\mathcal{K}$. Note that the link of a maximal-dimensional simplex is empty, whereas the link of a vertex v is the intersection of the star at v with the deletion of v.

In general, for any simplex $\alpha \in \mathcal{K}$, we have

$$\mathrm{lk}_{\mathcal{K}}(\alpha) = \mathrm{st}_{\mathcal{K}}(\alpha) \cap \Big(\bigcap_{v \in \alpha} \mathrm{dl}_{\mathcal{K}}(v) \Big).$$

Accordingly, one can think of $\mathrm{lk}_{\mathcal{K}}(\alpha)$ as the subcomplex along which α is attached to the rest of the simplicial complex: it is obtained from the closed star by deleting all the vertices of α.

All three concepts are illustrated in Figure 2.12.

2.6. Abstract simplicial complexes on finite ordered sets

Before proceeding with more constructions on abstract simplicial complexes, let us address the issue of defining homology groups.

2.6.1. Choosing an order on the vertex set. As mentioned above, one cannot define the boundary operator, and hence one cannot define the homology groups, for abstract simplicial complexes, without making some further assumptions. There are several options, and perhaps the simplest of them is to fix a total order on the vertex set.

Definition 2.25. An *abstract simplicial complex on the finite ordered set* S is simply an abstract simplicial complex on S, with a fixed choice of order on the vertex set S.

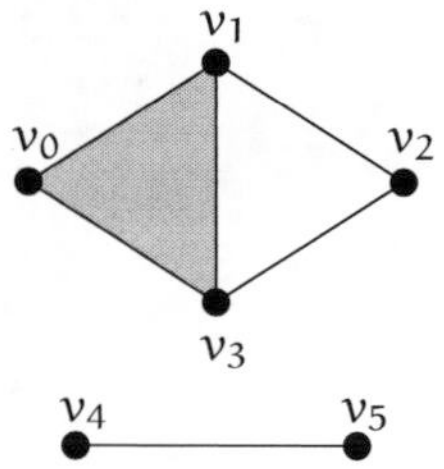

Figure 2.13. A simplicial complex $\widetilde{\mathcal{X}}$ on the ordered set $(v_0, v_1, v_2, v_3, v_4, v_5)$.

Any plain simplicial complex $\mathcal{K}$ on the set $[t]$ gives rise to a simplicial complex on the finite ordered set $\mathcal{K}(0)$, with the order on $\mathcal{K}(0)$ induced from the natural order on $[t]$. On the other hand, given a simplicial complex $\mathcal{K}$ on a finite ordered set, we can rename the vertices, preserving their relative order, so that $\mathcal{K}$ becomes a plain simplicial complex.

Most of the concepts and constructions from the plain simplicial complexes transfer verbatim to the simplicial complexes on finite ordered sets. One slight difference is that the subcomplexes may now have a different ground set, since we require that all the elements in the ground set must be vertices.

The existence of an order on S allows us to define the boundary operator in exactly the same way as in Definition 2.3, effortlessly leading to the definition of homology. Furthermore, the finiteness condition implies that we can still employ the classification of finitely generated abelian groups to derive the existence of Betti numbers and torsion coefficients. In a sense, there is not much which we cannot simply carry over from the plain simplicial complex case.

2.6.2. Homology is independent on the order of the vertex set. One new thing which we can do now is to contemplate how the homology groups depend on the order of the set S. Obviously, choosing a different order may result in a different boundary operator. Still, the homology groups will remain isomorphic, no matter which order is chosen, as the next lemma and the subsequent corollary formally demonstrate. The proof is simple, but it allows us to get a first taste of the important general concepts to come, so we do it in some detail.

Lemma 2.26. *Let* t *be an integer,* $t \geqslant 2$*, and assume* $S = (x_1, \dots, x_t)$ *is an ordered* t*-tuple. Pick any* $1 \leqslant k \leqslant t-1$*, and let* $\widetilde{S}$ *be the* t*-tuple obtained from* S *by swapping* x_k *and* x_{k+1}*, i.e., we set*

$$\widetilde{S} := (x_1, \dots, x_{k-1}, x_{k+1}, x_k, x_{k+2}, \dots, x_t).$$

Assume we are given a simplicial complex $\mathcal{K}$ *on the ordered set* S*. We construct a simplicial complex* $\widetilde{\mathcal{K}}$ *on the ordered set* $\widetilde{S}$ *by taking the same family of subsets as* $\mathcal{K}$.[7] *Then, the homology groups of* $\mathcal{K}$ *and* $\widetilde{\mathcal{K}}$ *are isomorphic.*

Proof. Given a tuple $\sigma \subseteq S$, which contains both x_k and x_{k+1}, we let $\widetilde{\sigma} \subseteq \widetilde{S}$ be the tuple obtained from σ by swapping x_k and x_{k+1}. Clearly, this is a bijection between the sets of those simplices of $\mathcal{K}$ and $\widetilde{\mathcal{K}}$, which contain both x_k and x_{k+1}.

For an arbitrary dimension n, we define a group isomorphism φ_n between the chain groups $C_n(\mathcal{K})$ and $C_n(\widetilde{\mathcal{K}})$. The map φ_n is specified on simplices as follows:

$$\varphi_n(\sigma) := \begin{cases} -\widetilde{\sigma}, & \text{if } x_k, x_{k+1} \in \sigma; \\ \sigma, & \text{otherwise.} \end{cases} \tag{2.10}$$

[7] Clearly, the tuples S and $\widetilde{S}$ coincide, when considered as sets.

Since the map φ_n is a bijection on the sets of generators, it is a group isomorphism between the chain groups $C_n(\mathcal{K})$ and $C_n(\widetilde{\mathcal{K}})$.

Let $\widetilde{\partial}_n : C_n(\widetilde{\mathcal{K}}) \to C_{n-1}(\widetilde{\mathcal{K}})$ denote the boundary operator of the simplicial complex $\widetilde{\mathcal{K}}$. We shall now see that for any $\alpha \in C_n(\mathcal{K})$, we have[8]

$$\widetilde{\partial}_n(\varphi_n(\alpha)) = \varphi_{n-1}(\partial_n \alpha). \tag{2.11}$$

Since both the boundary map and the maps φ_n, φ_{n-1} are linear, it is enough to verify Equation (2.11) when α is an n-simplex. If one of the elements x_k and x_{k+1} does not belong to α, then φ_n is the identity on α, and φ_{n-1} is the identity on the boundary simplices of α, so this case is immediate. (See Table 2.4.)

$$\begin{array}{ccc} C_n(\mathcal{K}) & \xrightarrow{\varphi_n} & C_n(\widetilde{\mathcal{K}}) \\ {\scriptstyle \partial_n}\big\downarrow & & \big\downarrow{\scriptstyle \widetilde{\partial}_n} \\ C_{n-1}(\mathcal{K}) & \xrightarrow{\varphi_{n-1}} & C_{n-1}(\widetilde{\mathcal{K}}) \end{array}$$

Table 2.4. The commuting diagram corresponding to Equation (2.11).

Assume now $x_k, x_{k+1} \in \alpha$. Let us say $\alpha = (y_0, \dots, y_p, x_k, x_{k+1}, z_0, \dots, z_q)$. First we calculate the left-hand side of Equation (2.11):

$$\begin{aligned} \widetilde{\partial}_n(\varphi_n(\alpha)) &= \widetilde{\partial}_n(-(y_0, \dots, y_p, x_{k+1}, x_k, z_0, \dots, z_q)) \\ &= -\widetilde{\partial}_n(y_0, \dots, y_p, x_{k+1}, x_k, z_0, \dots, z_q) \\ &= \sum_{i=0}^{p} (-1)^{i+1}(y_0, \dots, \widehat{y}_i, \dots, y_p, x_{k+1}, x_k, z_0, \dots, z_q) \\ &\quad + (-1)^p(y_0, \dots, y_p, x_k, z_0, \dots, z_q) \\ &\quad + (-1)^{p+1}(y_0, \dots, y_p, x_{k+1}, z_0, \dots, z_q) \\ &\quad + \sum_{j=0}^{q} (-1)^{p+j}(y_0, \dots, y_p, x_{k+1}, x_k, z_0, \dots, \widehat{z}_j, \dots, z_q). \end{aligned} \tag{2.12}$$

[8]Later on maps like φ will be called *chain maps*.

We then calculate the right-hand side of Equation (2.11):

(2.13)

$$\begin{aligned}
\varphi_{n-1}(\partial_n\alpha) &= \varphi_{n-1}(\partial_n(y_0,\dots,y_p,x_k,x_{k+1},z_0,\dots,z_q))\\
&= \varphi_{n-1}\Big(\sum_{i=0}^{p}(-1)^i(y_0,\dots,\widehat{y_i},\dots,y_p,x_k,x_{k+1},z_0,\dots,z_q)\\
&\qquad + (-1)^{p+1}(y_0,\dots,y_p,x_{k+1},z_0,\dots,z_q)\\
&\qquad + (-1)^{p}(y_0,\dots,y_p,x_k,z_0,\dots,z_q)\\
&\qquad + \sum_{j=0}^{q}(-1)^{p+j+1}(y_0,\dots,y_p,x_k,x_{k+1},z_0,\dots,\widehat{z_j},\dots,z_q)\Big)\\
&= \sum_{i=0}^{p}(-1)^{i+1}(y_0,\dots,\widehat{y_i},\dots,y_p,x_{k+1},x_k,z_0,\dots,z_q)\\
&\quad + (-1)^{p+1}(y_0,\dots,y_p,x_{k+1},z_0,\dots,z_q)\\
&\quad + (-1)^{p}(y_0,\dots,y_p,x_k,z_0,\dots,z_q)\\
&\quad + \sum_{j=0}^{q}(-1)^{p+j}(y_0,\dots,y_p,x_{k+1},x_k,z_0,\dots,\widehat{z_j},\dots,z_q).
\end{aligned}$$

The comparison of the final expressions of Equations (2.12) and (2.13) proves the validity of Equation (2.11).

It is instructive to see how an equation like Equation (2.11) can be put to use. To start with, take a cycle $\alpha \in Z_n(\mathcal{K})$. We have

$$\widetilde{\partial}_n(\varphi_n(\alpha)) = \varphi_{n-1}(\partial_n\alpha) = \varphi_{n-1}(0) = 0,$$

so $\varphi_n(\alpha) \in Z_n(\widetilde{\mathcal{K}})$. Put succinctly, the map φ_n *maps cycles to cycles,* that is, we have $\varphi_n(Z_n(\mathcal{K})) \subseteq Z_n(\widetilde{\mathcal{K}})$.

On the other hand, take $\alpha \in Z_n(\widetilde{\mathcal{K}})$, and set $\beta := \varphi_n^{-1}(\alpha)$, which is well-defined, since φ_n is an isomorphism. We have

$$\varphi_{n-1}(\partial_n\beta) = \widetilde{\partial}_n(\varphi_n(\beta)) = \widetilde{\partial}_n\alpha = 0.$$

The map φ_{n-1} is injective, so $\partial_n\beta = 0$, and hence $\beta \in Z_n(\mathcal{K})$. Altogether, we conclude that φ_n is a group isomorphism between $Z_n(\mathcal{K})$ and $Z_n(\widetilde{\mathcal{K}})$.

$$\begin{aligned}
\varphi_n &: Z_n(\mathcal{K}) \to Z_n(\widetilde{\mathcal{K}})\\
\varphi_n &: B_n(\mathcal{K}) \to B_n(\widetilde{\mathcal{K}})\\
\varphi_n^* &: H_n(\mathcal{K}) \to H_n(\widetilde{\mathcal{K}})
\end{aligned}$$

Table 2.5. The maps induced by φ.

We can deal with the boundaries in a similar way. Assume we have $\alpha \in B_n(\mathcal{K})$, so there exists $\beta \in C_{n+1}(\mathcal{K})$ such that $\partial_{n+1}\beta = \alpha$. We have

$$\varphi_n(\alpha) = \varphi_n(\partial_{n+1}\beta) = \widetilde{\partial}_{n+1}(\varphi_{n+1}(\beta)),$$

so $\varphi_n(B_n(\mathcal{K})) \subseteq B_n(\widetilde{\mathcal{K}})$, and φ_n *maps boundaries to boundaries*. On the other hand, take $\alpha \in B_n(\widetilde{\mathcal{K}})$, so there exists $\beta \in C_{n+1}(\widetilde{\mathcal{K}})$ such that $\widetilde{\partial}_{n+1}\beta = \alpha$. Set $\gamma := \varphi_{n+1}^{-1}(\beta)$. We have

$$\alpha = \widetilde{\partial}_{n+1}(\varphi_{n+1}(\gamma)) = \varphi_n(\partial_{n+1}\gamma),$$

so $\varphi_n^{-1}(\alpha) \in B_n(\mathcal{K})$. Again, we conclude that φ_n is a group isomorphism between $B_n(\mathcal{K})$ and $B_n(\widetilde{\mathcal{K}})$.

It follows that φ_n induces a group isomorphism φ_n^* between $H_n(\mathcal{K})$ and $H_n(\widetilde{\mathcal{K}})$. □

We summarize the maps induced by φ in Table 2.5.

Since any permutation can be represented as a product of elementary transpositions, the repeated use of Lemma 2.26 yields the following theorem.

Theorem 2.27. *Up to isomorphism, homology groups of an abstract simplicial complex on a finite ordered set do not depend on the order of that set.*

In other words, let $S = (x_1, \dots, x_t)$ be an ordered t-tuple, and let $\widetilde{S}$ be obtained from S by an arbitrary permutation. Let $\mathcal{K}$ be an abstract simplicial complex on S, and let $\widetilde{\mathcal{K}}$ be the abstract simplicial complex on $\widetilde{S}$, obtained by taking the same family of subsets. Then, the homology groups of $\mathcal{K}$ and $\widetilde{\mathcal{K}}$ are isomorphic.

Theorem 2.27 allows us, up to isomorphism, to define homology groups of an arbitrary abstract simplicial complex.

As an example, consider the plain simplicial complex $\widetilde{\mathcal{X}}$ shown in Figure 2.13. It is obtained from the sample plain simplicial complex $\mathcal{X}$ shown in Figure 2.3 by renaming the vertices, while also slightly changing their order. Accordingly, the homology groups are isomorphic, though the generators are different. The family of maps φ defined by Equation (2.10) provides the required isomorphisms.

2.7. Further constructions and associated homology

2.7.1. Disjoint union of simplicial complexes. Given two simplicial complexes, the simplest way to produce a new simplicial complex is to take their disjoint union.

Definition 2.28. Given two non-empty abstract simplicial complexes $\mathcal{K}_1$ and $\mathcal{K}_2$ with disjoint vertex sets, their *disjoint union* $\mathcal{K}_1 \amalg \mathcal{K}_2$ is defined by setting

$$(\mathcal{K}_1 \amalg \mathcal{K}_2)(t) := \mathcal{K}_1(t) \cup \mathcal{K}_2(t),$$

for all $t \geqslant 0$, where the union on the right-hand side is, of course, disjoint.

The disjoint union operation can be iterated, and it is clearly associative. Hence we can talk about multiple disjoint unions $\mathcal{K}_1 \amalg \ldots \amalg \mathcal{K}_q$.

Theorem 2.29. *Assume $\mathcal{K}_1, \ldots, \mathcal{K}_q$ are non-empty abstract simplicial complexes and set $\mathcal{K} := \mathcal{K}_1 \amalg \ldots \amalg \mathcal{K}_q$. For any non-negative integer n, we have the following isomorphism:*

$$H_n(\mathcal{K}) \approx H_n(\mathcal{K}_1) \oplus \cdots \oplus H_n(\mathcal{K}_q). \tag{2.14}$$

Proof. We clearly have $C_n(\mathcal{K}) = C_n(\mathcal{K}_1) \oplus \cdots \oplus C_n(\mathcal{K}_q)$ and $\partial_n(C_n(K_i)) \subseteq C_{n-1}(K_i)$, for all integers n and all $i = 1, \ldots, q$. It follows that $Z_n(\mathcal{K}) = Z_n(\mathcal{K}_1) \oplus \cdots \oplus Z_n(\mathcal{K}_q)$ and $B_n(\mathcal{K}) = B_n(\mathcal{K}_1) \oplus \cdots \oplus B_n(\mathcal{K}_q)$, again for all n. The Equation (2.14) then follows from the general algebraic theorem describing the quotients of direct sums of groups:

$$\begin{aligned} H_n(\mathcal{K}) = Z_n(\mathcal{K})/B_n(\mathcal{K}) =& \frac{Z_n(\mathcal{K}_1) \oplus \cdots \oplus Z_n(\mathcal{K}_q)}{B_n(\mathcal{K}_1) \oplus \cdots \oplus B_n(\mathcal{K}_q)} \\ \approx& (Z_n(\mathcal{K}_1)/B_n(\mathcal{K}_1)) \oplus \cdots \oplus (Z_n(\mathcal{K}_q)/B_n(\mathcal{K}_q)) \\ =& H_n(\mathcal{K}_1) \oplus \cdots \oplus H_n(\mathcal{K}_q). \end{aligned}$$

□

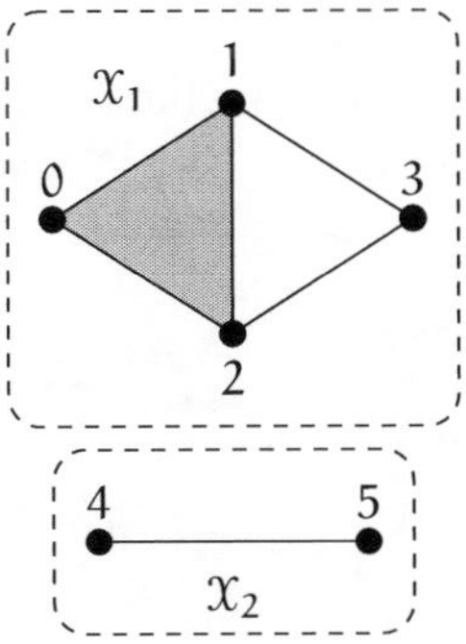

Figure 2.14. Connected components of $\mathcal{X}$.

Our sample simplicial complex $\mathcal{X}$ is a disjoint union of the subcomplexes $\mathcal{X}_1$ on vertices 0, 1, 2, and 3, and $\mathcal{X}_2$ on vertices 4 and 5; see Figure 2.14. Therefore, Theorem 2.29 can be applied with $q = 2$. We obtain $H_0(\mathcal{X}_1) \approx H_0(\mathcal{X}_2) \approx \mathbb{Z}$, and $H_1(\mathcal{X}_1) \approx \mathbb{Z}$, which fits with our previous computation of the homology groups of $\mathcal{X}$.

2.7.2. Wedge of simplicial complexes. Assume we are given two non-empty abstract simplicial complexes $\mathcal{K}_1$ and $\mathcal{K}_2$, with disjoint vertex sets, and let us pick vertices $v_1 \in \mathcal{K}_1(0)$ and $v_2 \in \mathcal{K}_2(0)$. The following definition makes formal the intuitive notion of gluing $\mathcal{K}_1$ with $\mathcal{K}_2$ by identifying v_1 with v_2.

Definition 2.30. The **wedge**, or **wedge sum**, of $\mathcal{K}_1$ and $\mathcal{K}_2$, with respect to the vertices v_1 and v_2, is the abstract simplicial complex W defined by

- $W(0) = \{v\} \cup (\mathcal{K}_1(0) \setminus \{v_1\}) \cup (\mathcal{K}_2(0) \setminus \{v_2\})$, where v is a new vertex;
- $\sigma \subseteq W(0)$, such that $|\sigma| = n+1$, is an n-simplex of W if and only if one of the following cases applies:
  (1) $v \notin \sigma$ and $\sigma \in \mathcal{K}_1(n) \cup \mathcal{K}_2(n)$;
  (2) $v \in \sigma$ and σ is an n-simplex of $\mathcal{K}_1$ once the vertex v is replaced with the vertex v_1;
  (3) $v \in \sigma$ and σ is an n-simplex of $\mathcal{K}_2$ once v is replaced with v_2.

We denote the wedge of $\mathcal{K}_1$ and $\mathcal{K}_2$ by $\mathcal{K}_1 \vee \mathcal{K}_2$.

We remark that, strictly speaking, the wedge sum is not an operation on simplicial complexes, since it also requires a choice of vertices. Rather it is an operation on the so-called *pointed simplicial complexes*, that is, pairs $(\mathcal{K}, v)$, where $\mathcal{K}$ is a simplicial complex and v is some vertex of $\mathcal{K}$.

Like the disjoint union, the wedge operation can be iterated. If we have a sequence $\mathcal{K}_1, \dots, \mathcal{K}_q$ of abstract simplicial complexes, we also need to choose a sequence of vertices $v_1, \dots, v_q$, such that $v_i \in \mathcal{K}_i$ for all $1 \leqslant i \leqslant q$. We can then define the multiple wedge sum $\mathcal{K}_1 \vee \dots \vee \mathcal{K}_q$ as a result of iterative wedging. It is easy to show that the end result does not depend, up to simplicial isomorphism, on the order in which the wedge operation is iterated.

Proposition 2.31. *Assume $\mathcal{K}_1, \dots, \mathcal{K}_q$ are abstract simplicial complexes. For all $n \geqslant 1$, we have the formula*

$$H_n(\mathcal{K}_1 \vee \dots \vee \mathcal{K}_q) \approx H_n(\mathcal{K}_1) \oplus \dots \oplus H_n(\mathcal{K}_q).$$

Furthermore, we have

$$H_0(\mathcal{K}_1 \vee \dots \vee \mathcal{K}_q) \oplus \mathbb{Z}^{q-1} \approx H_0(\mathcal{K}_1) \oplus \dots \oplus H_0(\mathcal{K}_q).$$

Proof. The proof is essentially the same as that of Theorem 2.29. We only need to pay a little bit closer attention to dimension 0. □

Note that Proposition 2.31 is valid independently of the choice of the wedge points in the simplicial complexes $\mathcal{K}_1, \dots, \mathcal{K}_q$.

2.7.3. Homology of graphs revisited. Let us now move up a notch and calculate the first homology group of a plain 1-dimensional simplicial complex $\mathcal{K}$.[9] Due to Theorem 2.29 we might as well assume that $\mathcal{K}$ is connected.

We have already considered homology of graphs in Chapter 1. In what follows we will describe a canonical basis of the first homology group associated to any given spanning tree.

Recall that a connected graph is called a *tree* if its number of vertices is one more than its number of edges, or, equivalently, one says that a tree is a connected graph without cycles.[10] The homology of a tree is especially easy to compute.

Lemma 2.32. *The first homology group of a tree is trivial.*

Proof. Let T be a 1-dimensional plain simplicial complex, which is also a tree. Take an arbitrary $\sigma \in Z_1(T)$. Let H be the subgraph of T consisting of all the edges which are summands of σ with a non-zero coefficient, and all the vertices which are adjacent to one of such edges. Any vertex of H must be adjacent to at least two edges from H, or else the boundary of σ would not be equal to 0 at this vertex. Clearly, a finite non-empty graph where all the vertices have valency at least 2 will contain a cycle. Thus, if H is non-empty, we will find a cycle in T, contradicting the fact that it is a tree. We conclude that H must be empty, hence $\sigma = 0$, and so $H_1(T) = Z_1(T) = 0$. □

Before dealing with the general case, it is handy to introduce new notation and to set $(v_1, v_0) := -(v_0, v_1)$, for $(v_0, v_1) \in \mathcal{K}(1)$, $v_0 < v_1$. In other words, (v_1, v_0) simply denotes the element of $C_1(\mathcal{K})$, which is equal to $-(v_0, v_1)$. We perform a simple calculation,

$$\partial_1(v_1, v_0) = \partial_1(-(v_0, v_1)) = -\partial_1(v_0, v_1) = -(v_1 - v_0) = v_0 - v_1,$$

to see that the formula $\partial_1(v, w) = w - v$ is valid no matter if $v < w$ or not. We also set $(v, v) := 0$, for all $v \in \mathcal{K}(1)$, and note that $\partial_1(v, w) = w - v$ even if $v = w$.

Set $n := |\mathcal{K}(0)|$ and $m := |\mathcal{K}(1)|$. Since $\mathcal{K}$ is connected we have $m + 1 \geqslant n$. Let T be any connected subgraph of $\mathcal{K}$ with n vertices and $n - 1$ edges. It always exists and is easy to generate by adding one edge at a time. Such a graph T is called a *spanning tree* of $\mathcal{K}$, since it is a tree and it spans the entire set of vertices. See Figure 2.15 for an example.

Let us fix a vertex $r \in \mathcal{K}(0)$, which we call a *root* of the tree T. For any vertex v, a sequence (r, v_1), (v_1, v_2), $\dots$, (v_{p-1}, v) of distinct edges in T is called a T*-path from* r *to* v. When $r = v$, we allow this sequence to be empty,

---

[9]Such complexes are essentially the same as simple graphs.

[10]The word *cycle* is used here in its graph-theoretic sense.

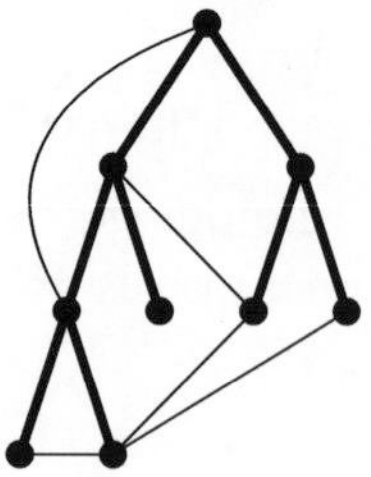

Figure 2.15. A spanning tree in a graph; fixing the vertex r makes it a *rooted* spanning tree.

giving us the unique T-path from r to r. The fact that T is a tree implies that for every $v \in \mathcal{K}(0)$ there exists a *unique* path from r to v.

Assume now that $e = (v, w)$ is an edge of $\mathcal{K}$ which does not belong to T. Let (r, v_1), (v_1, v_2), ..., (v_{p-1}, v) be the T-path from r to v, and let (r, w_1), (w_1, w_2), ..., (w_{q-1}, w) be the T-path from r to w. We now associate a 1-chain $\sigma_e \in C_1(\mathcal{K})$ to the edge e by setting

$$\sigma_e := (r, v_1) + (v_1, v_2) + \cdots + (v_{p-2}, v_{p-1}) + (v_{p-1}, v) + (v, w) + (w, w_{q-1}) + (w_{q-1}, w_{q-2}) + \cdots + (w_2, w_1) + (w_1, r). \tag{2.15}$$

An example is shown in Figure 2.16. We now have enough terminology to describe the first homology group of $\mathcal{K}$.

Theorem 2.33. *Assume $\mathcal{K}$ is a connected 1-dimensional plain simplicial complex with n vertices and m edges; then we have $H_1(\mathcal{K}) \approx \mathbb{Z}^{m-n+1}$.*

Furthermore, let T be some spanning tree of $\mathcal{K}$, and let e_1, ..., e_{m-n+1} be the complete list of edges of $\mathcal{K}$ which do not belong to T. Then the group $H_1(\mathcal{K})$ is freely generated by the homology classes $[\sigma_{e_1}]$, ..., $[\sigma_{e_{m-n+1}}]$.

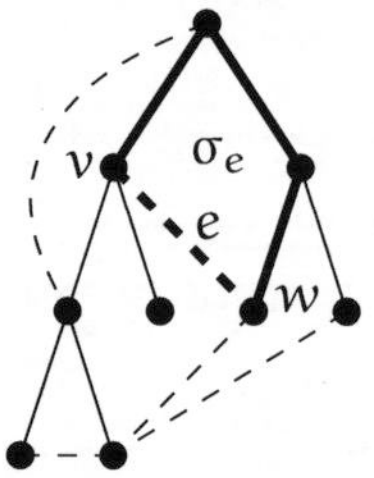

Figure 2.16. The 1-cycle σ_e.

Proof. A direct computation shows that

$$\partial_1 \sigma_e = (v_1 - r) + (v_2 - v_1) + \cdots + (r - w_1) = 0,$$

hence each σ_e is a 1-cycle, i.e., $\sigma_e \in Z_1(\mathcal{K})$, and the homology classes $[\sigma_{e_1}]$, $\dots$, $[\sigma_{e_{m-n+1}}]$ are well-defined.

Since $B_1(\mathcal{K}) = 0$, we might as well drop the square brackets and talk about the homology classes $\sigma_{e_1}, \dots, \sigma_{e_{m-n+1}}$. For each $1 \leqslant i \leqslant m - n + 1$ the 1-cycle σ_{e_i} contains the edge e_i, and for $j \neq i$, the 1-cycle σ_{e_j} does not contain the edge e_i, since the only edge outside of T which it contains is $e_j \neq e_i$. This implies that the 1-cycles $\sigma_{e_1}, \dots, \sigma_{e_{m-n+1}}$ are independent, because in any linear combination of $\sigma_{e_1}, \dots, \sigma_{e_{m-n+1}}$, the contributions of the edges e_i cannot cancel each other.

Finally, we can show that $Z_1(\mathcal{K})$ is generated by these 1-cycles. Indeed, pick an arbitrary 1-cycle $\sigma \in Z_1(\mathcal{K})$. We can write

$$\sigma = c_1\sigma_{e_1} + \dots + c_{m-n+1}\sigma_{e_{m-n+1}} + \tau,$$

where τ is a 1-chain which only has edges from T.

We now note that on one hand, the 1-chain τ is again a 1-cycle, since it is a linear combination of 1-cycles. On the other hand, it contains only the edges from T. This means that τ can be seen as a 1-cycle of T. Lemma 2.32 implies that $\tau = 0$, hence we have $\sigma = c_1\sigma_{e_1} + \dots + c_{m-n+1}\sigma_{e_{m-n+1}}$, and the proof is finished. □

2.7.4. Cones. Let us now look at a construction which is ubiquitous in topology.

Definition 2.34. A finite abstract simplicial complex $\mathcal{K}$ is called a *cone* if there exists a vertex $v \in \mathcal{K}(0)$ satisfying the following property: if $\sigma \in \mathcal{K}$, then $\sigma \cup v \in \mathcal{K}$.

Such a vertex v is called an *apex* of the cone. Note that $\mathrm{lk}_{\mathcal{K}}(v) = \mathrm{dl}_{\mathcal{K}}(v)$, and we call this subcomplex the *base* of the cone. Note that a cone is always non-empty.

The homology groups of any cone are the same as those of a point.

Proposition 2.35. *If the finite abstract simplicial complex* $\mathcal{K}$ *is a cone, then* $H_0(\mathcal{K}) \approx \mathbb{Z}$, *and* $H_n(\mathcal{K}) = 0$, *for all* $n \neq 0$.

Proof. Let v denote the apex of $\mathcal{K}$, and let $\mathcal{B}$ denote its base.

By Theorem 2.27 we will not lose any generality by assuming that v is the minimal vertex of $\mathcal{K}$. So $\mathcal{K}(0) = \{v_0, v_1, \dots, v_t\}$ and $v_0 = v$.

Furthermore, note that the 1-skeleton of a cone is clearly a connected graph, since any vertex of the base is connected by an edge to the apex. This means that $H_0(\mathcal{K}) \approx \mathbb{Z}$, and from now on we can consider the groups $H_n(\mathcal{K})$, for $n \geqslant 1$.

Since $\mathcal{K}$ is a cone, for any simplex $\sigma \in \mathcal{K}$ we also have $v \cup \sigma \in \mathcal{K}$. We extend this notation as follows: for any non-zero n-chain α in the base, where $n \geqslant 0$, we let $v \cup \alpha$ denote the $(n+1)$-chain in $\mathcal{K}$ obtained from α by adding the vertex v to each simplex in α. Note that $v \cup \alpha \neq 0$. A direct calculation shows that for any $\alpha \in C_n(\mathcal{B})$, $\alpha \neq 0$, we have

$$\partial_{n+1}(v \cup \alpha) = \begin{cases} \alpha - v \cup \partial_n \alpha, & \text{for } n \geqslant 1; \\ \alpha - cv, & \text{for } n = 0. \end{cases} \tag{2.16}$$

The integer c in the second case of Equation (2.16) is calculated as follows: for $\alpha = c_1 v_1 + \dots + c_p v_p$, where $v_1, \dots, v_p$ are vertices of the base, we have $c = c_1 + \dots + c_p$.

Let $n \geqslant 1$ and pick an arbitrary cycle $\gamma \in Z_n(\mathcal{K})$, $\gamma \neq 0$. Assume first that no simplices involved in γ contain the vertex v. Consider the $(n+1)$-chain $v \cup \gamma$. By Equation (2.16), we have $\partial_{n+1}(v \cup \gamma) = \gamma - v \cup \partial_n \gamma = \gamma$. This shows that $\gamma \in B_n(\mathcal{K})$; in other words, $[\gamma] = 0$, where $[\gamma] \in H_n(\mathcal{K})$.

In the general case, let us sort the simplices involved in γ into those which contain v and those which do not. We can write

$$\gamma = \tau + v \cup \mu, \tag{2.17}$$

where $\mu \in C_{n-1}(\mathcal{B})$, $\mu \neq 0$, and $\tau \in C_n(\mathcal{B})$.

First we consider the case $n \geqslant 2$. Taking the boundary of both sides in Equation (2.17), and applying Equation (2.16) to $v \cup \mu$, we obtain

$$\partial_n \gamma = \partial_n \tau + \mu - v \cup \partial_{n-1} \mu.$$

Since $\partial_n \gamma = 0$, this in turn implies that $\partial_n \tau = -\mu$ and $\partial_{n-1} \mu = 0$, where the latter follows from the first one anyway.

If $n = 1$, Equation (2.16) implies that $\partial_1 \gamma = \partial_1 \tau + \mu - cv$, where c is some integer. Also in this case we must have $\partial_1 \tau = -\mu$.

Again consider the $(n+1)$-chain $v \cup \tau$. Equation (2.16) combined with the equality $\partial_n \tau = -\mu$ yields

$$\partial_{n+1}(v \cup \tau) = \tau - v \cup \partial_n \tau = \tau - v \cup (-\mu) = \tau + v \cup \mu = \gamma.$$

Again, we conclude that $[\gamma] = 0$.

Since this is shown for any $\gamma \in Z_n(\mathcal{K})$, and any $n \geqslant 1$, it follows that $H_n(\mathcal{K}) = 0$, for all $n \geqslant 1$. □

2.7.5. Suspension. Let us define a useful operation on simplicial complexes which will allow us to shift homology groups to higher dimensions.

Definition 2.36. Let $\mathcal{K}$ be a non-empty finite abstract simplicial complex, and consider another finite abstract simplicial complex, denoted $\operatorname{susp} \mathcal{K}$, which is obtained from $\mathcal{K}$ by adding two new vertices v and w and then taking as a set of simplices the union

$$\{\sigma \mid \sigma \in \mathcal{K}\} \cup \{\sigma \cup v \mid \sigma \in \mathcal{K}\} \cup \{\sigma \cup w \mid \sigma \in \mathcal{K}\}.$$

The simplicial complex $\operatorname{susp} \mathcal{K}$ is called the *suspension* of $\mathcal{K}$.

Phrased colloquially, the set of simplices of $\operatorname{susp} \mathcal{K}$ is obtained as follows: in addition to the simplices which already exist in $\mathcal{K}$, we take those obtained from a simplex in $\mathcal{K}$ by adding a vertex v, or a vertex w, but not both. Note the special case when we take the empty simplex in $\mathcal{K}$, showing that vertices v and w are simplices of $\operatorname{susp} \mathcal{K}$.

Another way to see how suspension of $\mathcal{K}$ is constructed is to start with two cones, both having $\mathcal{K}$ as a base, but with different apexes, and then take the union of those copies over that common base. The complex $\mathcal{K}$ ends up being *suspended* between those apexes.

The following proposition says that the effect of taking the suspension on the homology of the underlying complex is a shift in dimension.

Proposition 2.37. *Assume $\mathcal{K}$ is a non-empty finite abstract simplicial complex; then we have*

$$\begin{cases} H_0(\operatorname{susp} \mathcal{K}) \approx \mathbb{Z}, \\ H_1(\operatorname{susp} \mathcal{K}) \oplus \mathbb{Z} \approx H_0(\mathcal{K}), \\ H_{n+1}(\operatorname{susp} \mathcal{K}) = H_n(\mathcal{K}), \qquad \text{for all } n \geqslant 1. \end{cases}$$

Proof. The fact that $H_0(\operatorname{susp} \mathcal{K}) \approx \mathbb{Z}$ is immediate, since for non-empty $\mathcal{K}$, the graph $\operatorname{sk}_1 \operatorname{susp} \mathcal{K}$ is connected.

Let us now show that $H_{n+1}(\operatorname{susp} \mathcal{K}) = H_n(\mathcal{K})$, for all $n \geqslant 1$. By Theorem 2.27 we can assume that w is the maximal vertex of $\operatorname{susp} \mathcal{K}$, and v is the next maximal one. In other words, the vertices of $\operatorname{susp} \mathcal{K}$ are $\{v_0, \dots, v_t\}$, with $v_t = w$ and $v_{t-1} = v$.

This is a slightly different assumption than the one we had in Proposition 2.35, but the signs in our calculation will work out better this way. Accordingly, we adopt adjusted notations from Proposition 2.35, so for any chain $\alpha \in C_n(\mathcal{K})$, $n \geqslant 0$, we let $\alpha \cup w$ and $\alpha \cup v$ denote the $(n+1)$-chains in $\operatorname{susp} \mathcal{K}$, which are obtained by adding the vertices w or v to each simplex in the linear combination α. Due to the ordering, these are added at the end of the ordered simplices.

Consider the map $\varphi : C_n(\mathcal{K}) \to C_{n+1}(\operatorname{susp} \mathcal{K})$, defined by

$$\alpha \mapsto \alpha \cup v - \alpha \cup w. \tag{2.18}$$

Obviously, φ is a linear map.

Assume now that $n \geqslant 1$. In analogy with Equation (2.16), we have the following calculation:

$$\begin{aligned}\partial_{n+1}(\varphi(\alpha)) &= \partial_{n+1}(\alpha \cup v - \alpha \cup w) \\ &= (\partial_n \alpha \cup v + (-1)^{n+1}\alpha) - (\partial_n \alpha \cup w + (-1)^{n+1}\alpha) \\ &= \partial_n \alpha \cup v - \partial_n \alpha \cup w = \varphi(\partial_n \alpha).\end{aligned}$$

This means that $\varphi(Z_n(\mathcal{K})) \subseteq Z_{n+1}(\text{susp } \mathcal{K})$ and $\varphi(B_n(\mathcal{K})) \subseteq B_{n+1}(\text{susp } \mathcal{K})$. Hence we have an induced map $\widetilde{\varphi} : H_n(\mathcal{K}) \to H_{n+1}(\text{susp } \mathcal{K})$.

Note that for any $\sigma \in C_{n+1}(\text{susp } \mathcal{K})$, we can write $\sigma = \alpha + \beta \cup v + \gamma \cup w$, where $\alpha \in C_{n+1}(\mathcal{K})$, $\beta, \gamma \in C_n(\mathcal{K})$. We then have

(2.19) $$\partial_{n+1}\sigma = \partial_{n+1}\alpha + (-1)^{n+1}\beta + (-1)^{n+1}\gamma + \partial_n \beta \cup v + \partial_n \gamma \cup w.$$

Let us show that the map $\widetilde{\varphi} : H_n(\mathcal{K}) \to H_{n+1}(\text{susp } \mathcal{K})$ is surjective. Take $\sigma \in Z_{n+1}(\text{susp } \mathcal{K})$, i.e., $\partial_{n+1}\sigma = 0$, and take the representation $\sigma = \alpha + \beta \cup v + \gamma \cup w$ as above. Equation (2.19) implies that

$$\partial_{n+1}\alpha + (-1)^{n+1}\beta + (-1)^{n+1}\gamma = 0,$$

or, equivalently, we have $\gamma = (-1)^n \partial_{n+1}\alpha - \beta$. We substitute this back into our representation for σ to obtain

$$\sigma = \alpha + \beta \cup v + (-1)^n \partial_{n+1}\alpha \cup w - \beta \cup w = \varphi(\beta) + (-1)^n \partial_{n+2}(\alpha \cup w).$$

This means that any homology class of susp $\mathcal{K}$ has a representative of the form $\varphi(\beta)$, which is the same as saying that $\widetilde{\varphi}$ is surjective.

To see that $\widetilde{\varphi}$ is injective, take $\sigma \in Z_n(\mathcal{K})$, such that $[\varphi(\sigma)] = \widetilde{\varphi}([\sigma]) = 0$. In other words, $[\sigma \cup v - \sigma \cup w] = 0$. This means that there exists $\alpha \in C_{n+2}(\mathcal{K})$ and $\beta, \gamma \in C_{n+1}(\mathcal{K})$, such that $\sigma \cup v - \sigma \cup w = \partial_{n+2}(\alpha + \beta \cup v + \gamma \cup w)$. It follows from Equation (2.19) that $\sigma = \partial_{n+1}\beta$. Hence $[\sigma] = 0$ and $\widetilde{\varphi}$ is injective.

The proof of the remaining statement that $H_1(\text{susp } \mathcal{K}) \oplus \mathbb{Z} \approx H_0(\mathcal{K})$ is similar, with a small twist. We leave it as an exercise for the interested reader; see Exercise (8). □

2.7.6. Simplicial join. The coning operation has a clear geometric connotation: given a geometric simplicial complex $\mathcal{K}$, add a new generic vertex a and span a cone over $\mathcal{K}$. Of course there are many situations where this will not work directly, as it will produce many self-intersections. What one can do instead is to add another dimension and choose a outside of the hyperplane containing $\mathcal{K}$.

This line of thought can be pursued further by starting with two simplicial complexes $\mathcal{K}_1$ and $\mathcal{K}_2$, placing them in complimentary Euclidean spaces, and then taking the convex hull. This is known as the *join* of the simplicial complexes. The next definition describes the obtained simplicial structure.

Definition 2.38. Let $\mathcal{K}_1$ and $\mathcal{K}_2$ be two finite ordered simplicial complexes whose vertices are indexed by disjoint sets. The *join* of $\mathcal{K}_1$ and $\mathcal{K}_2$, denoted $\mathcal{K}_1 * \mathcal{K}_2$, is the finite ordered simplicial complex $\mathcal{K}_1 * \mathcal{K}_2$ defined as follows:

- the set of vertices of $\mathcal{K}_1 * \mathcal{K}_2$ is a disjoint union $\mathcal{K}_1(0) \cup \mathcal{K}_2(0)$, where we can choose a new order by making all vertices of $\mathcal{K}_1$ preceed all the vertices of $\mathcal{K}_2$, and otherwise inheriting the order from $\mathcal{K}_1(0)$ and $\mathcal{K}_2(0)$;
- the set of simplices is given by

$$\begin{aligned}\mathcal{K}_1 * \mathcal{K}_2 &= \{\sigma \subseteq \mathcal{K}_1(0) \cup \mathcal{K}_2(0) \,|\, \sigma \cap \mathcal{K}_1(0) \in \mathcal{K}_1 \text{ and } \sigma \cap \mathcal{K}_2(0) \in \mathcal{K}_2\} \\ &= \{\sigma \cup \tau \,|\, \sigma \in \mathcal{K}_1,\ \tau \in \mathcal{K}_2\}.\end{aligned}$$

As an example, the simplicial join of a 1-simplex and the boundary of a 2-simplex is a union of three tetrahedra; see Figure 2.17.

In a certain sense we have commutativity: for arbitrary finite ordered simplicial complexes $\mathcal{K}_1$ and $\mathcal{K}_2$ the joins $\mathcal{K}_1 * \mathcal{K}_2$ and $\mathcal{K}_2 * \mathcal{K}_1$ can be obtained from each other by a straightforward permutation of vertices. The join is also associative, namely, for arbitrary abstract simplicial complexes $\mathcal{K}_1$, $\mathcal{K}_2$, and $\mathcal{K}_3$, the joins $(\mathcal{K}_1 * \mathcal{K}_2) * \mathcal{K}_3$ and $\mathcal{K}_1 * (\mathcal{K}_2 * \mathcal{K}_3)$ are equal.

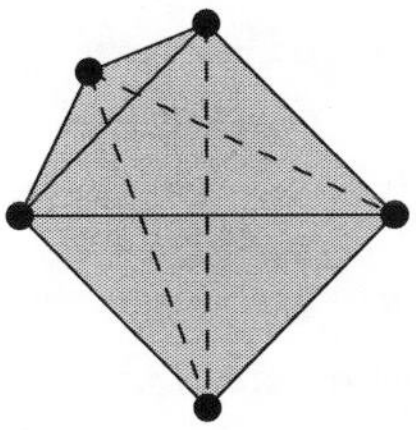

Figure 2.17. Simplicial join of a 1-simplex and the boundary of a 2-simplex.

Another important property of the join is that for any finite abstract simplicial complex $\mathcal{K}$ and any simplex $\tau \in \mathcal{K}$, the abstract simplicial complexes $\mathrm{lk}_{\mathcal{K}}(\tau) * \tau$ and $\mathrm{st}(\tau)$ are isomorphic.

As indicated above, joining with the finite ordered simplicial complex consisting of a single vertex is the same as coning. Joining with the simplicial complex consisting of two vertices is the same as suspension. In general, one can take a join with the finite ordered simplicial complex with n vertices and no simplices of dimension 1 and higher. This is the n-*coning*, giving the same result as taking the union of n single conings over a common base space.

2.7.7. Stellar subdivision. The simplest possible subdivision of a simplicial complex is obtained as follows. Pick a maximal simplex σ, and *star* it by

- putting a new vertex $\hat{\sigma}$ somewhere inside of σ, for instance, at its barycenter,
- coning over the boundary of σ, using $\hat{\sigma}$ as an apex.

More generally, one can pick any simplex, not necessarily the maximal one, and then star it in a similar way. The next definition makes this idea formal.

Definition 2.39. Let $\mathcal{K}$ be a finite ordered simplicial complex, and let σ be a simplex of $\mathcal{K}$. The *stellar subdivision of* $\mathcal{K}$ *at* σ is the abstract simplicial complex $\mathrm{Sd}_{\mathcal{K}}(\sigma)$ defined by the following:

- For the set of vertices we have $\mathrm{Sd}_{\mathcal{K}}(\sigma)(0) = \mathcal{K}(0) \cup \{\hat{\sigma}\}$, where $\hat{\sigma}$ denotes the new vertex *indexed by* σ.
- The simplex $\tau \in \mathcal{K}$ is a simplex of $\mathrm{Sd}_{\mathcal{K}}(\sigma)$ if and only if τ does not contain σ as a subset. Additionally, the abstract simplicial complex $\mathrm{Sd}_{\mathcal{K}}(\sigma)$ has simplices of the form $\tau \cup \{\hat{\sigma}\}$, where $\tau \in \mathcal{K}$, such that $\tau \cup \sigma \in \mathcal{K}$ and τ does not contain σ as a subset.

Note that in case σ itself is a vertex, we have $\hat{\sigma} = \sigma$, hence no new vertex is introduced, and in fact the subdivision does not change the simplicial complex $\mathcal{K}$.

An example of a stellar subdivision is shown in Figure 2.2. For those familiar with convex geometry, we remark that the stellar subdivision of an n-simplex is the Schlegel diagram of an $(n+1)$-simplex.

Proposition 2.40. *The stellar subdivision of a simplicial complex at an arbitrary simplex does not change the homology groups of that complex.*

The proof of Proposition 2.40 is a bit technical and is best done when we have more tools at our disposal.

2.7.8. Barycentric subdivision. Perhaps the most important subdivision operation on simplicial complexes is the so-called *barycentric subdivision.* The name comes from the fact that one adds a new vertex at the barycenter of each simplex. The next definition describes the obtained simplicial structure.

Definition 2.41. Let $\mathcal{K}$ be a finite ordered simplicial complex. The *barycentric subdivision* of $\mathcal{K}$ is also a finite ordered simplicial complex, which is denoted by $\mathrm{Bd}\ \mathcal{K}$. For each $n \geqslant 0$, the set of n-simplices of $\mathrm{Bd}\ \mathcal{K}$ is given by

$$\mathrm{Bd}\ \mathcal{K}(n) := \{\{\sigma_0, \dots, \sigma_n\} \mid \sigma_0 \supset \sigma_1 \supset \dots \supset \sigma_n, \sigma_i \in \mathcal{K} \setminus \emptyset\}.$$

Note that, in particular, the set of vertices of Bd $\mathcal{K}$ is indexed by the non-empty simplices of $\mathcal{K}$. For the definition of an ordered simplicial complex, we actually need to choose an order on the vertices of Bd $\mathcal{K}$, although homology calculations will yield the same result. There are many ways to choose such an order. Let us say that we first sort all the vertices according to the dimension t of the simplices indexing them, with smaller values of t coming first, and then sort the vertices with the same t lexicographically.

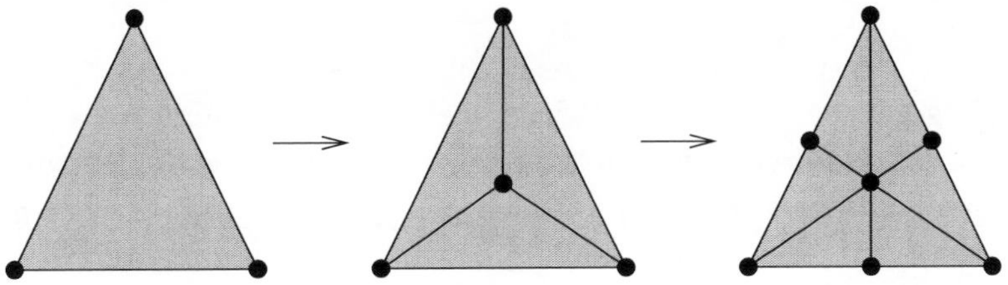

Figure 2.18. Barycentric subdivision as a sequence of stellar ones.

A simplex sequence $(\sigma_0, \dots, \sigma_n)$ such that $\sigma_0 \supset \cdots \supset \sigma_n$ is also called a *flag* of simplices. So the barycentric subdivision is composed of flags of the old simplices.

Note that if we forget the order of the vertices, Definitions 2.39 and 2.41 describe the constructions of stellar and barycentric subdivisions for an arbitrary finite abstract simplicial complex.

Theorem 2.42. *Barycentric subdivision of a finite abstract simplicial complex $\mathcal{K}$ can be represented as a sequence of stellar subdivisions. In particular, it does not change the homology of $\mathcal{K}$.*

Proof. Assume $\mathcal{K}$ has dimension d. The barycentric subdivision of $\mathcal{K}$ is obtained by the following process:

(1) take the stellar subdivision of all the d-simplices of $\mathcal{K}$,

(2) take the stellar subdivisions of those $(d-1)$-simplices of the obtained complex which were $(d-1)$-simplices in the original complex $\mathcal{K}$,

(3) repeat this for dimensions $d-2$ through 1.

The obtained abstract simplicial complex is the same as Bd $\mathcal{K}$, see Figure 2.18. The homology claim now follows from Proposition 2.40, together with the independence on the order of the vertices. □

2.8. Simplicial maps

As usual, it is important to consider the structure-preserving maps between simplicial complexes.

Definition 2.43. Assume $\mathcal{K}$ is an abstract simplicial complex with vertex set S, and $\mathcal{M}$ is an abstract simplicial complex with vertex set T. A map $f : S \to T$ is called a *simplicial map* if it maps simplices of $\mathcal{K}$ to simplices of $\mathcal{M}$. In other words, if $\sigma \in \mathcal{K}$, then $f(\sigma) \in \mathcal{M}$.

It is easy to see that composition of simplicial maps is again a simplicial map, and also the identity map is simplicial. This means we may consider the *category* of all abstract simplicial complexes and simplicial maps, called **SCpx**.

Assume σ is a geometric simplex with the set of vertices A and τ is a geometric simplex with the set of vertices B. A simplicial map $f : A \to B$ induces a continuous map from σ to τ: simply apply f to the barycentric coordinates. Gluing these maps together, a simplicial map between $\mathcal{K}$ and $\mathcal{M}$ will clearly induce a continuous map between geometric realizations $|\mathcal{K}|$ and $|\mathcal{M}|$.

Let n be a non-negative integer. The chain groups $C_n(\mathcal{K})$ and $C_n(\mathcal{M})$ are generated by the sets of n-simplices $\mathcal{K}(n)$ and $\mathcal{M}(d)$. Since f maps n-simplices to n-simplices, it induces group homomorphisms $f_n^\sharp : C_n(\mathcal{K}) \to C_n(\mathcal{M})$. We have the following important proposition.

Proposition 2.44. *In the situation above, the maps $\{f_n^\sharp\}_{n\in\mathbb{Z}}$ induce group homomorphisms on the homology groups $f_n^* : H_n(\mathcal{K}) \to H_n(\mathcal{M})$.*

Furthermore, if $\mathcal{N}$ is another abstract simplicial complex and $g : \mathcal{M} \to \mathcal{N}$ is a simplicial map, then these homomorphisms satisfy the property $g_n^* \circ f_n^* = (g \circ f)_n^*$.

We leave the proof of Proposition 2.44 as an exercise; see Exercise (12).

Exercises

(1) Assume G is a graph. The *neighborhood complex* of G is a simplicial complex $\mathcal{N}(G)$ defined as follows:
- the set of vertices of $\mathcal{N}(G)$ coincides with the set of vertices of G;
- the simplices of $\mathcal{N}(G)$ are all the sets of vertices which have a common neighbor.[11]

(a) Calculate the homology of $\mathcal{N}(C_n)$, where C_n is a cycle with n vertices, where $n \geqslant 3$.

(b) Calculate the homology of $\mathcal{N}(K_n)$, where K_n is the complete graph with n vertices, where $n \geqslant 2$.

[11] A set of vertices S is said to have a common neighbor if there exists a vertex adjacent to all the vertices in S.

(c) Calculate the homology of the neighborhood complex of the Petersen graph.

(2) Assume G is a graph. The *flag complex* of G, also called the *clique complex* of G, is the simplicial complex $F(G)$ defined as follows:
- the vertices of $F(G)$ are the vertices of G;
- the simplices of $F(G)$ are the complete subgraphs of G.

A simplicial complex $\mathcal{K}$ is called *flag* if there exists a graph G such that $\mathcal{K} = F(G)$. In fact, if it exists, the graph G must be the 1-skeleton of $\mathcal{K}$. For each $n \geqslant 1$ give an explicit example of the simplicial complex which is flag, but which has non-trivial homology in dimension n.

(3) Assume we are given a positive integer d, and consider the simplicial complex X_d defined as follows:
- the vertices of X_d are indexed by all proper subsets of $[d]$;
- the n-simplices of X_d are the collection of vertices $\{S_0, \dots, S_n\}$ which can be arranged so that $S_0 \subset S_1 \subset \dots \subset S_n$.

Calculate the homology groups of X_d.

(4) Assume we are given an integer $n \geqslant 1$, and consider the simplicial complex X_n defined as follows:
- the vertices of X_n are indexed by all proper partitions of the set $\{1, \dots, n\}$, where the partition is called proper if it has at least two blocks and does not entirely consist of singletons;
- the simplices of X_n are the collections of vertices $\{\pi_1, \dots, \pi_t\}$ which can be arranged so that π_1 refines π_2, π_2 refines π_3, and so on for the entire string.

Calculate the homology groups of X_4 and X_5.

(5) Let n and d be nonnegative integers such that $n \geqslant d$. Consider the simplicial complex $\text{sk}_d \Delta_n$ defined by

$$\text{sk}_d \Delta_n := \{\sigma \subseteq [n] \,|\, |\sigma| \leqslant d+1\}.$$

The simplicial complex $\text{sk}_d \Delta_n$ is called the *dth skeleton* of the n-simplex.
(a) Give a basis for the homology groups $H_0(\text{sk}_d \Delta_n)$ and $H_1(\text{sk}_d \Delta_n)$.
(b) Give a basis for the homology group $H_2(\text{sk}_d \Delta_n)$.
(c) Calculate the homology group $H_n(\text{sk}_d \Delta_n)$, for all n and d. Can you give a basis?

(6) Given a graph G, its *independence complex* $\text{Ind}(G)$ is defined as follows:
- the vertices of $\text{Ind}(G)$ are the vertices of G;
- the simplices of $\text{Ind}(G)$ are all possible independent[12] sets of vertices.

(a) Show that the independence complex of a graph G is the same as the clique complex of the complement of G.

[12] A set of vertices is called *independent* if no two vertices are connected by an edge.

(b) Let L_n be graph with the set of vertices $\{1, \dots, n\}$ and the set of edges $\{(1,2), (2,3), \dots, (n-1, n)\}$. Calculate the homology of the independence complex of the graph L_n.

(7) Assume $\mathcal{K}$ is an abstract simplicial complex, which can be represented as a union of simplices $\sigma_1, \dots, \sigma_n$ (and their boundary simplices), such that for some integer $d \geqslant 2$ we have
- $\dim \sigma_i \geqslant d$, for all i;
- for every $1 \leqslant i < j \leqslant n$ the intersection $\sigma_i \cap \sigma_j$ has dimension at most $d-2$.

Show that the homology of $\mathcal{K}$ vanishes in dimension d and above.

(8) Let $\mathcal{K}$ be a simplicial complex. Consider the subset S of $C_0(\mathcal{K})$ consisting of all linear combinations $c_1 v_1 + \cdots + c_q v_q$, such that $c_1 + \cdots + c_q = 0$.
(a) Show that S is a subgroup of $C_0(\mathcal{K})$.
(b) Show that S is a disjoint union of cosets of the boundary group $B_0(\mathcal{K})$, and that the corresponding homology classes form a subgroup of $H_0(\mathcal{K})$.
(c) Let T denote the subgroup of $H_0(\mathcal{K})$, which is described in (b). Finish the proof of Proposition 2.37 by showing that T is isomorphic to $H_1(\operatorname{susp} \mathcal{K})$.

(9) Assume $\mathcal{K}$ is an abstract simplicial complex of dimension d, $d < \infty$. The complex $\mathcal{K}$ is called a *pseudomanifold* if the following two conditions are satisfied:
- each $(d-1)$-simplex of $\mathcal{K}$ is contained in exactly one or in exactly two d-simplices of $\mathcal{K}$;
- for any two d-simplices $\sigma_1, \sigma_2 \in \mathcal{K}(d)$, there exists a sequence of d-simplices $\tau_1, \dots, \tau_k \in \mathcal{K}(d)$, such that $\tau_1 = \sigma_1$, $\tau_k = \sigma_2$, and for all $1 \leqslant i \leqslant k-1$ the d-simplices τ_i and τ_{i+1} share a common $(d-1)$-simplex.

Assume now that $\mathcal{K}$ is such a pseudomanifold of dimension d.
(a) Calculate $H_d(\mathcal{K}; \mathbb{Z}_2)$.
(b) What are the possibilities for $H_d(\mathcal{K}; \mathbb{Z})$? Give a combinatorial criterion determining this group.

(10) Investigate what happens to homology when we add a single simplex to a given simplicial complex. Differentiate between the cases of $\mathbb{Z}_2$ and integer coefficients.

(11) Let $\mathcal{K}$ be an abstract simplicial complex, and let t be a positive integer. Definition 2.36 can be generalized as follows. We construct a new abstract simplicial complex L, as obtained from $\mathcal{K}$ by adding n new vertices

$v_1, \ldots, v_n$ and then taking as a set of simplices the union

$$\{\sigma \mid \sigma \in \mathcal{K}\} \cup \bigcup_{i=1}^{n} \{\sigma \cup v_i \mid \sigma \in \mathcal{K}\}.$$

The abstract simplicial complex L is called the n-*coning* of $\mathcal{K}$. Which constructions do we recover for $n = 1$ and $n = 2$? In general, investigate what happens to homology when we perform an n-coning.

(12) Prove Proposition 2.44.

Chapter 3

Beyond the Simplicial Setting

Simplicial complexes constitute a major tool in algebraic topology. However, in several situations other structures will arise in a natural way. We use this short chapter to give the reader a glimpse into some of these frameworks. In order to avoid slowing down too much, we choose that in this chapter some of the proofs are left as sketches and others are left as exercises. We will resume a more rigorous treatment starting with the next chapter.

3.1. Polyhedral homology

3.1.1. Cubical homology. In many instances in practice, for example in vision recognition, the topological space is rendered in a rectangular grid. On the plane it is known as the *pixel* representation, whereas one speaks about *voxels* in the 3-dimensional space.

In general, this can be formalized as follows. Fix the dimension d and consider the integer grid $\mathbb{Z}^d$ in $\mathbb{R}^d$.

Definition 3.1. Assume $p = (p_1, \dots, p_d)$ is a vector with integer coordinates, and $l = (l_1, \dots, l_d)$ is a vector with 0/1 entries, i.e., $p \in \mathbb{Z}^d$ and $l \in \{0,1\}^d$. The set $c(p,l) := [p_1, p_1 + l_1] \times \cdots \times [p_d, p_d + l_d]$ is called the *grid cube* in $\mathbb{R}^d$ associated to the vectors p and l.

The integer grid point p is called the *base point* of $c(p,l)$. The dimension of $c(p,l)$ is equal to the number of 1's in the vector l, i.e., $\dim c(p,l) = l_1 + \cdots + l_d$. So the 0-dimensional grid cubes have $l = (0, \dots, 0)$ and correspond to the integer grid points themselves, and the d-dimensional grid cubes have $l = \underbrace{(1, \ldots, 1)}_{d}$.

Definition 3.2. A collection of grid cubes X is called a *grid cubical complex* if whenever $c \in X$, all the grid cubes contained as subsets in c also belong to X.

Given such a grid cubical complex X, the geometric union of all of its grid cubes is called the *geometric realization* of X and is denoted by $|X|$.

The cubical homology of X can then be defined as follows. For each $n \geqslant 0$, let $Q_n(X)$ denote the free abelian group generated by the n-dimensional grid cubes in X. We define the nth boundary operator of X by setting

$$(3.1)\quad \partial_n c(p, l)$$

$$:= \sum_{m=1}^{d} (-1)^{l_1+\cdots+l_m}([p_1, p_1 + l_1] \times \cdots \times \{p_m\} \times \cdots \times [p_d, p_d + l_d]$$

$$- [p_1, p_1 + l_1] \times \cdots \times \{p_m + l_m\} \times \cdots \times [p_d, p_d + l_d]),$$

where $n = \dim c(p, l) = l_1 + \cdots + l_d$.

We leave it to the reader to verify that (3.1) gives us maps which satisfy necessary conditions for being a boundary operator; see Exercise (1).

Definition 3.3. Let X be a grid cubical complex. Its *cubical homology groups* $QH_n(X)$ are defined by setting $QH_n(X) := \operatorname{Ker} \partial_n / \operatorname{Im} \partial_{n+1}$, for all $n \in \mathbb{Z}$.

Of course, as an alternative, we can subdivide each grid cube in a grid cubical complex into simplices, and then compute the resulting simplicial homology. The obtained homology groups will be the same, or to be more precise, they will be isomorphic to the cubical homology, which we just described. While true, this statement is rather difficult to prove. We suggest that the reader simply know and trust it at that point, including the general fact that the simplicial homology is independent of the triangulation.

3.1.2. General polyhedra.

While sufficient for many specific purposes, considering only grid cubical complexes is too restrictive in general. The following definition allows us to get rid of the grid and to allow more general shapes.

Definition 3.4. A *polyhedral complex* X consists of a finite set of closed convex polytopes in a Euclidean space, such that

(1) whenever a polytope P is contained in X, so are all its faces;

(2) the intersection of any two polytopes in X is either empty or is a face of each of them.

Accordingly, the *geometric realization of X* is just the union of all the polytopes in X.

Assume H is a hyperplane in a Euclidean space. Of course it divides the total space into two half-spaces. Assume furthermore that we have chosen an orientation in H, say by fixing an order of a certain basis of H. Then one of the half-spaces is called the positive half-space and is denoted by H^+, the other one is then the negative half-space. For any vector v outside of H, compute the sign of the determinant of the matrix whose columns are the basis vectors of H and v. H^+ consists of all the vectors for which this determinant is positive.

Assume now that K is a polytope of dimension m in a Euclidean space $\mathbb{R}^d$, and M is one of its boundary polytopes of dimension $m-1$. Assume furthermore that we have chosen an orientation on M. Then using the linear algebra fact above, we can define a sign $[K : M]$ as follows: let S be the linear span of K and let H be the linear span of M; then H is a hyperplane in S, and the orientation on M gives an orientation on H. We now set $[K : M] := 1$ if K lies in the positive half-space with respect to H, and set $[K : M] := -1$ if it lies in the negative half-space.

We can define polyhedral homology as follows. We let $P_n(X)$ be the free abelian group generated by all n-dimensional polytopes in X. The boundary operator is defined by

$$\partial_n K := \sum_M [K : M]\, M,$$

where the sum is taken over all $(n-1)$-dimensional boundary polytopes of K.

The polyhedral homology groups are then simply defined by setting $PH_n(X) = \operatorname{Ker} \partial_n / \operatorname{Im} \partial_{n+1}$.

3.2. Chain complexes of free abelian groups

Valiant as they are, the attempts from the previous section quickly reach their limits. To start with, the geometric realization of a polyhedral complex is by definition embedded in a Euclidean space. For various reasons, one would often like to avoid such specific embeddings.

It is possible to generalize the direct definition of polyhedral complexes which have been previously given by describing *polyhedral gluing schemes,* where the complex is given as an abstract set of disjoint polyhedra, equipped with an intricate system of identifying boundary subpolyhedra by means of various isometries. Though certainly doable, it is hardly practical. Instead, it is time to switch altogether to abstract algebra. This will both reduce the technical side of the arguments dramatically, as well as deliver a much more satisfactory generality.

We begin by considering the simplest, but also the most important, instance: the chain complexes of free abelian groups. These will also be our default gadgets unless explicitly stated otherwise.

3.2.1. Chain complexes of free abelian groups and their homology.

Definition 3.5. A *chain complex of free abelian groups* $\mathcal{C}$ consists of a family of free abelian groups $(C_n)_{n\in\mathbb{Z}}$, together with a family of group homomorphisms $(\partial_n^{\mathcal{C}})_{n\in\mathbb{Z}}$, $\partial_n^{\mathcal{C}} : C_n \to C_{n-1}$, such that $\partial_{n-1}^{\mathcal{C}} \circ \partial_n^{\mathcal{C}} = 0$, for all n:

$$\mathcal{C}: \quad \dots \xrightarrow{\partial_{n+2}^{\mathcal{C}}} C_{n+1} \xrightarrow{\partial_{n+1}^{\mathcal{C}}} C_n \xrightarrow{\partial_n^{\mathcal{C}}} C_{n-1} \xrightarrow{\partial_{n-1}^{\mathcal{C}}} \dots .$$

The shorthand notation, which we shall use for such a chain complex, will be $\mathcal{C} = (C_*, \partial_*^{\mathcal{C}})$. As mentioned earlier, the identity $\partial_{n-1}^{\mathcal{C}} \circ \partial_n^{\mathcal{C}} = 0$ often gets trivialized to the succinct statement $\partial^{\mathcal{C}} \circ \partial^{\mathcal{C}} = 0$. Informally, one says that

a chain complex is a sequence of groups, connected by the boundary operator, whose square is 0.

Inextricably connected to the concept of a chain complex is the concept of its homology.

Definition 3.6. Assume we are given a chain complex of free abelian groups $\mathcal{C} = (C_*, \partial_*^{\mathcal{C}})$. For every integer n, we define the n*th homology group of* $\mathcal{C}$ to be the quotient group

$$H_n(\mathcal{C}) := \operatorname{Ker} \partial_n^{\mathcal{C}} \big/ \operatorname{Im} \partial_{n+1}^{\mathcal{C}}. \tag{3.2}$$

We shall also write $H_*(\mathcal{C})$ to denote the totality of all homology groups of $\mathcal{C}$.

As mentioned in a previous chapter, the classification theorem of finitely generated abelian groups can be used to define the torsion part and the Betti numbers of the simplicial complexes. Since the statement is purely algebraic, we can do exactly the same for the homology groups of chain complexes, so we extend the use of these notions to that general framework.

For future reference we fix the following general notion.

Definition 3.7. A chain complex is called *acyclic* if all its homology groups are trivial.

Assume now that we have two chain complexes of free abelian groups. Denote them $\mathcal{C} = (C_*, \partial_*^{\mathcal{C}})$ and $\mathcal{D} = (D_*, \partial_*^{\mathcal{D}})$. The following definition provides an analog of simplicial maps in the context of chain complexes.

Definition 3.8. A *chain map* between $\mathcal{C}$ and $\mathcal{D}$ is a collection of group homomorphisms $(\varphi_n)_{n\in\mathbb{Z}}$, $\varphi_n : C_n \to D_n$, such that $\varphi_{n-1} \circ \partial_n^{\mathcal{C}} = \partial_n^{\mathcal{D}} \circ \varphi_n$ for all $n \in \mathbb{Z}$. In other words, the following diagram commutes:

$$\begin{array}{ccccccccc}
\dots & \xrightarrow{\partial_{n+2}^{\mathcal{C}}} & C_{n+1} & \xrightarrow{\partial_{n+1}^{\mathcal{C}}} & C_n & \xrightarrow{\partial_n^{\mathcal{C}}} & C_{n-1} & \xrightarrow{\partial_{n-1}^{\mathcal{C}}} & \dots \\
 & & \downarrow{\scriptstyle \varphi_{n+1}} & & \downarrow{\scriptstyle \varphi_n} & & \downarrow{\scriptstyle \varphi_{n-1}} & & \\
\dots & \xrightarrow{\partial_{n+2}^{\mathcal{D}}} & D_{n+1} & \xrightarrow{\partial_{n+1}^{\mathcal{D}}} & D_n & \xrightarrow{\partial_n^{\mathcal{D}}} & D_{n-1} & \xrightarrow{\partial_{n-1}^{\mathcal{D}}} & \dots
\end{array}$$

Clearly, when all φ_n are identity maps, the resulting collection is a chain map. Furthermore, the chain maps can be composed by setting $(\psi_n \circ \varphi_n)_{n\in\mathbb{Z}}$ to be the composition of the chain maps $(\psi_n)_{n\in\mathbb{Z}}$ and $(\varphi_n)_{n\in\mathbb{Z}}$. The result is again a chain map.

Finally, to define the analog of reduced homology, assume $\mathcal{C} = (C_*, \partial_*^{\mathcal{C}})$ is a chain complex of free abelian groups, such that $C_n = 0$, whenever n is negative. Assume furthermore that S is some fixed basis of C_0. Define a new chain complex $\widetilde{\mathcal{C}} = \left(\widetilde{C}_*, \partial_*^{\widetilde{\mathcal{C}}}\right)$ as follows. We set

$$\widetilde{C}_n := \begin{cases} C_n, & \text{if } n \neq -1, \\ \mathbb{Z}, & \text{if } n = -1. \end{cases}$$

The boundary maps of $\widetilde{\mathcal{C}}$ are defined by

$$\partial_n^{\widetilde{\mathcal{C}}} := \begin{cases} \partial_n^{\mathcal{C}}, & \text{if } n \neq 0, -1, \\ \varepsilon, & \text{if } n = 0, \\ 0\text{-map}, & \text{if } n = -1, \end{cases}$$

where $\varepsilon : C_0 \to \mathbb{Z}$ is uniquely defined by setting $\varepsilon(s) := 1$, for all $s \in S$:

$$\widetilde{\mathcal{C}}: \quad \dots \xrightarrow{\partial_2^{\mathcal{C}}} C_1 \xrightarrow{\partial_1^{\mathcal{C}}} C_0 \xrightarrow{\varepsilon} \mathbb{Z} \longrightarrow 0 \longrightarrow \dots$$

The homology of $\widetilde{\mathcal{C}}$ is called the *reduced homology* of $\mathcal{C}$.

3.2.2. First examples. The simplest possible chain complex is the one where $C_n = 0$, for all $n \in \mathbb{Z}$. The homology groups of this complex are all 0. The next simplest case would be where exactly one of the groups is non-trivial, say $C_0 \neq 0$, and $C_n = 0$, for all $n \in \mathbb{Z}$, $n \neq 0$:

$$\mathcal{C}: \qquad \dots \xrightarrow{\partial_2^{\mathcal{C}}} 0 \xrightarrow{\partial_1^{\mathcal{C}}} C_0 \xrightarrow{\partial_0^{\mathcal{C}}} 0 \xrightarrow{\partial_{-1}^{\mathcal{C}}} \dots .$$

In this case, we have $\operatorname{Ker}\partial_0^{\mathcal{C}} = C_0$, $\operatorname{Ker}\partial_n^{\mathcal{C}} = 0$, for all $n \neq 0$, and $\operatorname{Im}\partial_n^{\mathcal{C}} = 0$, for all n. It follows that $H_0(\mathcal{C}) = C_0$, and $H_n(\mathcal{C}) = 0$, for $n \neq 0$.

Let us now consider a different chain complex $\mathcal{C}$, where $C_0 = C_1 = \mathbb{Z}$, and $C_n = 0$, for $n \neq 0, 1$. The only potentially non-trivial boundary map is $\partial_1^{\mathcal{C}} : \mathbb{Z} \to \mathbb{Z}$, and this map must be a multiplication with some integer m:

$$\dots \xrightarrow{\partial_3^{\mathcal{C}}} 0 \xrightarrow{\partial_2^{\mathcal{C}}} \mathbb{Z} \xrightarrow[x \mapsto mx]{\partial_1^{\mathcal{C}}} \mathbb{Z} \xrightarrow{\partial_0^{\mathcal{C}}} 0 \xrightarrow{\partial_{-1}^{\mathcal{C}}} \dots . \tag{3.3}$$

The only non-trivial kernels of boundary operators are $\operatorname{Ker}\partial_0^{\mathcal{C}} = \mathbb{Z}$, and, if $m = 0$, also $\operatorname{Ker}\partial_1^{\mathcal{C}} = \mathbb{Z}$. The only potentially non-trivial image of a boundary operator is $\operatorname{Im}\partial_1^{\mathcal{C}} = |m| \cdot \mathbb{Z}$. We thus have $H_n(\mathcal{C}) = 0$, whenever $n \neq 0, 1$, and

$$H_0(\mathcal{C}) \approx \begin{cases} \mathbb{Z}, & m = 0, \\ \mathbb{Z}_m, & |m| \geqslant 2, \\ 0, & m = \pm 1; \end{cases} \qquad H_1(\mathcal{C}) \approx \begin{cases} \mathbb{Z}, & m = 0, \\ 0, & m \neq 0. \end{cases}$$

So there are three options for the pair of homology groups $(H_0(\mathcal{C}), H_1(\mathcal{C}))$, namely $(\mathbb{Z}, \mathbb{Z})$, $(\mathbb{Z}_m, 0)$, or $(0, 0)$. The chain complex (3.3) will play a role later on.

More general examples of chain complexes of free groups are provided by taking simplicial complexes, letting the chain groups be freely generated by simplices, and taking the usual simplicial boundary operator. The homology groups of this chain complex coincide with the simplicial homology groups.

It is also possible to arrive at the chain complexes directly from an arbitrary topological space X, bypassing any simplicial considerations. To do that, one will need to define the concept of a *singular simplex*, and then let these singular simplices freely generate the chain groups. The singular boundary operator will have to be defined in a separate way. This will result in the so-called *singular chain complex* of X, which will be treated in Chapter 7. The homology groups of that complex are called the *singular homology groups of* X, and we shall see that they are isomorphic to simplicial homology groups whenever the latter are defined. Even though the resulting chain complex is huge, it has the theoretical advantage of being defined for arbitrary topological spaces.

3.3. Cell complexes

Finally, we would like to take the polyhedral complex construction yet one step further and learn how to construct spaces by gluing topological balls using arbitrary continuous maps. There are three things which we need to learn in this context. First, we need to learn how to glue spaces together. Second, we need to fix what gluing schemes of balls we allow. Third, we need to define something called *cellular homology*. Unfortunately, the last concept requires quite a bit of technical development: either we need the notion of a connecting homomorphism, or we need to learn how to compute singular homology of spheres. Either way, it is best to postpone this until Part II. For now, we will simply be satisfied with being able to construct the spaces. We start by learning how the attaching procedure works.

3.3.1. Attaching spaces.

The next definition from point-set topology formalizes the intuitive notion of gluing.

Definition 3.9. Assume X and Y are topological spaces, A is a subspace of X, and f is a continuous map from A to Y. We define a new topological space Z as the quotient space $Z := (X \amalg Y)/\sim$, where

- $X \amalg Y$ is the disjoint union of X and Y,
- $\sim$ is the equivalence relation generated by $a \sim f(a)$, for all $a \in A$.

One says that the topologicial space Z is obtained by *attaching the space* X *to the space* Y *over the function* f. A standard notation is $Z := Y \cup_f X$, and the space Z is called the *adjunction space.*[1]

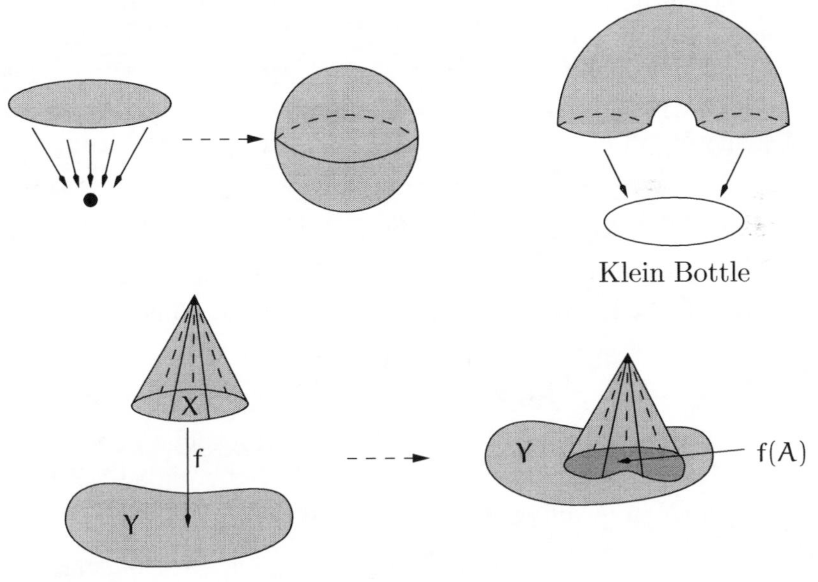

Figure 3.1. Examples of adjunction spaces: sphere, Klein bottle, and a mapping cone.

Many examples of spaces and general constructions in topology can be viewed through the prism of adjunction spaces. Figure 3.1 contains some examples. In the simplest one on the upper left of this figure, the space X is a 2-dimensional disc, A its boundary, and Y is a one-point space, which of

[1] Another frequently used name is *attaching space*.

course defines the map f uniquely. This yields $Y \cup_f X \cong S^2$. In the example in the upper right of this figure the space X is a cylinder, the space Y is a circle, the space A consists of the two circles constituting the boundary of the cylinder, and the map f is the identity on each boundary circle, preserving the orientation that we see in the figure. The resulting adjunction space $Y \cup_f X$ is a Klein bottle (choosing different orientations in the definition of the map f would have produced a torus). Finally, the bottom of the figure shows the construction for arbitrary topological spaces A and Y, and an arbitrary continuous map $f : A \to Y$. Here X is the cone over A and the adjunction space is obtained by gluing the cone onto Y over its base using the map f. We recognize the *mapping cone* construction: $Y \cup_f X$ is the mapping cone of f.

3.3.2. CW complexes. Let us now learn how to organize a space attachment in a scheme which will produce spaces, known as *CW complexes*.

To start with, here X will always be a closed ball, say of dimension d. It is customary to call such balls d-cells, and use the notation e^d. The subspace $A \subseteq e^d$ will always be the boundary of this ball, so A is homeomorphic to S^{d-1}, and we shall denote it by ∂e^d. The space Y will be the result of attaching a certain number of cells of dimension at most $d-1$ to each other. In this case, we just need to specify the continuous map $f : \partial e^d \to Y$, and the resulting space $Y \cup_f e^d$ is said to be obtained from Y by attaching a d-cell.

While the quotient topology definition for $Y \cup_f e^d$ is mathematically precise, that topology can also be understood intiutively as follows:

- the small neighborhoods of points of Y which do not belong to the image of f are not influenced by the cell attachment;
- the small neighborhoods of an internal point of e^d are just d-balls; here locally the space $Y \cup_f e^d$ looks like a d-dimensional manifold;
- for a point x in the image of f, the small neighborhoods of x inside $Y \cup_f e^d$ are just unions of the small neighborhoods of x inside Y with small neighborhoods of preimages of x inside e^d.

We can now consider all spaces obtained by successive attachments of cells. These are *almost* the CW complexes. The only further condition is that each attachment is done over lower-dimensional cells. In other words, the image of each f lies in the result of gluings of cells of dimensions at most $d-1$.

The technically easiest way to phrase this condition is to require that *all* cells of the same dimension are glued at once. This means that the space X is not just one d-cell, but rather a disjoint union of d-cells, i.e., $X = \amalg_i e_i^d$. We then have $A = \amalg_i \partial e_i^d$, and clearly we have a continuous map $f : \amalg_i \partial e_i^d \to Y$.

We then say that $Y \cup_f X$ is obtained from Y by the *simultaneous* attachment of a collection of d-cells.

We are now ready for the formal definition, which we phrase in a constructive way.

Definition 3.10. The notion of a *CW complex* is defined by the following three points:

- A 0-*dimensional CW complex* is any non-empty collection of points, equipped with the discrete topology.
- For $d \geqslant 1$, all d-*dimensional CW complexes* are obtained by a simultaneous attachment of a non-empty collection of d-cells to an arbitrary m-dimensional CW complex, where $0 \leqslant m < d$.
- Assume we have an infinite nested sequence of topological spaces $X_{d_0} \subset X_{d_1} \subset X_{d_2} \subset \dots$, such that
  - we have $0 = d_0 < d_1 < d_2 < \dots$;
  - the space X_0 is a 0-dimensional CW complex;
  - for each $k \geqslant 1$, the space X_{d_k} is obtained from $X_{d_{k-1}}$ by a simultaneous attachment of a non-empty collection of d_k-cells.

  Then the union $\bigcup_{k \geqslant 0} X_{d_k}$ is called the *infinite-dimensional CW complex*.

For each d, the intermediate space X_d from Definition 3.10 is called the d-*th skeleton* of X.

Usually, the empty space is also considered a CW complex.

Definition 3.11. A CW-complex is said to be *regular* if all its attaching maps are topological embeddings, i.e., homeomorphisms onto their images.

Regular CW-complexes are natural generalizations of polyhedral complexes.

In principle it is possible to define the so-called *cellular homology* starting from the structure of a CW complex. The cellular chain groups of dimension d are simply the free abelian groups generated by all the d-cells, just the same as in the simplicial case. Unfortunately, the definition of the boundary operator requires quite a bit more development, so we postpone it until Chapter 8.

For now, however, we remark that no matter how the boundary operator is defined, we can still make some conclusions about the cellular homology, based on the cell decomposition alone. This is because, different from the simplicial case, we may not have any cells at all in certain dimensions. There is an easy rule here:

> *if there are no cells in a certain dimension, then there is no homology in that dimension either.*

For example, a d-sphere can be represented as a CW complex with one 0-cell and one d-cell. Therefore, for $d \geqslant 2$, we immediately see that the d-th cellular homology of S^d is $\mathbb{Z}$. The same considerations will also work for a wedge of d-spheres. Later, we shall also see that for any triangulation of a CW complex its cellular and simplicial homologies are isomorphic.

3.4. Infinite abstract simplicial complexes

Next, we remove the requirement that the set of vertices of the simplicial complex is finite.

3.4.1. Removing the finiteness condition.

Definition 3.12. Assume that S is an arbitrary ordered set, and $\mathcal{K}$ is a collection of non-empty finite subsets of S. Then $\mathcal{K}$ is called an *abstract simplicial complex* if the following two conditions are satisfied:

- $\{x\} \in \mathcal{K}$, for all $x \in S$;
- if $\tau \subseteq \sigma$, and $\sigma \in \mathcal{K}$, then $\tau \in \mathcal{K}$.

The definition of the boundary of a simplex is unchanged, and it can linearly be extended to arbitrary chains, since these are finite linear combinations of simplices. All our calculations take place in this "finite setting", so everything we did goes through just the same, just make sure that we are working with *finite* linear combinations all the time.

Let us look at some examples which demonstrate possible occuring phenomena.

3.4.2. Infinite wedge of spheres. Let WS be the abstract simplicial complex defined as follows. For all integers $n \geqslant 0$ we set $V_n := \{x_i^n \,|\, 0 \leqslant i \leqslant n\}$, in particular, $|V_n| = n + 1$.

- The set of vertices of WS is $V := V_0 \cup V_1 \cup V_2 \cup \dots$.
- A subset $\sigma \subset V$ is a simplex of WS if and only if there exists $n \geqslant 1$ such that σ is a proper subset of $V_0 \cup V_n$.

The complex WS has infinitely many homology groups which are not 0, as the next proposition specifies. We leave the proof as an exercise.

Proposition 3.13. *We have* $H_n(WS) \approx \mathbb{Z}$, *for all* $n \geqslant 0$.

Proof. See Exercise (5). □

3.4.3. Infinite-dimensional sphere. Let S^∞ be the abstract simplicial complex defined as follows:

- The set of vertices of S^∞ is $V := \{x_n, y_n \,|\, n \geqslant 0\}$.
- A finite subset $\sigma \subset V$ is a simplex of S^∞ if and only if $\{x_n, y_n\} \not\subseteq \sigma$, for all n.

Proposition 3.14. *We have* $H_n(S^\infty) \approx 0$, *for all* $n \geqslant 1$, *and* $H_0(S^\infty) \approx \mathbb{Z}$.

Proof. Consider an arbitrary cycle σ, and let T be the union of the sets of the vertices of all simplices in the support of σ, that is, the simplices which occur with a non-zero coefficient when σ is viewed as a linear combination of simplices. Since that linear combination is required to be finite, the set T is finite as well. Set $I := \{i \,|\, x_i \in T \text{ or } y_i \in T\}$, and take $k \notin I$. Consider the subcomplex $\mathcal{K}_I$ consisting of all simplices of S^∞, whose vertex set is contained in the set $\bigcup_{i \in I}\{x_i, y_i\}$.

The chain σ is, of course, a cycle inside the cone with apex x_k and base $\mathcal{K}_I$. Since the homology of the cone is trivial, the chain σ must be a boundary inside this cone. Clearly, then it is also a boundary in S^∞, so it must represent the trivial homology element. Since σ was chosen to be arbitrary the proposition is proved. □

3.5. Semisimplicial sets

3.5.1. Direct definition. When considering non-simple graphs, we have realized that having simplicial complexes is not enough: both multiple edges as well as loops make simplicial structure, without further subdivision, impossible. Instead, we have seen that it is possible to define the boundary operator, and hence also homology, by specifying for each edge its initial and terminal vertices. These vertices are allowed to be the same, giving loops, and two edges can also have the same set of initial and terminal vertices, giving multiple edges.

Semisimplicial sets provide the formal context to describe such information for non-simple graphs, as well as their higher-dimensional analogs. Instead of having just two sets, the vertices and the edges, one has potentially infinitely many sets, one for each dimension. Furthermore, for each n-simplex, we need to specify who its boundary simplices are. Boundary simplices are indexed by subsets of the vertex sets of the simplex. For functorial reasons it is more elegant to replace the consideration of subsets by the equivalent concept of the *order-preserving injection.*

Definition 3.15. A *semisimplicial set* consists of the following data:

- a sequence of sets $S = (S_0, S_1, \dots)$,

- for every order-preserving injection $f : [m] \hookrightarrow [n]$ we have a set map $B_f : S_n \to S_m$.

The maps B_f are subject to the following two conditions:

(1) for the identity map $id_{[n]} : [n] \hookrightarrow [n]$ we have

$$B_{id_{[n]}} = id_{S_n}, \tag{3.4}$$

(2) for the composition of order-preserving injections $f : [k] \hookrightarrow [m]$ and $g : [m] \hookrightarrow [n]$, we have

$$B_f \circ B_g = B_{g \circ f}. \tag{3.5}$$

Following the intuition given before Definition 3.15, for each n, we shall call the elements of the set S_n, the n-*simplices*. An order-preserving injection $f : [m] \hookrightarrow [n]$ should equivalently be thought of as choosing a subset with $m+1$ elements from a subset with $n+1$ elements, which is the same as choosing an m-simplex on the boundary of an n-simplex. The value $B_f(\sigma)$ then specifies which of the simplices in S_m is the chosen boundary simplex of σ. Condition (3.4) simply says that when we choose the simplex itself as its degenerate boundary, the map B_f will give you back your simplex. Condition (3.5) says that the boundary simplex specifications are consistent with taking a subset of a subset, or, which is the same, taking the composition of order-preserving injections.

Definition 3.16. For a non-empty semisimplicial set Λ, the *dimension* of Λ is the maximal index n such that $S_n \neq \emptyset$. If no such n exists, we say that Λ has infinite dimension.

Note that for any $0 \leqslant t \leqslant \dim \Lambda$ we must have $S_t \neq \emptyset$, in other words, we must have *some* t-simplices. This is because if we have $S_t = \emptyset$ and $S_k \neq \emptyset$ for some $k > t$ then no map $B_f : S_t \to S_k$, where $f : [k] \hookrightarrow [t]$ is an order-preserving injection, can exist, as there are no set maps from a non-empty set to the empty one.

Definition 3.17. A finite-dimensional semisimplicial set Λ is called *pure* if for any $k < \dim \Lambda$ and any $\sigma \in S_k$, there exists an order-preserving injection $f : [k] \hookrightarrow [k+1]$, and $\tau \in S_{k+1}$, such that $B_f(\tau) = \sigma$.

Geometrically thinking, in a pure semisimplicial set, any simplex which is not in the top dimension is contained in a higher-dimensional one.

Another concept which generalizes easily from the simplicial context is that of a *skeleton*.

Definition 3.18. Assume a semisimplicial set Λ is given by the data $(S_k)_{k \geqslant 0}$, $\{B_f\}_f$. The d-*skeleton* of Λ is the semisimplicial set $\mathrm{sk}_d \Lambda$ given by the data

$(S'_k)_{k \geqslant 0}$, $\{B'_f\}_f$, where

$$S'_k = \begin{cases} S_k, & \text{if } 0 \leqslant k \leqslant d; \\ \emptyset, & \text{otherwise.} \end{cases}$$

For an arbitrary order-preserving injection $f : [l] \hookrightarrow [m]$ we have $B'_f = B_f$, if $0 \leqslant l \leqslant m \leqslant d$, and B'_f is the unique map from the empty set otherwise.

Finally, we have the following notion of maps between semisimplicial sets.

Definition 3.19. Assume we have two semisimplicial sets Λ and Λ' given by the data $(S_k)_{k \geqslant 0}$, $\{B_f\}_f$ and $(S'_k)_{k \geqslant 0}$, $\{B'_f\}_f$. A *semisimplicial set homomorphism* between Λ and Λ' is a family of set maps $\{\varphi_k\}_{k \geqslant 0}$, where $\varphi_k : S_k \to S'_k$, such that for any $k < l$ and any order-preserving injection $f : [k] \hookrightarrow [l]$ the following diagram commutes:

$$\begin{array}{ccc} S_l & \xrightarrow{B_f} & S_k \\ \Big\downarrow{\scriptstyle \varphi_l} & & \Big\downarrow{\scriptstyle \varphi_k} \\ S'_l & \xrightarrow{B'_f} & S'_k \end{array} \tag{3.6}$$

It is easy to construct an identity semisimplicial set homomorphism of a semisimplicial set onto itself, and also to show that a composition of two semisimplicial set homomorphisms is again a semisimplicial set homomorphism.

The objects described in Definition 3.15 have been known under different names. For example they are called *triangulated spaces* by Gelfand and Manin, see [**GM03**], *trisps* by this author, see [**Ko08**], and Δ-complexes by Hatcher, see [**Hat02**].

3.5.2. Semisimplicial sets as functors. A structural way to think about semisimplicial sets is as follows. Consider the category **Δ–Inj** such that

- the objects of **Δ–Inj** are the sets [0], [1], [2], and so on;
- the morpishms between [k] and [m] are indexed by order-preserving injections from [k] into [m];
- the composition of morphisms is given by the composition of the corresponding maps, which is itself of course also an order-preserving injection.

We can use the category **Δ–Inj** to give an alternative definition of semisimplicial sets.

Definition 3.20. A *semisimplicial set* is a contravariant[2] functor from **Δ–Inj** to **Sets**.[3]

Let us make three remarks illustrating advantages of the abstract approach used in Definition 3.20. First, we see that the semisimplicial sets themselves form a category, as a special case of the general notion of *functor category*. We call this category **ssSets**.

Second, there is no immediate reason to restrict ourselves in Definition 3.20 to only considering the category **Sets**. One can also look for example at the category of groups, obtaining *simplicial groups*, or any other category one finds interesting. There is also another category, closely related to **Δ–Inj**, where the injectivity condition is dropped. This will allow one to define *simplicial sets*, and in general other *simplical objects*. This is a very interesting subject, which however lies beyond the boundaries of the present text, and we refer the interested reader to the foundational text of May, [**May92**].

Third, the rather involved Definition 3.19 of maps between semisimplicial sets turns out to be an instance of a so-called *natural transformation* between the functors associated to the semisimplicial sets. Natural transformations are canonical tools to compare functors between given categories.

3.5.3. Examples. It is possible to associate a topological space to each semisimplicial complex, which, in line with the terminology for the simplicial complexes, is called its *geometric realization*. A rigorous definition using quotient topology can be given. We do not do this here, limiting ourselves to saying that each element of S_n will give an n-simplex, and the maps B_f are encoding the *gluing data*, telling precisely how the boundary simplices are to be glued to each other.

The simplest case of a non-empty semisimplicial set is the one consisting of just one 0-simplex, which we also call a point. In this semisimplicial set we have $|S_0| = 1$, and $S_n = \emptyset$ for all $n \neq 0$. All the maps B_f are of course uniquely determined since either the origin set is empty, or the origin and the target sets each have one element.

In general, when $S_n = \emptyset$ for all $n \neq 0$ (and all the maps B_f are trivial) we have a semisimplicial set corresponding to a set of isolated points. These are all the semisimplicial sets of dimension 0.

Passing on to the semisimplicial sets of dimension 1 we can see that these are precisely all directed graphs with loops and multiple edges allowed. Indeed, there exist two order-preserving injections from $[0] = \{0\}$ to $[1] = \{0, 1\}$. Let us call them f_0 and f_1, and let us say $f_0(0) = 1$ and $f_1(0) = 0$.

[2]Recall that the word *contravariant* means that all the arrows change directions.
[3]**Sets** denotes the category of sets.

Assume we are given a semisimplicial set of dimension 1. Construct a directed graph by taking the set S_0 to be the set of vertices, and set S_1 as the set of the edges. The map $B_{f_1} : C_1 \to C_0$ maps each edge to its endpoint, while the map $B_{f_0} : C_1 \to C_0$ maps each edge to its initial point. This way we get all possible directed graphs. Forgetting the edge orientation produces the geometric realization of that semisimplicial set.

One can use this point of view to define the notion of connectedness in the context of semisimplicial sets. Simply call a semisimplicial set Λ *connected* in case the directed graph corresponding to the 1-skeleton $\text{sk}_1 \Lambda$ is connected. Up to isomorphism, all pure connected semisimplicial sets of dimension 1 with two 1-simplices are shown in Figure 3.2.

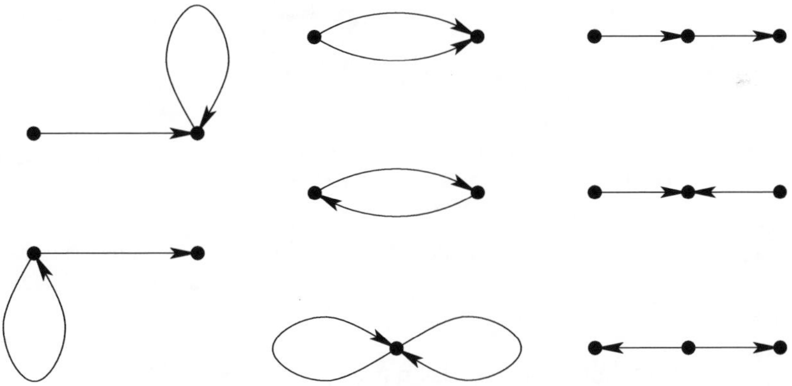

Figure 3.2. All pure connected semisimplicial sets of dimension 1 with two 1-simplices.

More interesting examples can be obtained starting from dimension 2. Even if we only have one 2-simplex, there are many options, see Figure 3.3, which up to isomorphism depicts all of them.

In higher dimensions, an interesting example is provided by the family of semisimplicial sets $\{\mathcal{D}_0, \mathcal{D}_1, \mathcal{D}_2, \dots\}$, where each $\mathcal{D}_n$ has exactly one simplex in each dimension between 0 and n, which defines it uniquely. These are the so-called *generalized Dunce hats*.

3.5.4. Simplicial homology of a semisimplicial set. For $0 \leqslant i \leqslant n$, the order-preserving injection $f_{n,i} : [n-1] \to [n]$ is uniquely defined by requiring $\text{Im}\, f_{n,i} = [n] \setminus \{i\}$. The precise formula is as follows:

$$f_{n,i}(j) = \begin{cases} j, & \text{if } j < i; \\ j+1, & \text{if } j \geqslant i. \end{cases}$$

Definition 3.21. Assume we are given a semisimplicial set Λ, with the simplex sets $(S_n)_{n \geqslant 0}$, and the attachment maps $\{B_f\}_f$.

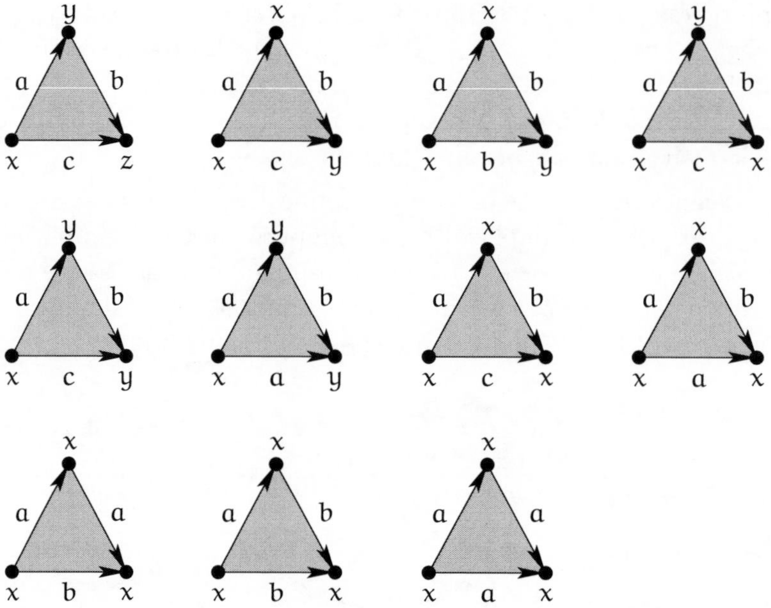

Figure 3.3. All pure semisimplicial sets of dimension 2 with one 2-simplex.

(1) For all n, we define the chain groups of Λ by setting $C_n(\Lambda) := \langle S_n \rangle$.

(2) For all $n \geqslant 1$, we define the boundary operator $\partial_n : S_n \to S_{n-1}$ by setting

$$\partial_n(\sigma) = \sum_{i=0}^{n} (-1)^i B_{f_{n,i}}(\sigma),$$

where the order-preserving injections $f_{n,i}$ are defined above.

Proposition 3.22. *We have* $\partial_{n-1} \circ \partial_n = 0$, *for all* $n \geqslant 1$.

Proof. For brevity, let us set $f_i := f_{n,i}$, for all i, and $g_j := f_{n-1,j}$, for all j. Furthermore, for all $i < j$ let $h_{i,j}$ denote the order-preserving injection $h_{i,j} : [n-2] \hookrightarrow [n]$ uniquely determined by the condition $\operatorname{Im} h_{i,j} = [n] \setminus \{i, j\}$.

We have the following formula:

$$f_i \circ g_j = \begin{cases} h_{j,i}, & \text{if } j < i; \\ h_{i,j+1}, & \text{otherwise.} \end{cases} \tag{3.7}$$

Pick an arbitrary $\sigma \in S_n$; we have the following calculation:

$$\begin{aligned}
\partial_{n-1}(\partial_n \sigma) &= \partial_{n-1}\Big(\sum_{i=0}^{n}(-1)^i B_{f_i}(\sigma)\Big) = \sum_{i=0}^{n}(-1)^i \partial_{n-1}(B_{f_i}(\sigma)) \\
&= \sum_{i=0}^{n}(-1)^i \sum_{j=0}^{n-1}(-1)^j B_{g_j}(B_{f_i}(\sigma)) \\
&= \sum_{\substack{0\leqslant i\leqslant n \\ 0\leqslant j\leqslant n-1}} (-1)^{i+j} B_{f_i \circ g_j}(\sigma) \\
&= \sum_{0\leqslant j<i\leqslant n} (-1)^{i+j} B_{h_{j,i}}(\sigma) + \sum_{0\leqslant i\leqslant j\leqslant n-1} (-1)^{i+j} B_{h_{i,j+1}}(\sigma),
\end{aligned} \tag{3.8}$$

where the last equality follows from Equation (3.7). Now replacing $j+1$ with k in the last term yields

$$\sum_{0\leqslant i\leqslant j\leqslant n-1} (-1)^{i+j} B_{h_{i,j+1}}(\sigma) = -\sum_{0\leqslant i<k\leqslant n} (-1)^{i+k} B_{h_{i,k}}(\sigma).$$

Substituting this into the last line of Equation (3.8) yields the desired identity $\partial_{n-1} \circ \partial_n = 0$, see Figure 3.4. □

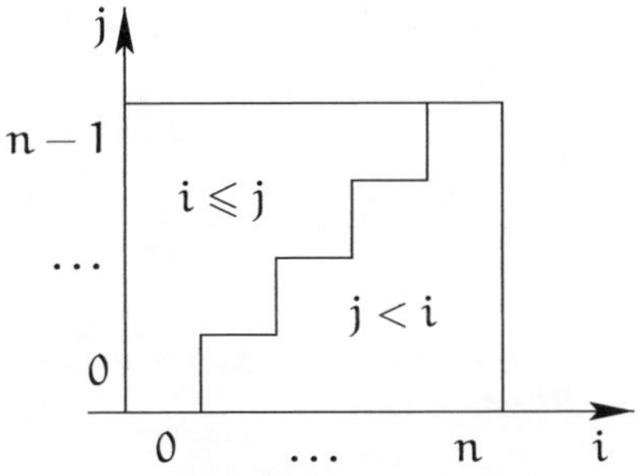

Figure 3.4. The index domain split in Equation (3.8).

Proposition 3.22 shows the crucial property of a boundary operator which allows one to define homology.

Definition 3.23. The n*th homology* of a semisimplicial set Λ is given by

$$H_n(\Lambda) = \operatorname{Ker} \partial_n / \operatorname{Im} \partial_{n+1}.$$

In the case of an ordered simplicial complex, Definition 3.23 specializes to the previously given homology definition.

In general, we know that $H_n(\Lambda)$ is an abelian group, and it is free when $n = \dim \Lambda$. The argument virtually identical to the previous one will show that $H_0(\Lambda)$ is again a free abelian group whose dimension is equal to the number of connected components of Λ.

3.5.5. Using semisimplicial sets for calculation. One of the main advantages of the semisimplicial sets is that they are excellent for explicit calculations. This is because all the input data is discrete and does not need general continuous maps.

Let us calculate the homology groups for a couple of examples. To start with, consider the semisimplicial set $\mathcal{D}$ shown as the last one in Figure 3.3. Topologically it corresponds to the space known as the *Dunce hat.* Assuming that $S_0(\mathcal{D}) = \{x\}$, $S_1(\mathcal{D}) = \{a\}$, and $S_2(\mathcal{D}) = \{t\}$, the chain groups and boundary operators are as follows:

$$\begin{aligned} C_0(\mathcal{D}) &= \langle x \rangle & \partial_1 &: \langle a \rangle \to \langle x \rangle \\ C_1(\mathcal{D}) &= \langle a \rangle & & a \mapsto x - x = 0 \\ C_2(\mathcal{D}) &= \langle t \rangle & \partial_2 &: \langle t \rangle \to \langle a \rangle \\ & & & t \mapsto a - a + a = a. \end{aligned}$$

This allows us to compute the homology groups

$$\begin{aligned} H_0(\mathcal{D}) &= \frac{\operatorname{Ker} \partial_0}{\operatorname{Im} \partial_1} = \frac{\langle x \rangle}{0} \approx \langle x \rangle \approx \mathbb{Z}, \\ H_1(\mathcal{D}) &= \frac{\operatorname{Ker} \partial_1}{\operatorname{Im} \partial_2} = \frac{\langle a \rangle}{\langle a \rangle} \approx 0, \\ H_2(\mathcal{D}) &= \frac{\operatorname{Ker} \partial_2}{\operatorname{Im} \partial_3} = \frac{0}{0} \approx 0, \end{aligned}$$

confirming the topological fact that the Dunce hat is actually contractible.

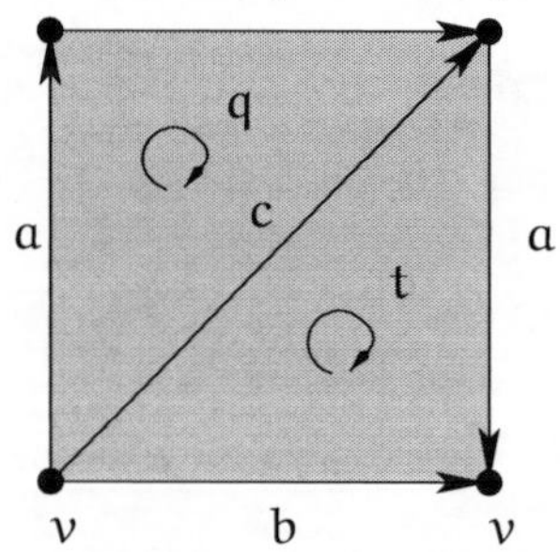

Figure 3.5. A semisimplicial set presentation of a Klein bottle.

As another example, consider the 2-dimensional semisimplicial set K shown schematically in Figure 3.5. Topologically it corresponds to the *Klein bottle.* We compute the homology of K, although to conclude that this in some sense computes the homology of the Klein bottle, one would need to show that the result is independent of the representation of the topological space as a semisimplicial set. For the chain groups and boundary operators we get:

$$
\begin{aligned}
C_0(K) &= \langle v \rangle & \partial_1 : \langle a, b, c \rangle &\to \langle v \rangle \\
C_1(K) &= \langle a, b, c \rangle & a &\mapsto v - v = 0 \\
& & b &\mapsto v - v = 0 \\
& & c &\mapsto v - v = 0 \\
C_2(K) &= \langle q, t \rangle & \partial_2 : \langle q, t \rangle &\to \langle a, b, c \rangle \\
& & q &\mapsto a + b - c \\
& & t &\mapsto a - b + c.
\end{aligned}
$$

This allows us to compute the homology groups

$$
\begin{aligned}
H_0(K) &= \frac{\operatorname{Ker} \partial_0}{\operatorname{Im} \partial_1} = \frac{\langle v \rangle}{0} \approx \langle v \rangle && \approx \mathbb{Z}, \\
H_1(K) &= \frac{\operatorname{Ker} \partial_1}{\operatorname{Im} \partial_2} = \frac{\langle a, b, c \rangle}{\langle a + b - c, a - b + c \rangle} && \approx \mathbb{Z} \oplus \mathbb{Z}_2, \\
H_2(K) &= \frac{\operatorname{Ker} \partial_2}{\operatorname{Im} \partial_3} = \frac{0}{0} && \approx 0.
\end{aligned}
$$

The second line deserves a little more attention. We have

$$
\begin{aligned}
H_1(K) = \frac{\langle a, b, c \rangle}{\langle a + b - c, a - b + c \rangle} &= \langle a, b, c \mid c = a + b, a + c = b \rangle \\
&\approx \langle a, b \mid 2a \rangle \approx \mathbb{Z} \oplus \mathbb{Z}_2,
\end{aligned}
$$

where for the sake of explanation we deviate a bit from our regular notation by writing the relations as actual equations, rather than group elements.

3.6. Arbitrary finitely generated abelian groups as homology groups

Let us return to considering a simplicial complex $\mathcal{K}$. We have seen that no torsion can occur in dimension 0 or in dimension $\dim \mathcal{K}$. So the first possibility for the torsion to appear would be in dimension 1, and we would need to require that $\dim \mathcal{K} \geqslant 2$. Curiously, it turns out that an arbitrary finitely generated abelian group can occur as the first homology group of a finite simplicial complex.

Theorem 3.24. *Let G be any finitely generated abelian group. Then there exists a 2-dimensional simplicial complex $\mathcal{Y}$, such that $H_1(\mathcal{Y}) \approx G$.*

Proof. Let C_k be a cyclic group of order k, $k \geqslant 2$. We construct a simplicial complex $\mathcal{Y}_k$, which satisfies $H_1(\mathcal{Y}_k) = C_k$. Start with a regular $3k$-gon with

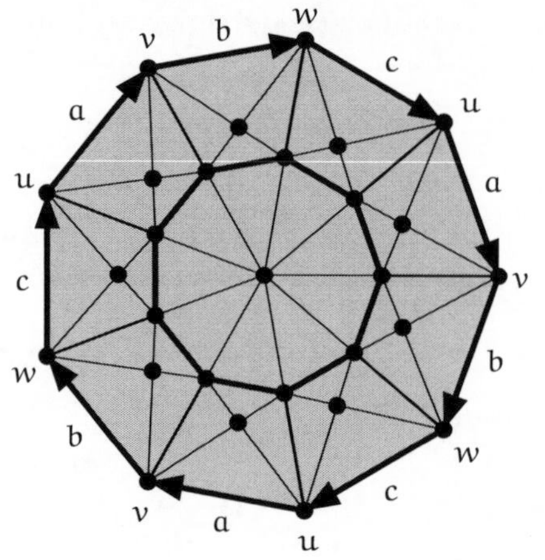

Figure 3.6. A simplicial complex $\mathcal{Y}_3$ with $H_1(\mathcal{Y}_3) \approx C_3$.

vertices labeled $u_1, v_1, w_1, \dots, u_k, v_k, w_k$. Add a center point r and connect r radially with all the vertices of this 3k-gon. Draw another regular 3k-gon centered at r, whose vertices are labeled $\tilde{u}_1, \tilde{v}_1, \tilde{w}_1, \dots, \tilde{u}_k, \tilde{v}_k, \tilde{w}_k$, where $\tilde{u}_i$ is a middle point of the edge (r, u_i), $\tilde{v}_i$ is a middle point of the edge (r, v_i), and $\tilde{w}_i$ is a middle point of the edge (r, w_i). Subdivide each of the $3k$ quadrangles by placing a vertex in the middle. We now identify the edges (u_i, v_i) for all $i = 1, \dots, k$ to make one edge, which we call a, identify the edges (v_i, w_i) for all $i = 1, \dots, k$ to make one edge called b, and finally, identify the edges (w_i, u_i) for all $i = 1, \dots, k$ to make one edge called c. Note that all the vertices u_i are now identified to a single vertex u, and the same is true for the vertices v_i and w_i, producing vertices v and w.

The resulting simplicial complex $\mathcal{Y}_k$ will have $7k + 1$ vertices, $22k$ edges and $15k$ 2-dimensional simplices. The example for $k = 3$ is shown in Figure 3.6.

We leave it as Exercise (7) to show that $H_1(\mathcal{Y}_k) = C_k$.

Furthermore, the complete graph on 3 vertices, or in fact any cycle, has the first homology group equal to $\mathbb{Z}$. By Theorem 2.29, taking disjoint unions of such complexes will yield complexes whose first homology groups range through all possible direct sums of cyclic groups. By the fundamental theorem mentioned above, this yields all finitely generated abelian groups. □

We remark that there are certainly complexes with the desired properties which have fewer simplices than $\mathcal{Y}_k$.

The following is the immediate consequence of Proposition 2.37, together with Theorem 3.24.

Corollary 3.25. *Let* G *be any finitely generated abelian group, and* d *any positive integer. There exists a plain* $(d+1)$*-dimensional simplicial complex* $\mathcal{Y}$*, such that* $H_d(\mathcal{Y}) \approx G$.

Proof. Choose an abstract simplicial complex as prescribed by Theorem 3.24 and suspend $d-1$ times. □

Exercises

(1) Verify that the cubical boundary operator defined in Equation (3.1) squares to 0.

(2) Calculate the cubical homology of the boundary of an n-dimensional cube.

(3) (a) Find a CW decomposition of the direct product $S^2 \times S^2$, which does not have any cells in dimensions 1 and 3.
   (b) In general, for any $d \geqslant 2$, find a CW decomposition of the direct product $S^d \times \cdots \times S^d$, which only has cells in dimensions, which are divisible by d.

(4) Find a CW decomposition of the complex projective space $\mathbb{CP}^n$, which does not have any cells in odd dimensions.

(5) (a) Compute the homology groups of the boundary complex of a d-simplex, for any $d \geqslant 1$. Find explicit generators.
   (b) Let WS be the simplicial complex defined in Subsection 3.4.2. Use (a) to prove Proposition 3.13 by a direct analysis of the cycles in WS.

(6) Find a semisimplicial set presentation of the 2-dimensional torus, similar to the one for the Klein bottle, shown in Figure 3.5. Use this presentation to compute the homology of the torus.

(7) Complete the proof of Theorem 3.24 by showing that $H_1(\mathcal{Y}_k) = C_k$.

(8) Find a 2-dimensional simplicial complex whose first homology group is isomorphic to $\mathbb{Z}_3$, and which has fewer triangles than 45. How low can one go?

(9) Assume we have t integers $1 \leqslant d_1 < \cdots < d_t$ and arbitrary abelian groups $G_1, \ldots, G_t$. Show that there exists an abstract simplicial complex $\mathcal{K}$ such that for all $1 \leqslant i \leqslant t$, we have $H_{d_i}(\mathcal{K}) \approx G_i$.

(10) Consider an infinite 2-dimensional abstract simplicial complex $\mathcal{K}$ defined by the following:

$$\mathcal{K}(0) = \{(a, b) \mid a, b \in \mathbb{Z}\},$$

$$\mathcal{K}(1) = \{\{(a, b), (a+1, b)\} \mid a, b \in \mathbb{Z}\} \cup \{\{(a, b), (a, b+1)\} \mid a, b \in \mathbb{Z}\} \cup \{\{(a, b), (a+1, b+1)\} \mid a, b \in \mathbb{Z}\},$$

$$\mathcal{K}(2) = \{\{(a, b), (a+1, b), (a+1, b+1)\} \mid a, b \in \mathbb{Z}\} \cup \{\{(a, b), (a, b+1), (a+1, b+1)\} \mid a, b \in \mathbb{Z}\}.$$

Calculate the homology of $\mathcal{K}$.

Part 2

Further Aspects of Homology Theory

Chapter 4

Category of Chain Complexes

As mentioned in Chapter 3, chain complexes provide a fairly general algebraic framework in which homology groups can be defined. Being a bit more abstract than the simplicial complexes, they avoid technical pitfalls, such as having to choose orientations, and are often more convenient to work with. We shall now look at the chain complexes in some detail. Following the functorial way of thinking, we shall actually consider the *category* of chain complexes, emphasizing the invaluable role the chain maps play in homology theory.

4.1. Chain complexes of modules over a ring

Our first step is to note that we can replace free abelian groups in the definition of chain complexes with vector spaces over a fixed field **k**, or, taking the abstraction one step further, with modules over any commutative ring $\mathcal{R}$ with a unit. The definition of the corresponding chain complex is virtually identical to Definition 3.5.

4.1.1. Definition of chain complexes of modules.

Definition 4.1. Let $\mathcal{R}$ be an arbitrary commutative ring with a unit. A *chain complex of* $\mathcal{R}$*-modules* is a family $(C_n)_{n\in\mathbb{Z}}$ of $\mathcal{R}$-modules, together with a family of module maps $(\partial_n)_{n\in\mathbb{Z}}$, $\partial_n : C_n \to C_{n-1}$, such that $\partial_{n-1} \circ \partial_n = 0$ for all $n \in \mathbb{Z}$.

Letting $\mathcal{R}$ be a field provides an important special case. It is customary to call this field **k**. The chain groups are then clearly vector spaces over **k**.

Hence, the homology groups are also vector spaces over **k**. This means that there can be no torsion in homology, and, when the homology groups are finitely generated, the Betti numbers provide us with complete information. The two most important choices of the field **k** will be the field of real numbers $\mathbb{R}$ and the 2-element field $\mathbb{Z}_2$.

In general, however, the structure of homology groups can be quite complicated.

4.1.2. Tensor product of a chain complex of abelian groups with a commutative ring.

The next definition provides a way of turning a given chain complex of abelian groups into a complex of modules over the chosen ring.

Definition 4.2. Let $\mathcal{C} = (C_*, \partial_*^{\mathcal{C}})$ be a chain complex of abelian groups, and let $\mathcal{R}$ be a ring. We define the tensor product $\mathcal{C} \otimes \mathcal{R}$ to be the chain complex

$$\dots \xrightarrow{\partial_{n+2}^{\mathcal{C}} \otimes \mathcal{R}} C_{n+1} \otimes \mathcal{R} \xrightarrow{\partial_{n+1}^{\mathcal{C}} \otimes \mathcal{R}} C_n \otimes \mathcal{R} \xrightarrow{\partial_n^{\mathcal{C}} \otimes \mathcal{R}} C_{n-1} \otimes \mathcal{R} \xrightarrow{\partial_{n-1}^{\mathcal{C}} \otimes \mathcal{R}} \dots,$$

where $\partial_n^{\mathcal{C}} \otimes \mathcal{R}$ is our abbreviated way to write $\partial_n^{\mathcal{C}} \otimes \mathrm{id}$. We shall write $\mathcal{C} \otimes \mathcal{R} = (C_* \otimes \mathcal{R}, \partial_*^{\mathcal{C}} \otimes \mathcal{R})$.

Tensoring the chain complex with a ring allows us to define homology groups with coefficients in that ring. Note that the tensor products $C_i \otimes \mathcal{R}$ are all $\mathcal{R}$-modules, and the boundary operators $\partial_n^{\mathcal{C}} \otimes \mathcal{R}$ are $\mathcal{R}$-module maps.

Definition 4.3. Let $\mathcal{C}$ be an arbitrary chain complex of abelian groups, and let $\mathcal{R}$ be arbitrary commutative ring with a unit. The homology groups $H_*(\mathcal{C} \otimes \mathcal{R})$ are called the *homology groups of* $\mathcal{C}$ *with coefficients in* $\mathcal{R}$.

As an example, let us again consider the chain complex from Subsection 3.2.2 with $m = 2$:

$$\mathcal{C}: \qquad \dots \xrightarrow{\partial_3} 0 \xrightarrow{\partial_2} \mathbb{Z} \xrightarrow[x \mapsto 2x]{\partial_1} \mathbb{Z} \xrightarrow{\partial_0} 0 \xrightarrow{\partial_{-1}} \dots .$$

Recall that $H_0(\mathcal{C}) \approx \mathbb{Z}_2$, $H_1(\mathcal{C}) = 0$, and all other homology groups are 0 as well. Let us tensor it with $\mathbb{Z}_2$ and with $\mathbb{Q}$, and then compare the homology groups of the resulting chain complexes.

First, tensoring with $\mathbb{Z}_2$ yields the chain complex

$$\mathcal{C} \otimes \mathbb{Z}_2: \qquad \dots \xrightarrow{\partial_3} 0 \xrightarrow{\partial_2} \mathbb{Z}_2 \xrightarrow[x \mapsto 0]{\partial_1} \mathbb{Z}_2 \xrightarrow{\partial_0} 0 \xrightarrow{\partial_{-1}} \dots,$$

so we get $H_0(\mathcal{C} \otimes \mathbb{Z}_2) \approx H_1(\mathcal{C} \otimes \mathbb{Z}_2) \approx \mathbb{Z}_2$.

On the other hand, tensoring with $\mathbb{Q}$ yields the chain complex

$$\mathcal{C} \otimes \mathbb{Q}: \qquad \dots \xrightarrow{\partial_3} 0 \xrightarrow{\partial_2} \mathbb{Q} \xrightarrow[x \mapsto 2x]{\partial_1} \mathbb{Q} \xrightarrow{\partial_0} 0 \xrightarrow{\partial_{-1}} \dots .$$

Here, the boundary map ∂_1 is an isomorphism, so we get $H_0(\mathcal{C} \otimes \mathbb{Q}) = H_1(\mathcal{C} \otimes \mathbb{Q}) = 0$.

4.2. Constructions with chain complexes

For technical simplicity we shall work with chain complexes of (not necessarily free) abelian groups for now.

Definition 4.4. A chain complex of abelian groups $\mathcal{C} = (C_*, \partial_*^{\mathcal{C}})$ is called *free* if C_n is free for all $n \in \mathbb{Z}$.

Let us look at a few constructions involving chain complexes. The simplest one is the so-called *shift*.

Definition 4.5. Let $\mathcal{C} = (C_*, \partial_*^{\mathcal{C}})$ be a chain complex of abelian groups, and let t be an arbitrary integer. The new chain complex $\mathcal{C}[t]$, called a *shift* or *translation* of $\mathcal{C}$ by t, is defined by $\mathcal{C}[t]_n := C_{n-t}$ and $\partial_n^{\mathcal{C}[t]} := \partial_{n-t}^{\mathcal{C}}$, for all $n \in \mathbb{Z}$.

If $\mathcal{C}$ is free, then so is $\mathcal{C}[t]$, for any t. Also, when a chain complex is shifted by t, then so is its homology.

Proposition 4.6. *For an arbitrary chain complex $\mathcal{C}$ of abelian groups, and any integer t, we have isomorphisms $H_n(\mathcal{C}[t]) \approx H_{n-t}(\mathcal{C})$, for all $n \in \mathbb{Z}$.*

Another operation which comes to mind is truncating the chain complex at a certain index. In order not to ruin the homology information, one has to be a little gentle at the point of truncation.

Definition 4.7. Let $\mathcal{C} = (C_*, \partial_*^{\mathcal{C}})$ be a chain complex of abelian groups, and let t be an arbitrary integer. The chain complex $\tau_t\mathcal{C}$, called a *truncation* of $\mathcal{C}$ at t, is defined as follows:

$$(\tau_t\mathcal{C})_n := \begin{cases} C_n, & \text{if } n < t, \\ \operatorname{Coker} \partial_{n+1}^{\mathcal{C}} = C_n / \operatorname{Im} \partial_{n+1}^{\mathcal{C}}, & \text{if } n = t, \\ 0, & \text{if } n > t. \end{cases}$$

Note that a truncation of a free chain complex may not in general be free. The truncation which we consider here is sometimes called the *canonical* truncation. There is also the direct, also known as the *stupid*, truncation, where one simply zeroes out all the chain groups above a certain index. The direct truncation of a free complex is clearly free again, however, it destroys the homology group at the truncation point, which is the reason why we do not consider it here. On the contrary, the canonical truncation behaves well, as the next proposition shows.

Proposition 4.8. *Let $\mathcal{C}$ be a chain complex of abelian groups, and let t be an arbitrary integer. The homology groups of the truncated complex $\tau_t\mathcal{C}$ are given by the following formula:*

$$H_n(\tau_t\mathcal{C}) \approx \begin{cases} H_n(\mathcal{C}), & \text{if } n \leqslant t; \\ 0, & \text{otherwise.} \end{cases}$$

The truncation in Definition 4.7 is done from *above.* We relegate the truncation from *below* to the exercises.

The reader will recognize the next few definitions as the standard ones in many categories.

Definition 4.9. Assume $\mathcal{C} = \left(C_*, \partial_*^{\mathcal{C}}\right)$ and $\mathcal{D} = \left(D_*, \partial_*^{\mathcal{D}}\right)$ are two chain complexes of abelian groups. We define a new chain complex $\mathcal{E} = \left(E_*, \partial_*^{\mathcal{E}}\right)$ by setting

$$E_n := C_n \oplus D_n \text{ and } \partial_n^{\mathcal{E}}(\sigma \oplus \tau) := \partial_n^{\mathcal{C}}(\sigma) \oplus \partial_n^{\mathcal{D}}(\tau), \text{ for all } n \in \mathbb{Z}.$$

This chain complex is called the *direct sum of the chain complexes* $\mathcal{C}$ and $\mathcal{D}$ and is denoted by $\mathcal{C} \oplus \mathcal{D}$.

When the complexes $\mathcal{C}$ and $\mathcal{D}$ are free, then so is their direct sum $\mathcal{C} \oplus \mathcal{D}$. Just as in the case of simplicial complexes, it is easy to calculate the homology groups of direct sums.

Proposition 4.10. *Assume $\mathcal{C} = \left(C_*, \partial_*^{\mathcal{C}}\right)$ and $\mathcal{D} = \left(D_*, \partial_*^{\mathcal{D}}\right)$ are two chain complexes of abelian groups. Then, the abelian groups $H_n(\mathcal{C}\oplus\mathcal{D})$ and $H_n(\mathcal{C})\oplus H_n(\mathcal{D})$ are isomorphic for all integers n.*

Proof. Assume $\mathcal{C}\oplus\mathcal{D} = \left(E_*, \partial_*^{\mathcal{E}}\right)$. Clearly, we have $\operatorname{Ker} \partial_n^{\mathcal{E}} = \operatorname{Ker} \partial_n^{\mathcal{C}} \oplus \operatorname{Ker} \partial_n^{\mathcal{D}}$, and $\operatorname{Im} \partial_n^{\mathcal{E}} = \operatorname{Im} \partial_n^{\mathcal{C}} \oplus \operatorname{Im} \partial_n^{\mathcal{D}}$. We can then derive

$$\begin{aligned} H_n(\mathcal{C} \oplus \mathcal{D}) = \frac{\operatorname{Ker} \partial_n^{\mathcal{E}}}{\operatorname{Im} \partial_{n+1}^{\mathcal{E}}} &= \frac{\operatorname{Ker} \partial_n^{\mathcal{C}} \oplus \operatorname{Ker} \partial_n^{\mathcal{D}}}{\operatorname{Im} \partial_{n+1}^{\mathcal{C}} \oplus \operatorname{Im} \partial_{n+1}^{\mathcal{D}}} \\ &\approx \frac{\operatorname{Ker} \partial_n^{\mathcal{C}}}{\operatorname{Im} \partial_{n+1}^{\mathcal{C}}} \bigoplus \frac{\operatorname{Ker} \partial_n^{\mathcal{D}}}{\operatorname{Im} \partial_{n+1}^{\mathcal{D}}} = H_n(\mathcal{C}) \oplus H_n(\mathcal{D}), \end{aligned}$$

where the existence of a group isomorphism in between the third and the fourth term is a standard fact from group theory. □

The concept of a simplicial subcomplex has its analog in the context of chain complexes as well.

Definition 4.11. Assume $\mathcal{C} = \left(C_*, \partial_*^{\mathcal{C}}\right)$ and $\mathcal{D} = \left(D_*, \partial_*^{\mathcal{D}}\right)$ are two chain complexes of abelian groups. The chain complex $\mathcal{D}$ is called the *chain subcomplex* of $\mathcal{C}$ if, for every $n \in \mathbb{Z}$, the group D_n is a subgroup of the group C_n, and the boundary homomorphism $\partial_n^{\mathcal{D}} : D_n \to D_{n-1}$ is well-defined as the restriction of the boundary homomorphism $\partial_n^{\mathcal{C}} : C_n \to C_{n-1}$ to the subgroup D_n, that is, $\partial_n^{\mathcal{D}} = \partial_n^{\mathcal{C}}|_{D_n}$.

If $\mathcal{C}$ is free, then so is $\mathcal{D}$, since any subgroup of a free abelian group is itself free abelian.

Definition 4.12. Assume $\mathcal{C} = \left(C_*, \partial_*^{\mathcal{C}}\right)$ is a chain complex of abelian groups, and $\mathcal{D} = \left(D_*, \partial_*^{\mathcal{D}}\right)$ is a subcomplex of $\mathcal{C}$. Then the *quotient chain complex* is the complex $\mathcal{Q} = (Q_*, \partial_*^{\mathcal{Q}})$ defined as follows:

- $Q_n := C_n/D_n$, for all $n \in \mathbb{Z}$,
- $\partial_n^{\mathcal{Q}} : C_n/D_n \to C_{n-1}/D_{n-1}$ is given by $\alpha + D_n \mapsto \partial_n^{\mathcal{C}}\alpha + D_{n-1}$, for all $n \in \mathbb{Z}$.

We shall denote $\mathcal{Q}$ by $\mathcal{C}/\mathcal{D}$. The boundary operator $\partial_*^{\mathcal{C}/\mathcal{D}}$ is well-defined, since $\partial_n^{\mathcal{C}}(D_n) \subseteq D_{n-1}$. However, even if $\mathcal{C}$ is free, the quotient chain complex $\mathcal{C}/\mathcal{D}$ may not be free.

Definition 4.13. Let G be a free abelian group, and let H be a subgroup of G. The subset A of G is called the *basis complement of* H *in* G if for any basis B of H, the union $A \cup B$ is a basis of G.

Assume now that in Definition 4.12 the chain complex $\mathcal{C}$ is free, and the following additional condition is satisfied: for each n there is a set A_n, which is a basis complement of D_n in C_n. In that case it is easy to see that the chain complex $\mathcal{C}/\mathcal{D}$ is also free.

4.3. Cones and cylinders based at chain complexes

Next, we look at the chain complex analogs of the geometric constructions of the cone and the cylinder.

Definition 4.14. Assume $\mathcal{C}$ is an arbitrary chain complex of abelian groups. We define a new chain complex of free abelian groups, which is denoted by $\mathcal{C}one(\mathcal{C}) = \left(\mathrm{Cone}_*, \partial_*^{\mathcal{C}one}\right)$,

$$\dots \xrightarrow{\partial_{n+2}^{\mathcal{C}one}} \mathrm{Cone}_{n+1} \xrightarrow{\partial_{n+1}^{\mathcal{C}one}} \mathrm{Cone}_n \xrightarrow{\partial_{n}^{\mathcal{C}one}} \mathrm{Cone}_{n-1} \xrightarrow{\partial_{n-1}^{\mathcal{C}one}} \dots$$

as follows: the chain groups Cone_n are the abelian groups given by

$$\mathrm{Cone}_n := C_{n-1} \oplus C_n, \text{ for all } n \in \mathbb{Z},$$

and the boundary operator $\partial_n^{\mathcal{C}one} : \mathrm{Cone}_n \to \mathrm{Cone}_{n-1}$ is given by the formula

$$\partial_n^{\mathcal{C}one}(\tau \oplus \rho) = \left(-\partial_{n-1}^{\mathcal{C}}\tau\right) \oplus \left(\partial_n^{\mathcal{C}}\rho + \tau\right). \tag{4.1}$$

We call the chain complex $\mathcal{C}one(\mathcal{C})$ the *cone with the base* $\mathcal{C}$.

If $\mathcal{C}$ is free, then so is $\mathcal{C}one(\mathcal{C})$.

Definition 4.15. Again let $\mathcal{C}$ be an arbitrary chain complex of abelian groups. We define a new chain complex of abelian groups $\mathcal{C}yl(\mathcal{C}) = \left(\mathrm{Cyl}_*, \partial_*^{\mathcal{C}yl}\right)$,

$$\cdots \xrightarrow{\partial_{n+2}^{\mathcal{C}yl}} \mathrm{Cyl}_{n+1} \xrightarrow{\partial_{n+1}^{\mathcal{C}yl}} \mathrm{Cyl}_n \xrightarrow{\partial_n^{\mathcal{C}yl}} \mathrm{Cyl}_{n-1} \xrightarrow{\partial_{n-1}^{\mathcal{C}yl}} \cdots$$

as follows: the chain groups Cyl_n are the abelian groups given by

$$\mathrm{Cyl}_n := C_n \oplus C_{n-1} \oplus C_n, \text{ for all } n,$$

and the boundary operator $\partial_n^{\mathcal{C}yl} : \mathrm{Cyl}_n \to \mathrm{Cyl}_{n-1}$ is given by the formula

$$\partial_n^{\mathcal{C}yl}(\sigma \oplus \tau \oplus \rho) = \left(\partial_n^{\mathcal{C}}\sigma - \tau\right) \oplus \left(-\partial_{n-1}^{\mathcal{C}}\tau\right) \oplus \left(\partial_n^{\mathcal{C}}\rho + \tau\right).$$

We call the chain complex $\mathcal{C}yl(\mathcal{C})$ the *cylinder with base* $\mathcal{C}$.

The intuitive picture for the cylinder is clear: there are two copies of $\mathcal{C}$, symbolizing the top and the bottom of the cylinder, and one more shifted copy of $\mathcal{C}$, symbolizing the stretched cells in between. For the intuition for the cone the reader should imagine forgetting about one of the copies of $\mathcal{C}$, which corresponds to considering the relative chain complex.

It easy to see that both $\mathcal{C}yl(\mathcal{C})$ and $\mathcal{C}one(\mathcal{C})$ are well-defined chain complexes, and that the chain groups are free abelian. To do that, we need to check that the boundary operators are actually differentials, that is, the composition of two subsequent maps is 0. In the case of the cone $\mathcal{C}one(\mathcal{C})$ we have the computation

$$\begin{aligned} \partial_{n-1}^{\mathcal{C}one}\left(\partial_n^{\mathcal{C}one}(\tau \oplus \rho)\right) &= \partial_{n-1}^{\mathcal{C}one}\left(\left(-\partial_{n-1}^{\mathcal{C}}\tau\right) \oplus \left(\partial_n^{\mathcal{C}}\rho + \tau\right)\right) \\ &= \left(-\partial_{n-2}^{\mathcal{C}}\left(-\partial_{n-1}^{\mathcal{C}}\tau\right)\right) \oplus \left(\partial_{n-1}^{\mathcal{C}}\left(\partial_n^{\mathcal{C}}\rho + \tau\right) + \left(-\partial_{n-1}^{\mathcal{C}}\tau\right)\right) = 0 \oplus 0 = 0. \end{aligned} \tag{4.2}$$

In the case of the cylinder $\mathcal{C}yl(\mathcal{C})$ we have the computation

$$\begin{aligned} &\partial_{n-1}^{\mathcal{C}yl}\left(\partial_n^{\mathcal{C}yl}(\sigma \oplus \tau \oplus \rho)\right) \\ &= \partial_{n-1}^{\mathcal{C}yl}\left(\left(\partial_n^{\mathcal{C}}\sigma - \tau\right) \oplus \left(-\partial_{n-1}^{\mathcal{C}}\tau\right) \oplus \left(\partial_n^{\mathcal{C}}\rho + \tau\right)\right) \\ &= \left(\partial_{n-1}^{\mathcal{C}}\left(\partial_n^{\mathcal{C}}\sigma - \tau\right) - \left(-\partial_{n-1}^{\mathcal{C}}\tau\right)\right) \oplus \left(-\partial_{n-2}^{\mathcal{C}}\left(-\partial_{n-1}^{\mathcal{C}}\tau\right)\right) \\ &\quad \oplus \left(\partial_{n-1}^{\mathcal{C}}\left(\partial_n^{\mathcal{C}}\rho + \tau\right) + \left(-\partial_{n-1}^{\mathcal{C}}\tau\right)\right) = 0 \oplus 0 \oplus 0 = 0. \end{aligned} \tag{4.3}$$

Let us now show the chain complex analog of Proposition 2.35.

Proposition 4.16. *For an arbitrary chain complex $\mathcal{C}$ of abelian groups, the cone $\mathcal{C}one(\mathcal{C})$ has trivial homology groups.*

Proof. Let us take an arbitrary cycle $\tau \oplus \rho$, where $\tau \in C_{n-1}$ and $\rho \in C_n$. We have

$$0 = \partial_n^{\mathcal{C}one}(\tau \oplus \rho) = \left(-\partial_{n-1}^{\mathcal{C}}\tau\right) \oplus \left(\partial_n^{\mathcal{C}}\rho + \tau\right)$$

$$\iff \begin{cases} -\partial_{n-1}^{\mathcal{C}}\tau = 0 \\ \partial_n^{\mathcal{C}}\rho + \tau = 0 \end{cases} \iff \tau = -\partial_n^{\mathcal{C}}\rho.$$

Now take the element $\rho \oplus 0 \in \mathrm{Cone}_{n+1}$. We have

$$\partial_{n+1}^{\mathcal{C}one}(\rho \oplus 0) = \left(-\partial_n^{\mathcal{C}}\rho\right) \oplus \rho = \tau \oplus \rho.$$

It follows that $[\tau \oplus \rho] = 0$. Since the choice of the cycle was arbitrary, we conclude that $H_n(\mathcal{C}one(\mathcal{C})) = 0$, for all n. □

Comparing our proof to that of Proposition 2.35 we observe the frequent and characteristic phenomenon that passing on to the more abstract framework actually makes the proofs easier. They become more structural and the abstraction provides us with a handy language for writing them down.

4.4. Chain maps

As mentioned above, bringing the maps between the chain complexes, the so-called chain maps, into the picture does not only provide aesthetically pleasing abstraction, but actually allows the consideration of the structures which help to understand the chain complexes themselves.

4.4.1. The category of chain complexes.

We generalize the notion of maps which we have seen for simplicial complexes.

Definition 4.17. Assume $\mathcal{C} = (C_*, \partial_*^{\mathcal{C}})$ and $\mathcal{D} = (D_*, \partial_*^{\mathcal{D}})$ are two chain complexes. A *chain map* f from $\mathcal{C}$ to $\mathcal{D}$ is a collection of group homomorphisms $(f_n)_{n\in\mathbb{Z}}$, $f_n : C_n \to D_n$, such that

$$\partial_n^{\mathcal{D}} \circ f_n = f_{n-1} \circ \partial_n^{\mathcal{C}}, \text{ for all } n \in \mathbb{Z}. \tag{4.4}$$

A graphical way to describe the identities (4.4) all at once is to present them as a commutative diagram (4.5). The identities then simply say that in each square of this diagram either of the two dashed arrows produces the same answer, which is just another way of saying that the squares commute.

(4.5)

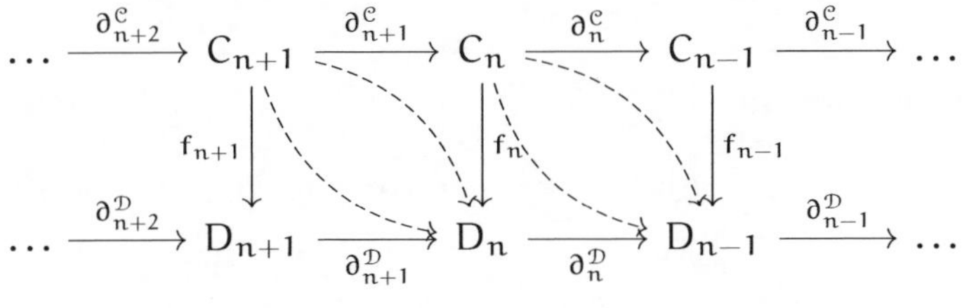

$\dots \xrightarrow{\partial_{n+2}^{\mathcal{C}}} C_{n+1} \xrightarrow{\partial_{n+1}^{\mathcal{C}}} C_n \xrightarrow{\partial_n^{\mathcal{C}}} C_{n-1} \xrightarrow{\partial_{n-1}^{\mathcal{C}}} \dots$
f_{n+1}
f_n
f_{n-1}
$\dots \xrightarrow{\partial_{n+2}^{\mathcal{D}}} D_{n+1} \xrightarrow{\partial_{n+1}^{\mathcal{D}}} D_n \xrightarrow{\partial_n^{\mathcal{D}}} D_{n-1} \xrightarrow{\partial_{n-1}^{\mathcal{D}}} \dots$

If the upper and the lower indices are dropped from Equation (4.4), it will simply say $\partial \circ f = f \circ \partial$. For this reason, one often describes chain maps as those which *commute with the boundary operator.*

It is easy to show that the identity map is a chain map, and a composition of two chain maps is again a chain map. Thus, the chain complexes (of R-modules), together with the chain maps, form a category.

Just as in the topological context, the cone over a chain complex comes equipped with the canonical inclusion map $\iota : \mathcal{C} \to \mathcal{C}one(\mathcal{C})$, defined by $\iota_n : \rho \mapsto (0, \rho)$, for each $\rho \in C_n$. Examining Equation (4.1) shows that ι is a chain map.

Similarly, for the cylinder we have two maps $t, b : \mathcal{C} \to \mathcal{C}yl(\mathcal{C})$, defined by $t_n : \sigma \mapsto (\sigma, 0, 0)$ and $b_n : \rho \mapsto (0, 0, \rho)$, for each $\sigma, \rho \in C_n$. These correspond to the embeddings as a top or a bottom copy into the cylinder, as described above. Again, it is immediate that both t and b are well-defined chain maps.

The next simple, but very important, proposition tells us that chain maps *induce* maps between homology groups.

Proposition 4.18. *Assume* $\mathcal{C} = (C_*, \partial_*^{\mathcal{C}})$ *and* $\mathcal{D} = (D_*, \partial_*^{\mathcal{D}})$ *are two chain complexes, and assume* $f = (f_n)_{n \in \mathbb{Z}}$ *is a chain map from* $\mathcal{C}$ *to* $\mathcal{D}$*. For each* $n \in \mathbb{Z}$*, the map* f_n^* *which takes* $[\alpha]$ *to* $[f_n(\alpha)]$*, whenever* $\alpha \in C_n$*, such that* $\partial_n^{\mathcal{C}} \alpha = 0$*, is a well-defined group homomorphism from* $H_n(\mathcal{C})$ *to* $H_n(\mathcal{D})$*.*

Furthermore, we have $\mathrm{id}_n^* = \mathrm{id}_{H_n(\mathcal{C})}$*, and* $(f \circ g)_n^* = f_n^* \circ g_n^*$*.*

Proof. Assume α is an n-cycle. Then $\partial_n^{\mathcal{D}}(f_n(\alpha)) = f_{n-1}(\partial_n^{\mathcal{C}} \alpha) = f_{n-1}(0) = 0$, so $f_n(\alpha)$ is an n-cycle as well. This means that $[f_n(\alpha)]$ is a well-defined homology class. Let us see that it only depends on $[\alpha]$, and not on the choice of the actual representative α. If $[\alpha] = [\beta]$, then $\alpha = \beta + \partial_{n+1}^{\mathcal{C}} \delta$, for some δ. Applying f_n to both sides of the last equality, we obtain

$$f_n(\alpha) = f_n(\beta) + f_n(\partial_{n+1}^{\mathcal{C}} \delta) = f_n(\beta) + \partial_{n+1}^{\mathcal{D}}(f_{n+1}(\delta)).$$

This of course implies that $[f(\alpha)] = [f(\beta)]$.

It is completely straightforward to see that f_n is a group homomorphism, since

$$\begin{aligned} f_n^*([\alpha] + [\beta]) = f_n^*([\alpha + \beta]) &= [f_n(\alpha + \beta)] = [f_n(\alpha) + f_n(\beta)] \\ &= [f_n(\alpha)] + [f_n(\beta)] = f_n^*([\alpha]) + f_n^*([\beta]). \end{aligned}$$

Furthermore, we have $\mathrm{id}_n^*([\alpha]) = [\mathrm{id}_n(\alpha)] = [\alpha]$, so $\mathrm{id}_n^* = \mathrm{id}_{H_n(\mathcal{C})}$. Finally,

$$(f \circ g)_n^*([\alpha]) = [(f \circ g)_n(\alpha)] = [f_n(g_n(\alpha))] = f_n^*([g_n(\alpha)]) = f_n^*(g_n^*([\alpha])),$$

which shows that $(f \circ g)_n^* = f_n^* \circ g_n^*$, and finishes the proof. □

Definition 4.19. A chain map f between the chain complexes $\mathcal{C}$ and $\mathcal{D}$ is called a *quasi-isomorphism* if the induced maps $f_n^* : H_n(\mathcal{C}) \to H_n(\mathcal{D})$ are group isomorphisms for all $n \in \mathbb{Z}$.

Note that an identity map is a quasi-isomorphism, and a composition of two quasi-isomorphisms is again a quasi-isomorphism.

4.4.2. Kernels and images of chain maps.

The notions of the kernel and the image of chain maps generalize those for linear maps defined in linear algebra.

Definition 4.20. Assume we are given two chain complexes, $\mathcal{C} = \left(C_*, \partial_*^{\mathcal{C}}\right)$ and $\mathcal{D} = \left(D_*, \partial_*^{\mathcal{D}}\right)$, and a chain map $f : \mathcal{C} \to \mathcal{D}$, $f = (f_n)_{n\in\mathbb{Z}}$. The chain complex $\operatorname{Ker}(f) = \left(\operatorname{Ker}(f)_*, \partial_*^{\operatorname{Ker}(f)}\right)$ is defined by $\operatorname{Ker}(f)_n := \operatorname{Ker}(f_n)$,[1] and the differential map $\partial_n^{\operatorname{Ker}(f)} : \operatorname{Ker}(f)_n \to \operatorname{Ker}(f)_{n-1}$ is the restriction of $\partial_n^{\mathcal{C}}$ to $\operatorname{Ker}(f_n)$:

$$\dots \xrightarrow{\partial_{n+2}^{\operatorname{Ker}(f)}} \operatorname{Ker}(f)_{n+1} \xrightarrow{\partial_{n+1}^{\operatorname{Ker}(f)}} \operatorname{Ker}(f)_n \xrightarrow{\partial_{n}^{\operatorname{Ker}(f)}} \operatorname{Ker}(f)_{n-1} \xrightarrow{\partial_{n-1}^{\operatorname{Ker}(f)}} \dots .$$

Furthermore, the chain complex $\operatorname{Im}(f) = \left(\operatorname{Im}(f)_*, \partial_*^{\operatorname{Im}(f)}\right)$ is defined by $\operatorname{Im}(f)_n := \operatorname{Im}(f_n)$, [2] and the differential map $\partial_n^{\operatorname{Im}(f)} : \operatorname{Im}(f)_n \to \operatorname{Im}(f)_{n-1}$ is the restriction of $\partial_n^{\mathcal{D}}$ to $\operatorname{Im}(f_n)$.

$$\dots \xrightarrow{\partial_{n+2}^{\operatorname{Im}(f)}} \operatorname{Im}(f)_{n+1} \xrightarrow{\partial_{n+1}^{\operatorname{Im}(f)}} \operatorname{Im}(f)_n \xrightarrow{\partial_{n}^{\operatorname{Im}(f)}} \operatorname{Im}(f)_{n-1} \xrightarrow{\partial_{n-1}^{\operatorname{Im}(f)}} \dots .$$

Proposition 4.21. *For any chain complexes $\mathcal{C}$ and $\mathcal{D}$, and an arbitrary chain map $f : \mathcal{C} \to \mathcal{D}$, the following statements are true:*

(1) *The chain complexes* $\operatorname{Ker}(f)$ *and* $\operatorname{Im}(f)$ *are well-defined.*

(2) *If $\mathcal{C}$ is a chain complex of free abelian groups, then so is* $\operatorname{Ker}(f)$.

(3) *If $\mathcal{D}$ is a chain complex of free abelian groups, then so is* $\operatorname{Im}(f)$.

Proof. Let us say that we have $\mathcal{C} = \left(C_*, \partial_*^{\mathcal{C}}\right)$, $\mathcal{D} = \left(D_*, \partial_*^{\mathcal{D}}\right)$, and $f = (f_n)_{n\in\mathbb{Z}}$. Take $\alpha \in \operatorname{Ker}(f)_n = \operatorname{Ker}(f_n)$. Then $f_{n-1}(\partial\alpha) = \partial(f_n(\alpha)) = \partial(0) = 0$, hence $\partial\alpha \in \operatorname{Ker}(f)_{n-1}$, which means that the chain complex $\operatorname{Ker}(f)$ is well-defined.

On the other hand, pick a chain $\beta \in \operatorname{Im}(f)_n = \operatorname{Im}(f_n)$. There exists $\alpha \in C_n$ such that $f_n(\alpha) = \beta$. Then, we have $\partial\beta = \partial(f_n(\alpha)) = f_{n-1}(\partial\alpha)$, which implies that $\partial\beta \in \operatorname{Im}(f_{n-1}) = \operatorname{Im}(f)_{n-1}$. Hence, also the chain complex $\operatorname{Im}(f)$ is well-defined, and the verification of (1) is finished.

[1] Note that $\operatorname{Ker}(f_n) \subseteq C_n$.
[2] Note that $\operatorname{Im}(f_n) \subseteq D_n$.

Finally, $\mathrm{Ker}(f_n) \subseteq C_n$ and $\mathrm{Im}(f_n) \subseteq D_n$, and since any subgroup of a free abelian group is itself free abelian, statements (2) and (3) follow. □

4.4.3. Mapping cylinder and mapping cone for chain complexes. Next, we would like to generalize Definitions 4.14 and 4.15, and to derive notions of cylinders and cones which depend on a given chain map.

Definition 4.22. Assume $\mathcal{C} = \left(C_*, \partial_*^{\mathcal{C}}\right)$ and $\mathcal{D} = \left(D_*, \partial_*^{\mathcal{D}}\right)$ are chain complexes, and $f = (f_n)_{n\in\mathbb{Z}}$ is a chain map from $\mathcal{C}$ to $\mathcal{D}$. We define a new chain complex $\mathcal{C}yl(f) = \left(\mathrm{Cyl}(f)_*, \partial_*^{\mathcal{C}yl(f)}\right)$, called the *mapping cylinder* of f, as follows:

- we set $\mathrm{Cyl}(f)_n := C_n \oplus C_{n-1} \oplus D_n$, for all integers n;
- the boundary maps $\partial_n^{\mathcal{C}yl(f)} : \mathrm{Cyl}(f)_n \to \mathrm{Cyl}(f)_{n-1}$, or stated more specifically, $\partial_n^{\mathcal{C}yl(f)} : C_n \oplus C_{n-1} \oplus D_n \to C_{n-1} \oplus C_{n-2} \oplus D_{n-1}$, are given by

$$\partial_n^{\mathcal{C}yl(f)}(\sigma \oplus \tau \oplus \rho) = \left(\partial_n^{\mathcal{C}}\sigma - \tau\right) \oplus \left(-\partial_{n-1}^{\mathcal{C}}\tau\right) \oplus \left(\partial_n^{\mathcal{D}}\rho + f_{n-1}(\tau)\right).$$

Furthermore, we define a new chain complex $\mathcal{C}one(f) = (\mathrm{Cone}\,(f)_*, \partial_*^{\mathcal{C}one(f)})$, which we call the *mapping cone* of f, as follows:

- we set $\mathrm{Cone}(f)_n := C_{n-1} \oplus D_n$, for all integers n;
- the boundary maps $\partial_n^{\mathcal{C}one(f)} : \mathrm{Cone}(f)_n \to \mathrm{Cone}(f)_{n-1}$, in alternative notations $\partial_n^{\mathcal{C}one(f)} : C_{n-1} \oplus D_n \to C_{n-2} \oplus D_{n-1}$, are given by

$$\partial_n^{\mathcal{C}one(f)}(\tau \oplus \rho) = \left(-\partial_{n-1}^{\mathcal{C}}\tau\right) \oplus \left(\partial_n^{\mathcal{D}}\rho + f_{n-1}(\tau)\right).$$

When $f : \mathcal{C} \to \mathcal{D}$ is the identity map, the constructions of the mapping cone and the mapping cylinder of f coincide with the constructions of the cone and the cylinder over the base $\mathcal{C}$, as defined in Section 4.3.

In general, when $\mathcal{C}$ and $\mathcal{D}$ are chain complexes of free abelian groups, and $f : \mathcal{C} \to \mathcal{D}$ is a chain map, then also $\mathcal{C}yl(f)$ and $\mathcal{C}one(f)$ are chain complexes of free abelian groups. The verification that the boundary operator squares to 0 is almost verbatim to Equation (4.2) and Equation (4.3). For the mapping cone, we have the computation

$$\begin{aligned}
\partial_{n-1}^{\mathcal{C}one(f)}\left(\partial_n^{\mathcal{C}one(f)}(\tau \oplus \rho)\right) &= \partial_{n-1}^{\mathcal{C}one(f)}\left(\left(-\partial_{n-1}^{\mathcal{C}}\tau\right) \oplus \left(\partial_n^{\mathcal{D}}\rho + f_{n-1}(\tau)\right)\right) \\
&= \left(-\partial_{n-2}^{\mathcal{C}}\left(-\partial_{n-1}^{\mathcal{C}}\tau\right)\right) \oplus \left(\partial_{n-1}^{\mathcal{D}}\left(\partial_n^{\mathcal{D}}\rho + f_{n-1}(\tau)\right) + f_{n-2}\left(-\partial_{n-1}^{\mathcal{C}}\tau\right)\right) \\
&= 0 \oplus \left(\partial_{n-1}^{\mathcal{D}} \circ f_{n-1} - f_{n-2} \circ \partial_{n-1}^{\mathcal{C}}\right)(\tau) = 0 \oplus 0 = 0,
\end{aligned}$$

and for the mapping cylinder, we have the computation

$$\begin{aligned}
&\partial_{n-1}^{\mathcal{C}yl(f)}\left(\partial_n^{\mathcal{C}yl(f)}(\sigma\oplus\tau\oplus\rho)\right)\\
&\quad=\partial_{n-1}^{\mathcal{C}yl(f)}\left(\left(\partial_n^{\mathcal{C}}\sigma-\tau\right)\oplus\left(-\partial_{n-1}^{\mathcal{C}}\tau\right)\oplus\left(\partial_n^{\mathcal{D}}\rho+f_{n-1}(\tau)\right)\right)\\
&\quad=\left(\partial_{n-1}^{\mathcal{C}}\left(\partial_n^{\mathcal{C}}\sigma-\tau\right)-\left(-\partial_{n-1}^{\mathcal{C}}\tau\right)\right)\oplus\left(-\partial_{n-2}^{\mathcal{C}}\left(-\partial_{n-1}^{\mathcal{C}}\tau\right)\right)\\
&\qquad\oplus\left(\partial_{n-1}^{\mathcal{D}}\left(\partial_n^{\mathcal{D}}\rho+f_{n-1}(\tau)\right)+f_{n-2}\left(-\partial_{n-1}^{\mathcal{C}}\tau\right)\right)\\
&\quad=0\oplus0\oplus\left(\partial_{n-1}^{\mathcal{D}}\circ f_{n-1}-f_{n-2}\circ\partial_{n-1}^{\mathcal{C}}\right)(\tau)=0\oplus0\oplus0=0.
\end{aligned}$$

One can show directly that $\mathcal{C}yl(f)$ has the same homology as $\mathcal{D}$ and also that when f is the inclusion map, the chain complex $\mathcal{C}one(f)$ has the same homology as $\mathcal{D}/\operatorname{Im}(f)$. However, the best way to do this is by using a special tool called chain homotopy.

Exercises

(1) Show that the cylinder construction in Definition 4.15 is a special case of the mapping cylinder of chain complexes. Show the same statement concerning the cone construction in Definition 4.14.

(2) Show that the identity map is a chain map, and a composition of two chain maps is again a chain map.

(3) Fill in the proofs of Propositions 4.6 and 4.8.

(4) Define the mirror version of Definition 4.7, where the truncation is done below a certain index, instead of above a certain index, and prove the analog of Proposition 4.8.

(5) Assume that we are given a free chain complex $\mathcal{C}=(C_*,\partial_*^{\mathcal{C}})$, and a subcomplex of $\mathcal{C}$, called $\mathcal{D}=(D_*,\partial_*^{\mathcal{D}})$, such that for each n there is a set A_n, which is a basis complement of D_n in C_n. Show that the chain complex $\mathcal{C}/\mathcal{D}$ is also free.

(6) Find a chain complex $\mathcal{C}$ of abelian groups such that $H_n(\mathcal{C})\neq 0$, for infinitely many values of n, and still $H_n(\mathcal{C}\otimes\mathbb{Z}_2)=0$, for all n.

(7) Let $\mathcal{C}$ and $\mathcal{D}$ be two arbitrary chain complexes, and let $f:\mathcal{C}\to\mathcal{D}$ be a chain map. Assuming f is a 0-map, compute the homology groups of its mapping cone, in terms of the homology groups of $\mathcal{C}$ and $\mathcal{D}$.

(8) Let $\mathcal{C} = (C_*, \partial_*^{\mathcal{C}})$ be the chain complex, whose chain groups are given by

$$C_n = \begin{cases} \mathbb{Z}, & \text{if } n = 0 \text{ or } 1, \\ 0, & \text{otherwise,} \end{cases}$$

and, for all $n \in \mathbb{Z}$, the boundary map $\partial_n^{\mathcal{C}}$ is the 0-map. Assume, furthermore, that $\mathcal{D}$ is a chain complex, which is isomorphic to $\mathcal{C}$, and assume $f : \mathcal{C} \to \mathcal{D}$ is a chain map.

Describe the mapping cone of f and calculate its homology, if the following is known:

(a) The map $f_0 : C_0 \to D_0$ is the identity map, and the map $f_1 : C_1 \to D_1$ is the multiplication by m, for some integer m.

(b) The map $f_0 : C_0 \to D_0$ is the multiplication by k, and the map $f_1 : C_1 \to D_1$ is the multiplication by m, for some integers k and m.

(9) Prove that the relation $\mathcal{C} \sim \mathcal{D}$ *if and only if there is a quasi-isomorphism from* $\mathcal{C}$ *to* $\mathcal{D}$ is reflexive and transitive, but not symmetric.

Chapter 5

Chain Homotopy

Chain homotopy is the right homotopy in the category of chain complexes. Defined in a purely algebraic way, it constitutes a very convenient tool to prove that two chain maps f and g between chain complexes $\mathcal{C}$ and $\mathcal{D}$ induce the same maps between the homology groups.

The general idea is to map each chain σ from $\mathcal{C}$ to a chain from $\mathcal{D}$ of dimension one higher. Intuitively, this should give an algebraic analog of a cylinder, whose two bases are the images of σ under the maps f and g, and whose other sides constitute the homotopy on the boundary of σ.

5.1. Chain homotopy

Let us now be more specific. Given two chain complexes $\mathcal{C}$ and $\mathcal{D}$, and two chain maps f and g between them, a chain homotopy Φ is a sequence of maps, and each map takes a chain of $\mathcal{C}$ to a chain of $\mathcal{D}$ of dimension one higher. This new chain is supposed to embody the topological homotopy. It turns out that for the actual homology computation, we do not need to define the chain homotopy on *all* the chains, but in fact it suffices to define Φ for the cycles only. We shall accordingly deviate from the standard literature on the subject, and define what we call an *abridged chain homotopy* on par with the regular one.

5.1.1. Abridged and unabridged. Before we give the first definition let us recall the previously introduced piece of notation. Whenever $\mathcal{C} = (C_*, \partial_*^{\mathcal{C}})$ is a chain complex, we let $Z_n^{\mathcal{C}}$ denote the kernel of the boundary map $\partial_n^{\mathcal{C}}$, and let $B_n^{\mathcal{C}}$ denote the image of the boundary map $\partial_{n+1}^{\mathcal{C}}$. Clearly, $Z_n^{\mathcal{C}} \supseteq B_n^{\mathcal{C}}$, since $\mathcal{C}$ is a chain complex.

Definition 5.1. Assume that we have two chain complexes $\mathcal{C} = (C_*, \partial_*^{\mathcal{C}})$ and $\mathcal{D} = (D_*, \partial_*^{\mathcal{D}})$, and chain maps $f = (f_n)_{n\in\mathbb{Z}}$ and $g = (g_n)_{n\in\mathbb{Z}}$ from $\mathcal{C}$ to $\mathcal{D}$.

An *abridged chain homotopy* between the chain maps f and g is a family of maps $(\Psi_n : Z_n^{\mathcal{C}} \to D_{n+1})_{n\in\mathbb{Z}}$, such that

$$\partial_{n+1}^{\mathcal{D}} \circ \Psi_n = f_n - g_n : \tag{5.1}$$

$$\begin{array}{ccccccccc}
\cdots & & Z_{n+1}^{\mathcal{C}} & & Z_n^{\mathcal{C}} & & Z_{n-1}^{\mathcal{C}} & & \cdots \\
 & & f_{n+1}\Big\downarrow\Big\downarrow g_{n+1} & \swarrow \Psi_n & f_n\Big\downarrow\Big\downarrow g_n & \swarrow \Psi_{n-1} & f_{n-1}\Big\downarrow\Big\downarrow g_{n-1} & & \\
\cdots & \xrightarrow{\partial_{n+2}^{\mathcal{D}}} & D_{n+1} & \xrightarrow{\partial_{n+1}^{\mathcal{D}}} & D_n & \xrightarrow{\partial_n^{\mathcal{D}}} & D_{n-1} & \xrightarrow{\partial_{n-1}^{\mathcal{D}}} & \cdots
\end{array}$$

The intuitive idea behind the abridged chain homotopy is that we want to construct a certificate of the fact that the difference between f and g evaluated on cycles is a boundary of some chain; cf. Equation (5.1). Defining the maps $\Psi = (\Psi_n)_{n\in\mathbb{Z}}$ allows us to do that in an organized manner.

More classically, we have the following definition.

Definition 5.2. Assume that $\mathcal{C}$, $\mathcal{D}$, f, and g are the same as in Definition 5.1. A *chain homotopy* between f and g is a family of maps $(\Phi_n : C_n \to D_{n+1})_{n\in\mathbb{Z}}$, such that

$$\partial_{n+1}^{\mathcal{D}} \circ \Phi_n + \Phi_{n-1} \circ \partial_n^{\mathcal{C}} = f_n - g_n : \tag{5.2}$$

$$\begin{array}{ccccccccc}
\cdots & \xrightarrow{\partial_{n+2}^{\mathcal{C}}} & C_{n+1} & \xrightarrow{\partial_{n+1}^{\mathcal{C}}} & C_n & \xrightarrow{\partial_n^{\mathcal{C}}} & C_{n-1} & \xrightarrow{\partial_{n-1}^{\mathcal{C}}} & \cdots \\
 & & f_{n+1}\Big\downarrow\Big\downarrow g_{n+1} & \swarrow \Phi_n & f_n\Big\downarrow\Big\downarrow g_n & \swarrow \Phi_{n-1} & f_{n-1}\Big\downarrow\Big\downarrow g_{n-1} & & \\
\cdots & \xrightarrow{\partial_{n+2}^{\mathcal{D}}} & D_{n+1} & \xrightarrow{\partial_{n+1}^{\mathcal{D}}} & D_n & \xrightarrow{\partial_n^{\mathcal{D}}} & D_{n-1} & \xrightarrow{\partial_{n-1}^{\mathcal{D}}} & \cdots
\end{array}$$

The chain maps f and g are said to be *chain homotopic* if there exists a chain homotopy between them.

5.1.2. Chain homotopy is an equivalence relation.

Assume we are given chain complexes $\mathcal{C}$ and $\mathcal{D}$, and let $\mathcal{M}(\mathcal{C}, \mathcal{D})$ denote the set of all chain maps from $\mathcal{C}$ to $\mathcal{D}$.

Proposition 5.3. *Being chain homotopic is an equivalence relation on* $\mathcal{M}(\mathcal{C}, \mathcal{D})$.

Proof. Let us simply check the three axioms of equivalence relations.

Reflexivity. For any chain map $f : \mathcal{C} \to \mathcal{D}$, the map $\Phi = 0$ is a chain homotopy between f and f; so $f \sim f$.

Symmetry. If $\Phi = (\Phi_n)_{n\in\mathbb{Z}}$ is a chain homotopy between chain maps f and g, for some $f, g : \mathcal{C} \to \mathcal{D}$, then $\Psi = (\Psi_n)_{n\in\mathbb{Z}}$, defined by $\Psi_n = -\Phi_n$, for all $n \in \mathbb{Z}$, is a chain homotopy between g and f; since for all $n \in \mathbb{Z}$ we have:

$$\begin{aligned}\partial^{\mathcal{D}}_{n+1} \circ \Psi_n + \Psi_{n-1} \circ \partial^{\mathcal{C}}_n &= \partial^{\mathcal{D}}_{n+1} \circ (-\Phi_n) + (-\Phi_{n-1}) \circ \partial^{\mathcal{C}}_n \\ &= -\left(\partial^{\mathcal{D}}_{n+1} \circ \Phi_n + \Phi_{n-1} \circ \partial^{\mathcal{C}}_n\right) = -(f_n - g_n) = g_n - f_n.\end{aligned}$$

So $f \sim g$ implies $g \sim f$.

Transitivity. Assume that for some chain maps f, g, and h, where $f, g, h : \mathcal{C} \to \mathcal{D}$, we have a chain homotopy between f and g, called $\Phi = (\Phi_n)_{n\in\mathbb{Z}}$, and a chain homotopy between g and h, called $\Psi = (\Psi_n)_{n\in\mathbb{Z}}$. Consider the family of maps $\Omega = (\Omega_n)_{n\in\mathbb{Z}}$, given by $\Omega_n = \Phi_n + \Psi_n$, for all $n \in \mathbb{Z}$. The following direct computation verifies that it is a chain homotopy between f and h:

$$\begin{aligned}\partial^{\mathcal{D}}_{n+1} \circ \Omega_n + \Omega_{n-1} \circ \partial^{\mathcal{C}}_n &= \partial^{\mathcal{D}}_{n+1} \circ (\Phi_n + \Psi_n) + (\Phi_{n-1} + \Psi_n) \circ \partial^{\mathcal{C}}_n \\ &= \partial^{\mathcal{D}}_{n+1} \circ \Phi_n + \partial^{\mathcal{D}}_{n+1} \circ \Psi_n + \Phi_{n-1} \circ \partial^{\mathcal{C}}_n + \Psi_n \circ \partial^{\mathcal{C}}_n \\ &= \left(\partial^{\mathcal{D}}_{n+1} \circ \Phi_n + \Phi_{n-1} \circ \partial^{\mathcal{C}}_n\right) + \left(\partial^{\mathcal{D}}_{n+1} \circ \Psi_n + \Psi_n \circ \partial^{\mathcal{C}}_n\right) \\ &= (f_n - g_n) + (g_n - h_n) = f_n - h_n.\end{aligned}$$

So $f \sim g$, together with $g \sim h$, implies that $f \sim h$. We have therefore verified the last equivalence relation axiom. □

5.1.3. Chain homotopy and homology. Obviously, the restriction of an arbitrary chain homotopy to the subgroups of cycles is an abridged chain homotopy, since the term $(\Phi_{n-1} \circ \partial^{\mathcal{C}}_n)(\sigma)$ vanishes when σ is a cycle. On the other hand, as Theorem 5.4 and Corollary 5.5 show, having an abridged chain homotopy is just the right tool to show that the chain maps induce the same maps between the homology groups of free chain complexes.

Theorem 5.4. *Assume $\mathcal{C}$ and $\mathcal{D}$ are chain complexes of abelian groups, such that $\mathcal{C}$ is free. For an arbitrary chain map $f : \mathcal{C} \to \mathcal{D}$ the following three statements are equivalent:*

(1) *f induces trivial maps on the homology groups of $\mathcal{C}$, that is, we have $f^* = 0$, which is shorthand notation for $f^*_n = 0$, for all n;*

(2) *f maps each cycle in $\mathcal{C}$ to a boundary of $\mathcal{D}$, that is, for all n we have $f(Z^{\mathcal{C}}_n) \subseteq B^{\mathcal{D}}_n$;*

(3) *there exists an abridged chain homotopy between the chain map f and the 0-map.*

Proof. Let $\alpha \in Z_n^{\mathcal{C}}$ represent a homology class $[\alpha] \in H_n(\mathcal{C})$. By definition of f_n^*, we have $f_n^*([\alpha]) = [f_n(\alpha)]$. Thus, for all $\alpha \in Z_n^{\mathcal{C}}$, we have the following chain of equivalences:

$$f_n^*([\alpha]) = 0 \iff [f_n(\alpha)] = 0 \iff f_n(\alpha) \in B_n^{\mathcal{D}}.$$

This shows the equivalence of (1) and (2).

Assume now that there exists an abridged chain equivalence Ψ between the map f and the 0-map. This means that for all n, there exist $\Psi_n : Z_n^{\mathcal{C}} \to D_{n+1}$, such that $\partial_{n+1}^{\mathcal{D}} \circ \Psi_n = \tilde{f}_n$, where $\tilde{f}_n$ is the restriction of f_n to $Z_n^{\mathcal{C}}$. Clearly, this implies $\operatorname{Im} \tilde{f}_n \subseteq \operatorname{Im} \partial_{n+1}^{\mathcal{D}}$, and so (3) implies (2).

Finally, assume condition (2) holds, and let us construct an abridged chain equivalence Ψ between the map f and the 0-map. All subgroups of free abelian groups are free abelian, so there exists a basis A which generates $Z_n^{\mathcal{C}}$ freely. For each $a \in A$, choose $b \in D_{n+1}$, such that $\partial_{n+1}^{\mathcal{D}} b = f_n(a)$. Such an element must exist, since $f_n(Z_n^{\mathcal{C}}) \subseteq B_n^{\mathcal{D}}$. We now set $\Psi(a) := b$ and extend uniquely by linearity to the entire subgroup $Z_n^{\mathcal{C}}$. Since the identity $\partial_{n+1}^{\mathcal{D}} \circ \Psi_n = f_n$ is true for the basis elements of $Z_n^{\mathcal{C}}$, it must hold for the entire group $Z_n^{\mathcal{C}}$. □

Note that the freeness of $\mathcal{C}$ was only used to prove the implication (2) ⇒ (3). The implication (3) ⇒ (2) is valid for all chain complexes.

Corollary 5.5. *Assume $\mathcal{C}$ and $\mathcal{D}$ are chain complexes, $\mathcal{C}$ is free, and $f, g : \mathcal{C} \to \mathcal{D}$ are chain maps. Then f and g induce the same homomorphisms on the homology groups if and only if there exists an abridged chain homotopy between them.*

Proof. If we have two chain maps f and g then $f^* = g^*$ if and only if $(f - g)^* = 0$. We can therefore use Theorem 5.4 to conclude that $f^* = g^*$ if and only if there exists an abridged chain homotopy between $f - g$ and the 0-map. This is, of course, the same as an abridged chain homotopy between f and g. □

Corollary 5.6. *Assume $\mathcal{C}$ and $\mathcal{D}$ are arbitrary chain complexes of abelian groups, and $f, g : \mathcal{C} \to \mathcal{D}$ are chain maps, which are chain homotopic. Then f and g induce the same maps on the homology groups.*

Proof. Since the restriction of a chain homotopy yields an abridged chain homotopy, this follows from Corollary 5.5, together with the previous observation that the implication (3) ⇒ (2) in Theorem 5.4 is valid for all chain complexes. □

Let us now consider an example of two chain complexes and chain maps between them such that no chain homotopy exists, whereas an abridged chain homotopy does exist. Let $\mathcal{C} = (C_*, \partial_*^{\mathcal{C}})$ be the chain complex defined by saying that the only non-trivial chain groups and maps are $C_1 = \mathbb{Z}$, $C_0 = \mathbb{Z}_2$, and $\partial_1^{\mathcal{C}} : x \mapsto x \mod 2$. Furthermore, let $\mathcal{D} = (D_*, \partial_*^{\mathcal{D}})$ be the chain complex whose only non-trivial chain groups and maps are $D_2 = D_1 = \mathbb{Z}$, and $\partial_2^{\mathcal{D}} : x \to 2x$. Consider the chain maps $f = (f_n)_{n\in\mathbb{Z}}$ and $g = (g_n)_{n\in\mathbb{Z}}$ from $\mathcal{C}$ to $\mathcal{D}$, such that $f_1 = \text{id}$, and all other f_i's and g_i's are 0. The situation is depicted in Figure 5.1. We leave it as an exercise to show that f and g are not chain homotopic, but there does exist an abridged chain homotopy.

For the interested reader we note that the only non-trivial homology groups of $\mathcal{C}$ and $\mathcal{D}$ are $H_1(\mathcal{C}) \approx \mathbb{Z}$ and $H_1(\mathcal{D}) \approx \mathbb{Z}_2$. Looking at representing chains, one can see that the chain map f induces a 0-map on the homology groups. This cannot be certified by presenting a chain homotopy, but it can, by presenting an abridged chain homotopy!

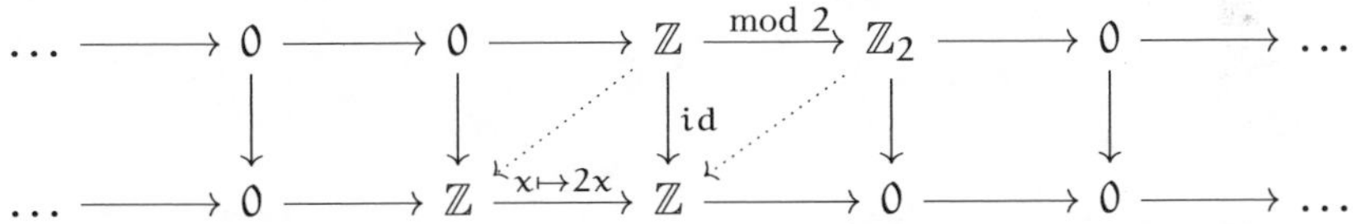

Figure 5.1. Diagram of chain complexes and chain maps where the chain homotopy does not exist, but the abridged one does.

5.2. Some applications of chain homotopy

We would now like to make our first foray into the vast field of applications of chain homotopy. The topological homotopy has deep connections with mapping cones and mapping cylinders. The same turns out to be true for the chain homotopy.

5.2.1. Null homotopy and maps from mapping cones.

Definition 5.7. A chain map f is called *null-homotopic* if there exists a chain homotopy between f and the 0-map.

Intuitively, one might think that it should somehow be possible to *contract* a null-homotopic map. That intuition is made formal by the following proposition.

Proposition 5.8. *Let $\mathcal{C} = (C_*, \partial_*^{\mathcal{C}})$ and $\mathcal{D} = (D_*, \partial_*^{\mathcal{D}})$ be two chain complexes of abelian groups, and let $f = (f_n)_{n\in\mathbb{Z}}$ be a chain map from $\mathcal{C}$ to $\mathcal{D}$. The chain map f is null-homotopic if and only if it can be extended to a chain map from the cone over $\mathcal{C}$ to $\mathcal{D}$.*

Formally, this means that there exists a chain map $g : \mathrm{Cone}(\mathcal{C}) \to \mathcal{D}$, *such that* $g \circ \iota = f$, *where* $\iota : \mathcal{C} \to \mathrm{Cone}(\mathcal{C})$ *is the canonical inclusion map of* $\mathcal{C}$ *into the base of* $\mathrm{Cone}(\mathcal{C})$.

Proof. Recall that the canonical inclusion map ι of $\mathcal{C}$ into the base of $\mathrm{Cone}(\mathcal{C})$ is defined by $\iota_n : C_n \to C_{n-1} \oplus C_n$, $\sigma \mapsto 0 \oplus \sigma$.

Assume first that $\Phi = (\Phi_n)_{n\in\mathbb{Z}}$ is a chain homotopy between f and the 0-map, that is, $\Phi_{n-1} \circ \partial_n^{\mathcal{C}} + \partial_{n+1}^{\mathcal{D}} \circ \Phi_n = f_n$, for all n. Define $g_n : C_{n-1} \oplus C_n \to D_n$ by setting

$$g_n(\tau \oplus \sigma) := \Phi_{n-1}(\tau) + f_n(\sigma).$$

Clearly, this is a group homomorphism. The next calculation verifies that it commutes with the differentials:

$$\begin{aligned}
&\partial_n^{\mathcal{D}}(g_n(\tau \oplus \sigma)) - g_{n-1}(\partial_n^{\mathrm{Cone}(\mathcal{C})}(\tau \oplus \sigma)) \\
&\qquad = \partial_n^{\mathcal{D}}(\Phi_{n-1}(\tau) + f_n(\sigma)) - g_{n-1}((-\partial_{n-1}^{\mathcal{C}}\tau) \oplus (\partial_n^{\mathcal{C}}\sigma + \tau)) \\
&\qquad = \partial_n^{\mathcal{D}}(\Phi_{n-1}(\tau)) + \partial_n^{\mathcal{D}}(f_n(\sigma)) - \Phi_{n-2}(-\partial_{n-1}^{\mathcal{C}}\tau) - f_{n-1}(\partial_n^{\mathcal{C}}\sigma + \tau) \\
&= (\partial_n^{\mathcal{D}} \circ \Phi_{n-1} + \Phi_{n-2} \circ \partial_{n-1}^{\mathcal{C}} - f_{n-1})(\tau) + (\partial_n^{\mathcal{D}} \circ f_n - f_{n-1} \circ \partial_n^{\mathcal{C}})(\sigma) = 0.
\end{aligned}$$

Furthermore, we have

$$(g_n \circ \iota_n)(\sigma) = g_n(\iota_n(\sigma)) = g_n(0 \oplus \sigma) = f_n(\sigma),$$

hence $g \circ \iota = f$ as chain maps.

Reversely, assume that there exists a chain map $g : \mathrm{Cone}(\mathcal{C}) \to \mathcal{D}$, such that $g \circ \iota = f$. For each $n \in \mathbb{Z}$, define the map $\Phi_n : C_n \to D_{n+1}$ by sending $\tau \mapsto g_n(\tau \oplus 0)$. Clearly, these maps are group homomorphisms. The fact that $\Phi = (\Phi_n)_{n\in\mathbb{Z}}$ is a chain homotopy between f and the 0-map is verified by the following calculation, where for brevity we skip the indices:

$$\begin{aligned}
\partial(\Phi(\tau)) + \Phi(\partial\tau) &= \partial(g(\tau \oplus 0)) + g(\partial\tau \oplus 0) = g(\partial(\tau \oplus 0)) + g(\partial\tau \oplus 0) \\
&= g((-\partial\tau) \oplus \tau) + g(\partial\tau \oplus 0) = g((-\partial\tau) \oplus \tau + \partial\tau \oplus 0) = g(0 \oplus \tau) = f(\tau).
\end{aligned}$$

This finishes the proof. □

5.2.2. Chain homotopy of mapping cylinders.

Proposition 5.9. *Let* $\mathcal{C} = (C_*, \partial_*^{\mathcal{C}})$ *and* $\mathcal{D} = (D_*, \partial_*^{\mathcal{D}})$ *be two chain complexes of abelian groups, and let* $f = (f_n)_{n\in\mathbb{Z}}$ *be a chain map from* $\mathcal{C}$ *to* $\mathcal{D}$. *Then, the homology groups of the chain complex* $\mathcal{C}yl(f)$ *are isomorphic to the homology groups of* $\mathcal{D}$. *Specifically, this isomorphism is induced by the chain map* $\varphi : \mathcal{D} \to \mathcal{C}yl(f)$, *given by* $\rho \mapsto (0 \oplus 0 \oplus \rho)$.

Proof. In addition to the chain map φ, which is described in the formulation of the proposition, we consider the chain map $\psi : \mathcal{C}yl(f) \to \mathcal{D}$, defined by

$$\psi_n : \sigma \oplus \tau \oplus \rho \mapsto f_n(\sigma) + \rho.$$

First, we clearly have $\psi_n \circ \varphi_n : \rho \mapsto \rho$, i.e., the chain map $\psi \circ \varphi : \mathcal{D} \to \mathcal{D}$ is simply the identity map. For the induced maps on the homology groups, this means that $\psi^* \circ \varphi^* = \mathrm{id}_{H_*(\mathcal{D})}$, since $\psi^* \circ \varphi^* = (\psi \circ \varphi)^* = (\mathrm{id}_{\mathcal{D}})^* = \mathrm{id}_{H_*(\mathcal{D})}$.

Let us investigate the chain map $\varphi \circ \psi : \mathcal{C}yl(f) \to \mathcal{C}yl(f)$. We consider the family of homomorphisms $\Phi = (\Phi_n)_{n\in\mathbb{Z}}$, with each $\Phi_n : \mathrm{Cyl}(f)_n \to \mathrm{Cyl}(f)_{n+1}$ given by

$$\Phi_n : \sigma \oplus \tau \oplus \rho \mapsto 0 \oplus \sigma \oplus 0.$$

We claim that Φ is a chain homotopy between the identity map $\mathrm{id}_{\mathcal{C}yl(f)}$ and the map $\varphi \circ \psi$. This is verified by the following computation:

$$\text{(5.3)} \quad \left(\partial_{n+1}^{\mathcal{C}yl(f)} \circ \Phi_n + \Phi_{n-1} \circ \partial_n^{\mathcal{C}yl(f)}\right)(\sigma \oplus \tau \oplus \rho)$$
$$= \partial_{n+1}^{\mathcal{C}yl(f)}(0 \oplus \sigma \oplus 0) + \Phi_{n-1}\left(\left(\partial_n^{\mathcal{C}}\sigma - \tau\right) \oplus \left(-\partial_{n-1}^{\mathcal{C}}\tau\right) \oplus \left(\partial_n^{\mathcal{D}}\rho + f_{n-1}(\tau)\right)\right)$$
$$= (-\sigma) \oplus \left(-\partial_n^{\mathcal{C}}\sigma\right) \oplus f_n(\sigma) + 0 \oplus \left(\partial_n^{\mathcal{C}}\sigma - \tau\right) \oplus 0 = (-\sigma) \oplus (-\tau) \oplus f_n(\sigma)$$
$$= 0 \oplus 0 \oplus (f_n(\sigma) + \rho) - \sigma \oplus \tau \oplus \rho = (\varphi_n \circ \psi_n - \mathrm{id})(\sigma \oplus \tau \oplus \rho).$$

Since $\varphi \circ \psi$ is chain homotopic to the identity map, both maps induce the same map on homology groups. This means that $\varphi^* \circ \psi^* = (\varphi \circ \psi)^* = (\mathrm{id}_{\mathcal{C}yl(f)})^* = \mathrm{id}_{H_*(\mathcal{C}yl(f))}$. Combined with the identity $\psi^* \circ \varphi^* = \mathrm{id}_{H_*(\mathcal{D})}$, this tells us that ψ^* and φ^* are isomorphisms, which finishes the proof. □

Note how the computation Equation (5.3) would have been much simpler if we restricted ourselves to verifying that Φ is an abridged chain homotopy. In this case, we would have taken an element $\sigma \oplus \tau \oplus \rho$, which is a cycle. This, in particular, means we would have $\partial_n^{\mathcal{C}}\sigma = \tau$. Then we could replace Equation (5.3) with

$$\left(\partial_{n+1}^{\mathcal{C}yl(f)} \circ \Phi_n\right)(\sigma \oplus \tau \oplus \rho) = \partial_{n+1}^{\mathcal{C}yl(f)}(0 \oplus \sigma \oplus 0) = (-\sigma) \oplus \left(-\partial_n^{\mathcal{C}}\sigma\right) \oplus f_n(\sigma)$$
$$= (-\sigma)\oplus(-\tau)\oplus f_n(\sigma) = 0\oplus 0\oplus(f_n(\sigma)+\rho)-\sigma\oplus\tau\oplus\rho = (\varphi_n\circ\psi_n-\mathrm{id})(\sigma\oplus\tau\oplus\rho).$$

5.3. Alternative definition of chain homotopy via chain maps of cylinders

We find it instructive that rather than defining the chain homotopy ad hoc, we derive this concept by combining the notion of the cylinder of the chain complex with the topological intuition of homotopies of maps.

Recall that in point-set topology two continuous maps f and g between topological spaces X and Y are called homotopic if there exists a family of continuous maps which *continuously* deforms f to g. The concept of a continuous family is formalized by requiring the existence of a continuous map $F : X \times I \to Y$, where I is the closed interval $[0, 1]$ and the space $X \times I$ is equipped with the standard direct product topology.

Clearly, $X \times I$ is nothing but the cylinder with a base X. To mimic this topological definition in the chain complex setting we can do the following:

- replace the topological spaces X and Y with chain complexes $\mathcal{C}$ and $\mathcal{D}$;
- replace the continuous maps f and g with chain maps;
- replace the direct product space $X \times I$ with the cylinder over $\mathcal{C}$.

Furthermore, recall at this time that we have structural embedding maps $b, t : \mathcal{C} \to \mathcal{C}yl(\mathcal{C})$ mimicking the inclusion as the top or bottom copy in the cylinder.

As a result, we obtain the following alternative definition of a chain homotopy.

Theorem 5.10. *Assume $\mathcal{C}$ and $\mathcal{D}$ are chain complexes, and $f, g : \mathcal{C} \to \mathcal{D}$ are chain maps. The maps f and g are chain homotopic if and only if there exists a chain map $F : \mathcal{C}yl(\mathcal{C}) \to \mathcal{D}$, such that $F \circ b = f$ and $F \circ t = g$.*

Proof. Indeed, a chain map $F : \mathcal{C}yl(\mathcal{C}) \to \mathcal{D}$ consists of group homomorphisms $F_n : C_n \oplus C_{n-1} \oplus C_n \to D_n$. Each such homomorphism can be split into three homomorphisms $\tilde{f}_n, \tilde{g}_n : C_n \to D_n$, and $\varphi_{n-1} : C_{n-1} \to D_n$, so that $F_n(\sigma \oplus \tau \oplus \rho) = \tilde{g}_n(\sigma) + \varphi_{n-1}(\tau) + \tilde{f}_n(\rho)$.

Clearly, the conditions $F \circ b = f$ and $F \circ t = g$ translate into $f = \tilde{f}$ and $g = \tilde{g}$. Let us now write out the meaning of the condition $\partial \circ F = F \circ \partial$, where again for brevity we shall skip the indices. First, we have

$$
\begin{aligned}
(5.4)\quad (\partial \circ F)(\sigma \oplus \tau \oplus \rho) = \partial(g(\sigma) + \varphi(\tau) + f(\rho)) &= \partial g(\sigma) + \partial\varphi(\tau) + \partial f(\rho) \\
&= f(\partial\rho) + g(\partial\sigma) + \partial\varphi(\tau),
\end{aligned}
$$

where the last equality used the fact that f and g are chain maps. On the other hand, we get

$$
\begin{aligned}
(5.5)\quad & (F \circ \partial)(\sigma \oplus \tau \oplus \rho) = F((\partial\sigma - \tau) \oplus (-\partial\tau) \oplus (\partial\rho + \tau)) \\
&= g(\partial\sigma - \tau) + \varphi(-\partial\tau) + f(\partial\rho + \tau) = g(\partial\sigma) - g(\tau) - \varphi(\partial\tau) + f(\partial\rho) + f(\tau) \\
&= f(\partial\rho) + g(\partial\sigma) + f(\tau) - g(\tau) - \varphi(\partial\tau).
\end{aligned}
$$

The left-hand sides of Equations (5.4) and (5.5) must be equal. Comparing the right-hand sides of these equations yields precisely the identity $\partial\varphi(\tau) = f(\tau) - g(\tau) - \varphi(\partial\tau)$ which is used to define the concept of chain homotopy. □

Exercises

(1) Let $\mathcal{C}$, $\mathcal{D}$, and $\mathcal{E}$ be chain complexes. Assume we are given chain maps $f, g : \mathcal{C} \to \mathcal{D}$ and $h, k : \mathcal{D} \to \mathcal{E}$, such that f is chain homotopic to g and h is chain homotopic to k. Show that the compositions $h \circ f$ and $k \circ g$ are chain homotopic.

(2) Show that in the example on Figure 5.1 there can be no chain homotopy between the chain maps f and g. Contrast that by presenting an abridged chain homotopy between the two maps.
Hint: make use of the different domains of an abridged and unabridged homotopy.

(3) Assume $\mathcal{C} = (C_*, \partial_*)$ is a chain complex of free abelian groups, such that $C_i = 0$, for all $i < 0$. Show that $\mathcal{C}$ is acyclic (see Definition 3.7) if and only if the identity map $\mathrm{id}_{\mathcal{C}}$ is null-homotopic.

Chapter 6

Connecting Homomorphism

6.1. Homology map induced by inclusion

Assume that our goal is to calculate homology groups of a certain chain complex of abelian groups $\mathcal{X} = (X_*, \partial_*^{\mathcal{X}})$. Assume, furthermore, that $\mathcal{A} = (A_*, \partial_*^{\mathcal{A}})$ is some given chain subcomplex of $\mathcal{X}$. Recall that being a chain subcomplex can be phrased as two conditions:

- for each $n \in \mathbb{Z}$, the group A_n is a subgroup of X_n;
- each boundary operator $\partial_n^{\mathcal{A}} : A_n \to A_{n-1}$ is well-defined as the restriction of $\partial_n^{\mathcal{X}} : X_n \to X_{n-1}$ to A_n.

Because of that second property, we will mostly drop the letters $\mathcal{A}$ and $\mathcal{X}$ from $\partial_*^{\mathcal{A}}$ and from $\partial_*^{\mathcal{X}}$, and just use ∂_* in our notations. We also say that we have a *pair of chain complexes* $(\mathcal{X}, \mathcal{A})$.

We would like to investigate in what way that having the information about the homology groups of the subcomplex $\mathcal{A}$ and, importantly, about how these groups *sit inside* the homology groups of the complex $\mathcal{X}$, would help us to gain some understanding of the groups $H_*(\mathcal{X})$.

6.1.1. Replacing chain subcomplexes by inclusion chain maps, and the associated subgroups.

Following the *functorial way of thinking*, it is natural to supplant by saying that $\mathcal{A}$ is a chain subcomplex of $\mathcal{X}$, by considering the chain map $\iota : \mathcal{A} \to \mathcal{X}$ defined by the inclusion. This, in turn, means that we have induced maps $\iota^n : H_n(\mathcal{A}) \to H_n(\mathcal{X})$, $\forall n$, on the homology groups. The next task which we undertake is to study this map ι_n^*:

$$\begin{array}{ccccccccc}
\mathcal{A}: & \dots \xrightarrow{\partial_{n+2}^{\mathcal{A}}} & A_{n+1} & \xrightarrow{\partial_{n+1}^{\mathcal{A}}} & A_n & \xrightarrow{\partial_n^{\mathcal{A}}} & A_{n-1} & \xrightarrow{\partial_{n-1}^{\mathcal{A}}} & \dots \\
& & \downarrow{\scriptstyle \iota_{n+1}} & & \downarrow{\scriptstyle \iota_n} & & \downarrow{\scriptstyle \iota_{n-1}} & & \\
\mathcal{X}: & \dots \xrightarrow{\partial_{n+2}^{\mathcal{X}}} & X_{n+1} & \xrightarrow{\partial_{n+1}^{\mathcal{X}}} & X_n & \xrightarrow{\partial_n^{\mathcal{X}}} & X_{n-1} & \xrightarrow{\partial_{n-1}^{\mathcal{X}}} & \dots
\end{array}$$

To start with, note that just the fact that the map ι is an inclusion does not by itself mean anything - the induced maps ι_n^* certainly do not need to be injective. This is because cycles in $\mathcal{A}$, which are not boundaries of some chain *in* $\mathcal{A}$, may just happen to be boundaries of some chain *in* $\mathcal{X}$ instead. The kernel of ι_n^* will essentially consist of such cycles.

To phrase the relation precisely, we need to have notations for the plethora of the groups involved in this situation. To start with, we already have A_n and X_n denote the chain groups of the chain complexes $\mathcal{A}$ and $\mathcal{X}$, and we know that $A_n \subseteq X_n$, $\partial_n(X_n) \subseteq X_{n-1}$, and $\partial_n(A_n) \subseteq A_{n-1}$. We then set

$$Z_n := \text{Ker}\,\partial_n, \quad B_n := \partial_{n+1}(X_{n+1}),$$
$$Z_n^{\mathcal{A}} := \text{Ker}\,(\partial_n|_{A_n}), \text{ and } B_n^{\mathcal{A}} := \partial_{n+1}(A_{n+1}),$$

where $\partial_n|_{A_n}$ denotes the restriction of the boundary operator ∂_n to the subgroup A_n.

As far as the inclusions are concerned, we certainly have both $X_n \supseteq Z_n \supseteq B_n$ and $A_n \supseteq Z_n^{\mathcal{A}} \supseteq B_n^{\mathcal{A}}$. In fact, by the definition of homology, we have

$$H_n(\mathcal{X}) = Z_n/B_n \text{ and } H_n(\mathcal{A}) = Z_n^{\mathcal{A}}/B_n^{\mathcal{A}}.$$

Furthermore, the group $Z_n^{\mathcal{A}}$ consists of those chains from X_n, whose boundary is 0, and which are at the same time chains of $\mathcal{A}$. In other words, we have $Z_n^{\mathcal{A}} = Z_n \cap A_n$. Crucially, and notwithstanding the formal temptation, we *do not* have the identity $B_n^{\mathcal{A}} = B_n \cap A_n$. Instead, we can only claim the inclusion $B_n^{\mathcal{A}} \subseteq B_n \cap A_n$. That motivates the need for further notations, and we set

$$B_n^{\mathcal{A} \leftarrow \mathcal{X}} := B_n \cap A_n.$$

This is the subgroup of those chains in A_n, which are boundaries of some chain from X_{n+1}. Clearly, the boundary of a chain from X_{n+1} is automatically a cycle, so we have $B_n^{\mathcal{A} \leftarrow \mathcal{X}} = Z_n^{\mathcal{A}} \cap B_n$.

The collection of subgroups of X_n which arises in our simple construction is illustrated in Figure 6.1.

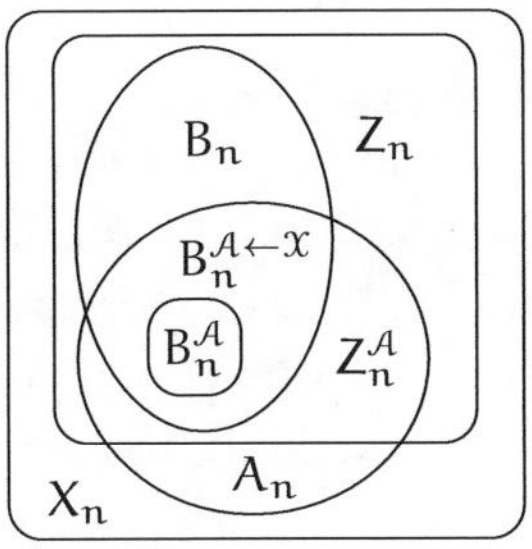

Figure 6.1. Cycle and boundary subgroups.

6.1.2. The kernel and the image of the induced homology map.

Utilizing the notations which we have introduced, the group homomorphism $\iota_n^* : H_n(\mathcal{A}) \to H_n(\mathcal{X})$ is given by

$$\iota_n^* : \alpha + B_n^{\mathcal{A}} \longmapsto \alpha + B_n.$$

It is not difficult to find the kernel of the map ι_n^*. Indeed, for any cycle $\alpha \in Z_n^{\mathcal{A}}$, we have $\alpha + B_n^{\mathcal{A}} \in \text{Ker}\ \iota_n^*$ if and only if $\alpha \in B_n$; or, equivalently, if and only if $\alpha \in Z_n^{\mathcal{A}} \cap B_n = B_n^{\mathcal{A}\leftarrow\mathcal{X}}$. Hence, we can write

$$\text{Ker}\ \iota_n^* = B_n^{\mathcal{A}\leftarrow\mathcal{X}} / B_n^{\mathcal{A}}. \tag{6.1}$$

This is our formal way of saying that the kernel of ι_n^* consists of cycles in $\mathcal{A}$ which happen to be boundaries in $\mathcal{X}$. The set of elements of X_n contained in these cosets is $B_n^{\mathcal{A}\leftarrow\mathcal{X}} = A_n \cap \partial_{n+1}(X_{n+1})$.

Let us now turn to describing the image of the homomorphism ι_n^*. Clearly, the subgroup $\text{Im}\ \iota_n^*$ consists of all homology classes $h \in H_n(\mathcal{X})$, for which there exists a cycle $\alpha \in Z_n^{\mathcal{A}}$, such that $[\alpha] = h$. To spell this out: these are precisely the homology classes of $\mathcal{X}$, which can be *represented* by a cycle from $\mathcal{A}$. Here is a formal way to express this fact:

$$\text{Im}\ \iota_n^* = (Z_n^{\mathcal{A}} + B_n)/B_n. \tag{6.2}$$

The set of all elements of X_n that represent these cosets can be written as

$$Z_n^{\mathcal{A}} + B_n = \text{Ker}\ \partial_n^{\mathcal{A}} + \partial_{n+1}(X_{n+1}).$$

It follows from the Second Isomorphism Theorem for abelian groups that

$$(Z_n^{\mathcal{A}} + B_n)/B_n \approx Z_n^{\mathcal{A}}/(Z_n^{\mathcal{A}} \cap B_n) = Z_n^{\mathcal{A}} / B_n^{\mathcal{A}\leftarrow\mathcal{X}}.$$

In other words, the following two procedures will yield isomorphic groups:

- take all the cycles in $\mathcal{A}$, add to them all the boundaries in $\mathcal{X}$, and then divide by the boundaries in $\mathcal{X}$;
- take all the cycles of $\mathcal{A}$ and then divide by those which are also boundaries in $\mathcal{X}$.

This gives us another group, which is isomorphic to $\text{Im}\ \iota_n^*$.

6.2. Relative homology

With all the new notations of the previous section, one might start getting the feeling that, to phrase the relation between homology of a chain complex and homology of its subcomplex, a succinct mathematical language would be imperative. Such a language can be provided by the concepts of relative homology, and the associated, so-called *long exact sequence.*

6.2.1. Calculating modulo a subcomplex. Assume as above that we are given a chain complex $\mathcal{X} = (X_*, \partial_*)$ and its chain subcomplex $\mathcal{A} = (A_*, \partial_*)$. Consider the quotient complex $\mathcal{X}/\mathcal{A}$. Recall that by definition the n-th chain group of $\mathcal{X}/\mathcal{A}$ is X_n/A_n. So, a typical n-chain of $\mathcal{X}/\mathcal{A}$ is a coset $\alpha + A_n$, where $\alpha \in X_n$. Furthermore, recall that the boundary operator $\partial_n^{\mathcal{X}/\mathcal{A}} : X_n/A_n \to X_{n-1}/A_{n-1}$ is given by the formula

$$\partial_n^{\mathcal{X}/\mathcal{A}} : \alpha + A_n \longmapsto \partial_n \alpha + A_{n-1}.$$

In the context of relative homology one typically uses a slightly different terminology to which we shall now revert. Namely, the chain complex $\mathcal{X}/\mathcal{A} = (X_*/A_*, \partial_*^{\mathcal{X}/\mathcal{A}})$ is called the *chain complex of* $\mathcal{X}$ *relative to* $\mathcal{A}$. Its homology groups $H_*(\mathcal{X}/\mathcal{A})$ are called the *homology groups of* $\mathcal{X}$ *relative to* $\mathcal{A}$ or simply the *relative homology groups*. Accordingly, one can talk about *relative cycles, relative boundaries*, and *relative homology classes.*

To simplify notations, we shall drop the upper index from $\partial_n^{\mathcal{X}/\mathcal{A}}$ most of the time, as it is clear from the context which boundary operator we are using.

By definition, a relative n-cycle is an element $\alpha + A_n \in X_n/A_n$ whose relative boundary is 0, that is, $\partial_n(\alpha + A_n) = 0$. Untangling the notations, we get

$\alpha + A_n$ is a relative n-cycle if and only if $\partial_n \alpha \in A_{n-1}$.

We let $Z_n^{\mathcal{X}/\mathcal{A}} \subseteq X_n/A_n$ denote the subgroup of all relative n-cycles.

A relative n-boundary, again by definition, is an element $\alpha + A_n \in X_n/A_n$, for which there exists $\beta + A_{n+1} \in X_{n+1}/A_{n+1}$, such that $\partial_{n+1}\beta + A_n = \alpha + A_n$. This is the same as saying that $\alpha - \partial_{n+1}\beta \in A_n$. Thus:

$\alpha + A_n$ is a relative n-boundary if and only if $\alpha \in A_n + B_n$, where B_n is the subgroup of all n-boundaries.

We let $B_n^{\mathcal{X}/\mathcal{A}} \subseteq X_n/A_n$ denote the subgroup of all relative n-boundaries. Clearly, we have $H_n(\mathcal{X}/\mathcal{A}) = Z_n^{\mathcal{X}/\mathcal{A}} / B_n^{\mathcal{X}/\mathcal{A}}$.

By comparison, the relative homology classes are more interesting creatures. These are obtained by a double quotient process, where we first take the quotient by A_n, and then by $B_n^{\mathcal{X}/\mathcal{A}}$. Therefore, the full and correct name for $[\alpha] \in H_n(\mathcal{X}/\mathcal{A})$ should be $(\alpha + A_n) + B_n^{\mathcal{X}/\mathcal{A}}$, where $B_n^{\mathcal{X}/\mathcal{A}}$ itself is a group consisting of cosets of A_n. Viewing the union of these cosets as a subset of X_n, we obtain the set $\alpha + A_n + B_n$. When practical, we shall use this alternative notation, and view the relative homology class as a coset of $A_n + B_n$, with the latter perceived as a subgroup of X_n. Figure 6.2 provides the summary of various names for $[\alpha]$, which we use.

$$[\alpha] \in H_n(\mathcal{X}/\mathcal{A})$$

$$(\alpha + A_n) + B_n^{\mathcal{X}/\mathcal{A}}$$

$$\alpha + A_n + B_n$$

Figure 6.2. Different names of the same relative homology class, where $\alpha \in X_n$, $\partial_n \alpha \in A_{n-1}$.

6.2.2. Examples of relative homology. The two simplest cases of relative homology are found when one sets $\mathcal{X} := \mathcal{A}$ or $\mathcal{A} := 0$. Indeed, if $\mathcal{X} = \mathcal{A}$, then $\mathcal{X}/\mathcal{A}$ is simply the trivial complex, that is, the chain complex where all the chain groups are trivial. So the relative homology in this case is also trivial in all dimensions.

If $\mathcal{A} = 0$, then $\mathcal{X} \approx \mathcal{X}/\mathcal{A}$, so the relative homology is the same as the homology of $\mathcal{X}$.

If we have a direct sum decomposition $\mathcal{X} = \mathcal{A} \oplus \mathcal{B}$, then one can prove that the chain complex $\mathcal{X}/\mathcal{A}$ is isomorphic to $\mathcal{B}$. In particular, the relative homology is simply the homology of $\mathcal{B}$.

We remark that often the relative homology arises in the case when $\mathcal{X}$ is the chain complex of some simplicial complex $\mathcal{K}$, and $\mathcal{A}$ is the chain complex associated to some simplicial subcomplex of $\mathcal{K}$.

6.2.3. Mapping cones, mapping cylinders, and the quotient construction. Let $\mathcal{C} = (C_*, \partial_*)$ be an arbitrary chain complex of abelian groups. In Section 4.3 we have defined chain complexes $\mathcal{C}yl(\mathcal{C}) = (\mathrm{Cyl}_*, \partial_*^{\mathcal{C}yl})$ and $\mathcal{C}one(\mathcal{C}) = (\mathrm{Cone}_*, \partial_*^{\mathcal{C}one})$ as algebraic analogs of the cylinder and the cone based at $\mathcal{C}$.

Let us start with the cylinder. Recall that $\mathrm{Cyl}_n = C_n \oplus C_{n-1} \oplus C_n$ and $\partial_n^{\mathcal{C}yl}(\sigma \oplus \tau \oplus \rho) = (\partial\sigma - \tau) \oplus (-\partial\tau) \oplus (\partial\rho + \tau)$. In particular, $\partial(\sigma \oplus 0 \oplus 0) = \partial\sigma \oplus 0 \oplus 0$ and $\partial(0 \oplus 0 \oplus \rho) = 0 \oplus 0 \oplus \partial\rho$. This means that the first and the third coordinates correspond to chain subcomplexes $\mathcal{B}$ and $\mathcal{B}'$ isomorphic to $\mathcal{C}$. Let us set $\mathcal{D} := \mathcal{C}yl(\mathcal{C})/\mathcal{B}$ and $\mathcal{D}' := \mathcal{C}yl(\mathcal{C})/\mathcal{B}'$. Assume $\mathcal{D} = (D_*, \partial_*^{\mathcal{D}})$. By definition of the quotient complex, we have $D_n = C_{n-1} \oplus C_n$ and $\partial_n^{\mathcal{D}}(\tau \oplus \rho) = (-\partial\tau) \oplus (\partial\rho + \tau)$. Furthermore, we have $D'_n = C_n \oplus C_{n-1}$ and $\partial_n^{\mathcal{D}'}(\sigma \oplus \tau) = (\partial\sigma - \tau) \oplus (-\partial\tau)$.

Recall that $\text{Cone}_n = C_{n-1} \oplus C_n$ and $\partial_n^{\mathcal{C}one}(\tau \oplus \rho) = (-\partial\tau) \oplus (\partial\rho + \tau)$. We immediately see that $\mathcal{D}$ is evidently isomorphic to $\mathcal{C}one(\mathcal{C})$. Furthermore, swapping the terms and changing the sign shows that $\mathcal{D}'$ is also isomorphic to $\mathcal{C}one(\mathcal{C})$. This is the algebraic analog of the topological fact that the quotient of a cylinder by its base is homeomorphic to the cone over that base.

Let us now consider the quotient of the cone by its base. Formally, the chain complex $\mathcal{C}one(\mathcal{C})$ has the following subcomplex $\mathcal{D} = (D_*, \partial_*^{\mathcal{D}})$: for all n, the subgroup D_n consists of all elements $0 \oplus \rho$. Note that $\partial_*^{\mathcal{C}one}(0 \oplus \rho) = 0 \oplus \partial\rho$, so this is indeed a subcomplex, which is isomorphic to $\mathcal{C}$. The quotient complex $\mathcal{C}one(\mathcal{C})/\mathcal{D} = \mathcal{E} = (E_*, \partial_*^{\mathcal{E}})$ is given by $E_n \approx \{\tau \,|\, \tau \in C_{n-1}\}$ and $\partial_n^{\mathcal{E}}(\tau) = -\partial_{n-1}^{\mathcal{C}}\tau$. This complex is isomorphic to the shifted complex $\mathcal{C}[1]$. The isomorphism is given by changing the sign in every second chain group.

6.2.4. Homology map induced by the quotient. For every $n \in \mathbb{Z}$ we have a standard quotient map $q_n : X_n \to X_n/A_n$, which maps each element $\alpha \in X_n$ to its coset $\alpha + A_n$. This is of course a group homomorphism. On the level of the chain complexes we have the following proposition.

Proposition 6.1. *The family of group homomorphisms* $q = \{q_n\}_{n\in\mathbb{Z}}$ *is a well-defined chain map* $q : \mathcal{X} \to \mathcal{X}/\mathcal{A}$.

Proof. For an arbitrary chain $\alpha \in X_n$ we have the following calculation:

$$q_{n-1}(\partial_n^{\mathcal{X}}\alpha) = \partial_n^{\mathcal{X}}\alpha + A_{n-1} = \partial_n^{\mathcal{X}/\mathcal{A}}(\alpha + A_n) = \partial_n^{\mathcal{X}/\mathcal{A}}(q_n(\alpha)).$$

This shows that $q_{n-1} \circ \partial_n^{\mathcal{X}} = \partial_n^{\mathcal{X}/\mathcal{A}} \circ q_n$, for all $n \in \mathbb{Z}$, and hence q is a chain map. □

The chain map q induces maps on homology groups, $q^* : H_*(\mathcal{X}) \to H_*(\mathcal{X}/\mathcal{A})$, $q^* = \{q_n^*\}_n$, given by

$$\begin{aligned} q_n^* : H_n(\mathcal{X}) &\longrightarrow H_n(\mathcal{X}/\mathcal{A}), \\ \alpha + B_n &\longmapsto \alpha + A_n + B_n. \end{aligned}$$

The kernel of q_n^* consists of all $\alpha + B_n$ for which $\alpha \in Z_n$ and $\alpha + A_n + B_n = A_n + B_n$. In other words, $\alpha \in Z_n \cap (A_n + B_n) = Z_n^{\mathcal{A}} + B_n$, and so, using Equation (6.2), we get

$$\text{Ker } q_n^* = (Z_n^{\mathcal{A}} + B_n)/B_n = \text{Im } \iota_n^*. \tag{6.3}$$

The image of q_n^* consists of all $\alpha + A_n + B_n$, such that $\alpha \in Z_n$. The elements from such cosets constitute the subset $Z_n + A_n + B_n = Z_n + A_n$. We therefore obtain

$$\text{Im } q_n^* = (Z_n + A_n)/(A_n + B_n). \tag{6.4}$$

We now have the formulae for kernels and images of the maps ι_n^* and q_n^*.

6.3. Connecting homomorphism

While it is simple to find a map from the homology of $\mathcal{A}$ to the homology of $\mathcal{X}$ (it is induced by inclusion, and it is simple to find the map from the homology of $\mathcal{X}$ to the homology of $\mathcal{X}/\mathcal{A}$; it is induced by the quotient map), it is not as straightforward to connect the homology of $\mathcal{X}/\mathcal{A}$ with the homology of $\mathcal{A}$. It turns out that there is a canonical way to map $H_*(\mathcal{X}/\mathcal{A})$ to $H_*(\mathcal{A})$, but not in the same dimension. In fact, as this map is induced by the boundary operator, the homology index will shift down by one.

6.3.1. The definition and the first examples.

Definition 6.2. Assume $\mathcal{X}$ is a chain complex, and $\mathcal{A}$ is a subcomplex of $\mathcal{X}$. For any integer n, the *connecting homomorphism* is a map

$$\partial_n^c : H_n(\mathcal{X}/\mathcal{A}) \to H_{n-1}(\mathcal{A})$$

given by

$$\partial_n^c : \alpha + A_n + B_n \longmapsto \partial_n \alpha + B_{n-1}^{\mathcal{A}}. \tag{6.5}$$

One often uses the shorthand notation $\partial_*^c : H_*(\mathcal{X}/\mathcal{A}) \to H_{*-1}(\mathcal{A})$ to denote the collection of connecting homomorphisms for all indices.

The map (6.5) can be viewed as follows. Take the set on the left-hand side of (6.5) and apply the regular boundary operator to it. The boundary operator takes α to $\partial_n \alpha$, takes A_n to $B_{n-1}^{\mathcal{A}}$, and takes B_n to 0. As the result we obtain the set on the right-hand side of (6.5).

By definition, the kernel of the connecting homomorphism ∂_n^c consists of all $\alpha + A_n + B_n$, such that $\partial_n \alpha \in B_{n-1}^{\mathcal{A}}$. In other words, $\alpha \in \partial_n^{-1}(B_{n-1}^{\mathcal{A}})$. On the other hand, we note that

$$\partial_n^{-1}(B_{n-1}^{\mathcal{A}}) = \partial_n^{-1}(\partial_n(A_n)) = Z_n + A_n.$$

This is because the set of all n-chains of $\mathcal{X}$, whose boundary is equal to the boundary of some n-chain of $\mathcal{A}$, is the same as the set of all n-chains of $\mathcal{X}$ which differ from some n-chain of $\mathcal{A}$ by a cycle. Indeed, two chains have the same boundary if and only if they differ by a cycle.

Comparing with Equation (6.4), we can thus conclude that

$$\text{Ker } \partial_n^c = (Z_n + A_n)/(A_n + B_n) = \text{Im } q_n^*. \tag{6.6}$$

Finally, again directly from (6.5), we see that the image of the connecting homomorphism consists of all $\beta + B_{n-1}^{\mathcal{A}}$, such that

(1) $\beta \in A_{n-1}$,

(2) there exists $\alpha \in X_n$, such that $\beta = \partial_n \alpha$.

We conclude from Equation (6.1) that

$$\operatorname{Im} \partial_n^c = B_{n-1}^{\mathcal{A}\leftarrow\mathcal{X}}/B_{n-1}^{\mathcal{A}} = \operatorname{Ker} \iota_{n-1}^*. \tag{6.7}$$

6.3.2. Recalling the formalism of exact sequences. Let us take a brief step back into the realm of abstract algebra and recall the concept of exact sequences.

Definition 6.3. Assume we have a set of abelian groups $\{A_i\}_{i\in\mathbb{Z}}$ together with a set of group homomorphisms $\{\varphi_i\}_{i\in\mathbb{Z}}$, with each $\varphi_i : A_i \to A_{i-1}$, so that these can conveniently be arranged into a sequence:

$$\dots \xrightarrow{\varphi_{n+2}} A_{n+1} \xrightarrow{\varphi_{n+1}} A_n \xrightarrow{\varphi_n} A_{n-1} \xrightarrow{\varphi_{n-1}} \dots . \tag{6.8}$$

Such a sequence is called *exact* if $\operatorname{Im} \varphi_{n+1} = \operatorname{Ker} \varphi_n$, for all $n \in \mathbb{Z}$.

We stress that the abelian groups in Definition 6.3 do not necessarily have to be free.

When we have a sequence as in (6.8) and the condition $\operatorname{Im} \varphi_{n+1} = \operatorname{Ker} \varphi_n$ is satisfied for some specific n, we say that this sequence *is exact at* A_n.

Definition 6.4. A sequence (6.8) is called *short* if all but three consequent entries in the sequence are trivial.

Consider a short exact sequence

$$0 \longrightarrow A \xrightarrow{\varphi} B \xrightarrow{\psi} C \longrightarrow 0 . \tag{6.9}$$

The exactness condition breaks down into the following three statements:

(1) the map φ is injective;

(2) the map ψ is surjective;

(3) we have $\operatorname{Im} \varphi = \operatorname{Ker} \psi$.

It is easy to show that C is always isomorphic to the quotient group $B/\operatorname{Im} \varphi$. However, in general, it does not have to be the case that B is isomorphic to the direct sum $A \oplus C$. A notable exception is provided by the case of free groups; see the exercises for this chapter.

6.3.3. Long Exact Sequence of a pair of chain complexes.

A succinct way to summarize these findings is provided by the helpful formalism of the associated long exact sequence

$$
\begin{array}{c}
\cdots \xrightarrow{\iota_n^*} H_n(\mathcal{X}) \xrightarrow{q_n^*} H_n(\mathcal{X}/\mathcal{A}) \\
\xrightarrow{\partial_n^c} \\
H_{n-1}(\mathcal{A}) \xrightarrow{\iota_{n-1}^*} H_{n-1}(\mathcal{X}) \xrightarrow{q_{n-1}^*} \cdots
\end{array}
\tag{6.10}
$$

This can be depicted by a spiral diagram.

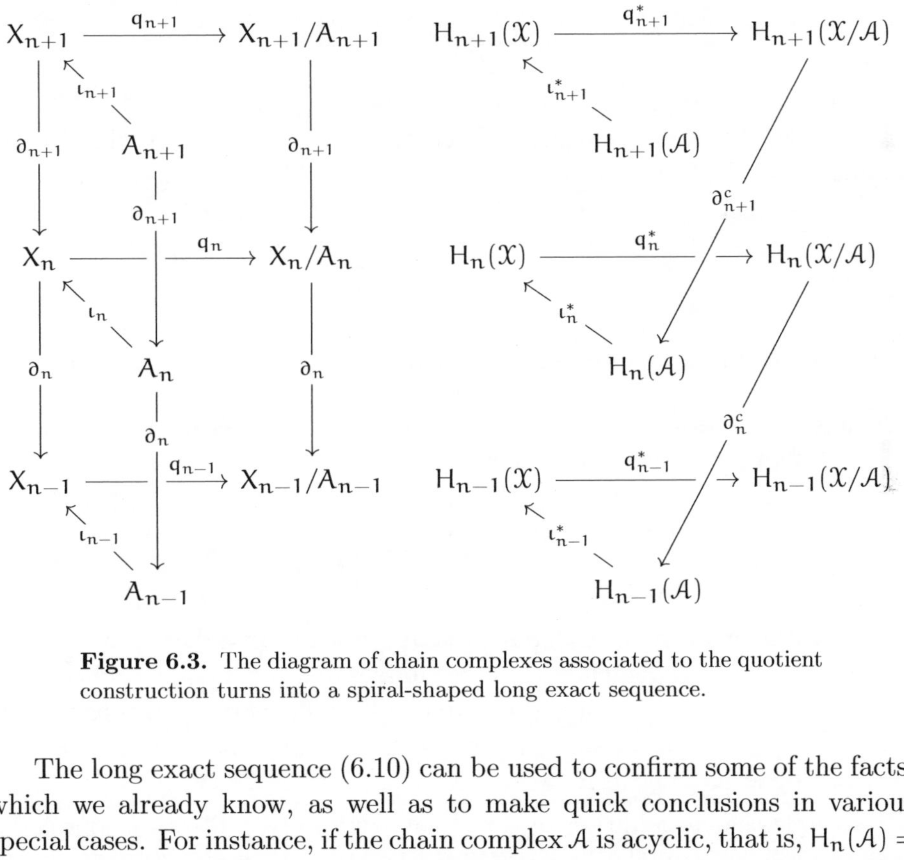

Figure 6.3. The diagram of chain complexes associated to the quotient construction turns into a spiral-shaped long exact sequence.

The long exact sequence (6.10) can be used to confirm some of the facts, which we already know, as well as to make quick conclusions in various special cases. For instance, if the chain complex $\mathcal{A}$ is acyclic, that is, $H_n(\mathcal{A}) = 0$, for all $n \in \mathbb{Z}$, then $H_n(\mathcal{X}) \approx H_n(\mathcal{X}/\mathcal{A})$, and the maps q_n^* give the necessary isomorphisms. This is of course hardly surprising as it simply says that dividing by a homology-trivial complex will not change homology.

Similarly, if the quotient complex $\mathcal{X}/\mathcal{A}$ is acyclic, we get $H_n(\mathcal{X}) \approx H_n(\mathcal{A})$, and the maps ι_n^*, which are induced by the inclusion, are isomorphisms. This is also intuitively rather clear, as it simply means that when the quotient is "trivial" the chain complexes $\mathcal{X}$ and $\mathcal{A}$ have the same homology.

More interesting is the special case when the chain complex $\mathcal{X}$ is the acyclic one. In this case, the homology groups of the quotient complex $\mathcal{X}/\mathcal{A}$ and the chain complex $\mathcal{A}$ are nearly the same, just the index gets shifted. Formally, we have $H_n(\mathcal{X}/\mathcal{A}) \approx H_{n-1}(\mathcal{A})$, for all $n \in \mathbb{Z}$, and the connecting homomorphism provides a canonical isomorphism.

The next level of complexity is reached when we start assuming that the maps, rather than the groups, are trivial. For example, we can consider the natural question: what happens when the homology maps $\iota_n^* : H_n(\mathcal{A}) \to H_n(\mathcal{X})$, induced by inclusion, are trivial? In this case, the long exact sequence (6.10) splits into a multitude of short ones. Namely, for all $n \in \mathbb{Z}$ we have the short exact sequence

$$0 \longrightarrow H_n(\mathcal{X}) \xrightarrow{q_n^*} H_n(\mathcal{X}/\mathcal{A}) \xrightarrow{\partial_n^c} H_{n-1}(\mathcal{A}) \longrightarrow 0. \tag{6.11}$$

As mentioned above, this does not automatically mean that $H_n(\mathcal{X}/\mathcal{A}) \approx H_n(\mathcal{X}) \oplus H_{n-1}(\mathcal{A})$, as things can become entangled in the middle of the sequence (6.11). To make this conclusion we would need to have additional conditions, such as requiring that $H_{n-1}(\mathcal{A})$ should be free. Still there are many cases when this is true, for example if we consider homology with field coefficients.

6.4. Maps between pairs and connecting homomorphism

The long exact sequence of a pair of chain complexes is frequently a rather efficient tool for computing homology. However, in many situations, its true power first unfolds when put in the functorial context of maps between pairs of chain complexes, and hence maps between the associated long exact sequences.

6.4.1. Functorial properties of relative homology.

We recall that chain maps between chain complexes induce families of group homomorphisms between their homology groups. The same is true for pairs, each consisting of a chain complex and its subcomplex. The concept of a chain map is then replaced by a map between pairs.

Assume that in addition to the chain complex $\mathcal{X}$ and its subcomplex $\mathcal{A}$ we have a chain complex $\mathcal{Y} = (Y_*, \partial_*^{\mathcal{Y}})$ and its subcomplex $\mathcal{D} = (D_*, \partial_*^{\mathcal{D}})$. Furthermore, assume we are given a chain map $\varphi : \mathcal{X} \to \mathcal{Y}$, $\varphi = \{\varphi_n\}_n$, $\varphi_n : X_n \to Y_n$, such that for each $n \in \mathbb{Z}$ we have an inclusion $\varphi_n(A_n) \subseteq D_n$. For brevity, we shall phrase that condition as $\varphi(\mathcal{A}) \subseteq \mathcal{D}$.

Definition 6.5. Given pairs of chain complexes $(\mathcal{X}, \mathcal{A})$ and $(\mathcal{Y}, \mathcal{D})$, a chain map $\varphi : \mathcal{X} \to \mathcal{Y}$ is called *a chain map between pairs* $(\mathcal{X}, \mathcal{A})$ and $(\mathcal{Y}, \mathcal{D})$ if $\varphi(\mathcal{A}) \subseteq \mathcal{D}$.

As expected, chain maps between pairs induce maps between appropriate homology groups, and these maps behave in a functorially nice way.

Proposition 6.6. *Any chain map between pairs of complexes* $\varphi : (\mathcal{X}, \mathcal{A}) \to (\mathcal{Y}, \mathcal{D})$ *induces a family of group homomorphisms on the relative homology*

$$\varphi^* : H_*(\mathcal{X}, \mathcal{A}) \to H_*(\mathcal{Y}, \mathcal{D}), \quad \varphi^* = \{\varphi_n^*\}_{n \in \mathbb{Z}}, \quad \varphi_n^* : H_n(\mathcal{X}, \mathcal{A}) \to H_n(\mathcal{Y}, \mathcal{D}).$$

These homomorphisms are given by the formula $\varphi_n^*([\alpha]) := [\varphi_n(\alpha)]$, *for all* $\alpha \in X_n$, *such that* $\partial_n^{\mathcal{X}} \alpha \in A_{n-1}$.

Proof. Assume we have $\alpha \in X_n$, such that $\partial_n^{\mathcal{X}} \alpha \in A_{n-1}$. Since we have the inclusion $\varphi_{n-1}(A_{n-1}) \subseteq D_{n-1}$, and $\partial_n^{\mathcal{Y}} \circ \varphi_n = \varphi_{n-1} \circ \partial_n^{\mathcal{X}}$, we have $\partial_n^{\mathcal{Y}}(\varphi_n(\alpha)) = \varphi_{n-1}(\partial_n^{\mathcal{X}} \alpha) \in D_{n-1}$, so the homology class $[\varphi_n(\alpha)]$ is well-defined.

Let us see that $[\varphi_n(\alpha)]$ depends only on the choice of the homology class $[\alpha]$, and it is independent of the choice of the actual α. Pick an arbitrary $\beta \in A_n$ and $\gamma \in X_{n+1}$. We need to show that $[\varphi_n(\alpha)] = [\varphi_n(\alpha + \beta + \partial_{n+1}\gamma)]$. We have

$$\begin{aligned} [\varphi_n(\alpha + \beta + \partial_{n+1}\gamma)] &= [\varphi_n(\alpha) + \varphi_n(\beta) + \varphi_n(\partial_{n+1}\gamma)] \\ &= [\varphi_n(\alpha) + \varphi_n(\beta) + \partial_{n+1}(\varphi_{n+1}(\gamma))] = [\varphi_n(\alpha)], \end{aligned}$$

where the last equality follows from the fact that $\varphi_n(\beta)$ and $\partial_{n+1}(\varphi_{n+1}(\gamma))$ both belong to D_n.

The fact that φ_n^* is a group homomorphism follows from the following two calculations:

$$\varphi_n^*(k[\alpha]) = \varphi_n^*([k\alpha]) = [\varphi_n(k\alpha)] = [k\varphi_n(\alpha)] = k[\varphi_n(\alpha)] = k\varphi_n^*([\alpha]),$$

$$\begin{aligned} \varphi_n^*([\alpha] + [\beta]) = \varphi_n^*([\alpha + \beta]) &= [\varphi_n(\alpha + \beta)] = [\varphi_n(\alpha) + \varphi_n(\beta)] \\ &= [\varphi_n(\alpha)] + [\varphi_n(\beta)] = \varphi_n^*([\alpha]) + \varphi_n^*([\beta]), \end{aligned}$$

for all $\alpha, \beta \in X_n$, and $k \in \mathbb{Z}$. □

6.4.2. Naturality of the connecting homomorphism. The property stated in the next theorem is often referred to as *naturality of the connected homomorphism*; alternative phrasing is to say that the connecting homomorphism *is natural*.

Theorem 6.7. *Assume we are given chain complexes* $\mathcal{X}$ *and* $\mathcal{Y}$, *their respective subcomplexes* $\mathcal{A}$ *and* $\mathcal{D}$, *and a chain map* φ *between pairs* $(\mathcal{X}, \mathcal{A})$ *and* $(\mathcal{Y}, \mathcal{D})$. *Let* φ^* *denote the map induced on homology. Then, for all* n, *the following diagram commutes:*

$$
\begin{array}{ccc}
H_n(\mathcal{X}/\mathcal{A}) & \xrightarrow{\partial_n^c[\mathcal{X},\mathcal{A}]} & H_{n-1}(\mathcal{A}) \\
\downarrow \varphi_n^* & & \downarrow \varphi_{n-1}^* \\
H_n(\mathcal{Y}/\mathcal{D}) & \xrightarrow{\partial_n^c[\mathcal{Y},\mathcal{D}]} & H_{n-1}(\mathcal{D})
\end{array}
\tag{6.12}
$$

where $\partial_n^c[\mathcal{X},\mathcal{A}]$ and $\partial_n^c[\mathcal{Y},\mathcal{D}]$ are connecting homomorphisms from the long exact sequence of the pairs $(\mathcal{X},\mathcal{A})$ and $(\mathcal{Y},\mathcal{D})$.

Proof. The verification is completely straightforward. Take any $\alpha \in X_n$, such that $\partial_n \alpha \in A_{n-1}$. The two-way calculation in diagram (6.12) yields

$$
\begin{aligned}
\partial(\varphi^*(\alpha + A_n + B_n^{\mathcal{X}})) &= \partial(\varphi^*(\alpha) + D_n + B_n^{\mathcal{Y}}) = \partial(\varphi^*(\alpha) + D_n),\\
\varphi^*(\partial(\alpha + A_n + B_n^{\mathcal{X}})) &= \varphi^*(\partial(\alpha + A_n)) = \varphi^*(\partial(\alpha) + A_{n-1}).
\end{aligned}
$$

The two final expressions are equal by Proposition 6.6. This confirms the commutativity of diagram (6.12). □

The commutative diagram (6.12) can be extended to maps of long exact sequences.

The naturality of the connecting homomorphism is also very useful for concrete calculations.

6.5. Zig-Zag Lemma

The crucial feature of the connecting homomorphism is that it allows one to translate the statement about exact sequences of chain complexes to the statements about exact sequences of homology groups. In its full generality, the corresponding algebraic statement is known as the *Zig-Zag Lemma.* Its verbal meta-formulation is as follows:

> *a short exact sequence of chain complexes induces a long exact sequence of the corresponding homology groups.*

Before we can formulate the precise formal statement, we need to define short exact sequences of chain complexes.

Definition 6.8. *A short exact sequence of chain complexes* is a sequence of chain complexes and chain maps

$$0 \longrightarrow \mathcal{C} \xrightarrow{\varphi} \mathcal{D} \xrightarrow{\psi} \mathcal{E} \longrightarrow 0, \tag{6.13}$$

such that for each n, the corresponding short sequence

$$0 \longrightarrow C_n \xrightarrow{\varphi_n} D_n \xrightarrow{\psi_n} E_n \longrightarrow 0$$

is exact.

We are now ready for a *short exact sequence* version of what we did in Section 6.3. The proof is essentially the same as the derivation in the section, just formulated in a more abstract language. We choose to include it here for the purposes of providing an exercise in the frequently used algebraic technique known as *diagram chasing.*

Theorem 6.9. (Zig-Zag Lemma)

Assume we have a short exact sequence of chain complexes (6.13). *Then we have a long exact sequence*

$$\dots \xrightarrow{\partial^c_{n-1}} H_n(\mathcal{C}) \xrightarrow{\varphi^*_n} H_n(\mathcal{D}) \xrightarrow{\psi^*_n} H_n(\mathcal{E}) \xrightarrow{\partial^c_n} H_{n-1}(\mathcal{C}) \xrightarrow{\varphi^*_{n-1}} \dots,$$

where φ^* *and* ψ^* *are induced by* φ *and* ψ*, and* ∂^c_* *is the connecting homomorphism.*

Proof. We shall define $\partial^c_n : H_n(\mathcal{E}) \to H_{n-1}(\mathcal{C})$, which we do in two steps. We start by constructing an auxiliary map $\zeta : Z_n(\mathcal{E}) \to H_{n-1}(\mathcal{C})$, where we recall that $Z_n(\mathcal{E}) = \operatorname{Ker} \partial^{\mathcal{E}}_n$. After that we combine it with the usual quotient map $Z_n(\mathcal{E}) \to Z_n(\mathcal{E})/B_n(\mathcal{E}) = H_n(\mathcal{E})$.

Take $\gamma \in E_n$, such that $\partial_n \gamma = 0$. Since ψ_n is surjective, there exists $\beta \in D_n$, such that $\psi_n(\beta) = \gamma$. Since ψ_* is a chain map, we have $\partial_n \circ \psi_n = \psi_{n-1} \circ \partial_n$. We have chosen γ, so that $\partial_n \gamma = 0$ and $\psi_n(\beta) = \gamma$. We get that $\psi_{n-1}(\partial_n \beta) = \partial_n(\psi_n(\beta)) = 0$. However, we know that $\operatorname{Ker} \psi_{n-1} = \operatorname{Im} \varphi_{n-1}$, so there must exist $\alpha \in C_{n-1}$, such that $\varphi_{n-1}(\alpha) = \partial_n \beta$. We now define $\zeta([\gamma]) := [\alpha]$, see Figure 6.4.

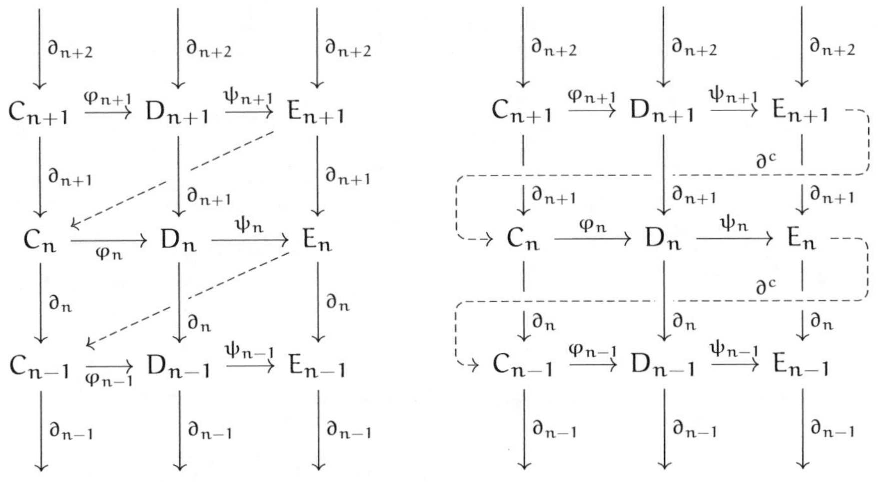

Figure 6.4. The two most frequently used graphic depictions of the connecting homomorphisms.

To see that homology class $[\alpha]$ is well-defined, we need to show that $\partial_n \alpha = 0$. Since φ is a chain map and $\varphi_n(\alpha) = \partial_{n+1}\beta$, we have

$$\varphi_{n-2}(\partial_n \alpha) = \partial_{n-1}\big(\varphi_n(\alpha)\big) = \partial_n(\partial_{n+1}\beta) = 0.$$

The map φ_{n-2} is injective, and hence $\partial_n \alpha = 0$.

Let us show that $[\alpha]$ is independent of the choice of α and β. Assume we have $\beta_1, \beta_2 \in D_n$, such that $\psi_n(\beta_1) = \psi_n(\beta_2) = \gamma$. We have $\psi_n(\beta_1 - \beta_2) = 0$. Since $\operatorname{Ker}\psi_n = \operatorname{Im}\varphi_n$, there exists $\tilde{\alpha} \in C_n$, such that $\varphi_n(\tilde{\alpha}) = \beta_1 - \beta_2$. Then

$$\partial_n \beta_1 - \partial_n \beta_2 = \partial_n(\beta_1 - \beta_2) = \partial_n\big(\varphi(\tilde{\alpha})\big) = \varphi_{n-1}(\partial_n \tilde{\alpha}).$$

Pick $\alpha_1, \alpha_2 \in C_{n-1}$, such that $\varphi_{n-1}(\alpha_1) = \partial_n \beta_1$ and $\varphi_{n-1}(\alpha_2) = \partial_n \beta_2$. We then have $\varphi_{n-1}(\alpha_1 - \alpha_2) = \partial_n \beta_1 - \partial_n \beta_2$. Since φ is injective, we conclude that $\alpha_1 - \alpha_2 = \partial_n \tilde{\alpha}$. It follows that $[\alpha_1] = [\alpha_2]$.

It is easy to see that ζ is a group homomorphism. Indeed, take $\gamma_1, \gamma_2 \in E_n$, such that $\partial_n \gamma_1 = \partial_n \gamma_2 = 0$, and take $k_1, k_2 \in \mathbb{Z}$. Set $\gamma := k_1\gamma_1 + k_2\gamma_2$. Assume we have chosen $\beta_1, \beta_2 \in D_n$, such that $\psi_n(\beta_1) = \gamma_1$ and $\psi_n(\beta_2) = \gamma_2$. Take $\alpha_1, \alpha_2 \in C_{n-1}$, such that $\varphi_{n-1}(\alpha_1) = \partial_n \beta_1$ and $\varphi_{n-1}(\alpha_2) = \partial_n \beta_2$. Set $\beta := k_1\beta_1 + k_2\beta_2$ and $\alpha := k_1\alpha_1 + k_2\alpha_2$. On one hand, we have $\psi_n(\beta) = \gamma$. On the other hand, we have $\varphi_{n-1}(\alpha) = \partial_n \beta$. It follows that $\zeta(\gamma) = [\alpha]$, and hence ζ is a group homomorphism.

Assume now that $\gamma \in E_n$, such that $\gamma = \partial_{n+1}\tilde{\gamma}$, for some $\tilde{\gamma} \in E_{n+1}$. Since ψ_{n+1} is surjective, we can find $\tilde{\beta} \in D_{n+1}$, such that $\psi_{n+1}(\tilde{\beta}) = \tilde{\gamma}$. But then

$$\psi_n(\partial_{n+1}\tilde{\beta}) = \partial_{n+1}\big(\psi_{n+1}(\tilde{\beta})\big) = \partial_{n+1}(\tilde{\gamma}) = \gamma.$$

Since $\zeta(\gamma)$ is independent of the choice of β, we might as well choose $\partial_{n+1}\tilde{\beta}$. Of course, we have $\partial_n(\partial_{n+1}\tilde{\beta}) = 0$, which implies that $\zeta(\gamma) = 0$.

We have shown that $B_n^{\mathcal{E}} \subseteq \operatorname{Ker}\zeta$, hence, passing on to the quotient, we have a well-defined group homomorphism ∂_n^c from $H_n(\mathcal{E}) = Z_n^{\mathcal{E}}/B_n$ to $H_{n-1}(\mathcal{C})$.

Let us now determine $\operatorname{Ker}\partial_n^c$. First, take $[\gamma] \in H_n(\mathcal{E})$, such that $\partial_n^c([\gamma]) = 0$. Assume $\beta \in D_n$, such that $\psi_n(\beta) = \gamma$, and $\alpha \in C_{n-1}$, such that $\varphi_{n-1}(\alpha) = \partial_n \beta$. We have $\partial_n^c([\gamma]) = [\alpha]$. Since $\partial_n^c([\gamma]) = 0$, there must exist $\tilde{\alpha} \in C_n$, such that $\alpha = \partial_n \tilde{\alpha}$. Using the fact that φ is a chain map, we have

$$\partial_n\big(\varphi_n(\tilde{\alpha})\big) = \varphi_{n-1}(\partial_n \tilde{\alpha}) = \varphi_{n-1}(\alpha) = \partial_n \beta.$$

In particular, $\partial_n\big(\beta - \varphi_n(\tilde{\alpha})\big) = 0$; in other words, $\beta - \varphi_n(\tilde{\alpha}) \in Z_n^{\mathcal{D}}$. On the other hand, we have

$$\psi_n\big(\beta - \varphi_n(\tilde{\alpha})\big) = \psi_n(\beta) - \psi_n\big(\varphi_n(\tilde{\alpha})\big) = \psi_n(\beta) = \gamma.$$

This means that $[\gamma] \in \operatorname{Im}\psi_n^*$, where ψ_n^* is the induced map $\psi_n^* : H_n(\mathcal{D}) \to H_n(\mathcal{E})$, and we conclude that $\operatorname{Ker}\partial_n^c \subseteq \operatorname{Im}\psi_n^*$.

On the other hand, take $\gamma \in E_n$, such that $[\gamma] \in \operatorname{Im} \psi_n^*$. This means that there exists $\beta \in Z_n^{\mathcal{D}}$, such that $\psi_n(\beta) = \gamma$. Use this β when defining $\partial_n^c([\gamma])$. Since $\partial_n \beta = 0$, we immediately obtain $\partial_n^c([\gamma]) = 0$, and hence the reverse inclusion $\operatorname{Ker} \partial_n^c \supseteq \operatorname{Im} \psi_n^*$. In total, we get $\operatorname{Ker} \partial_n^c = \operatorname{Im} \psi_n^*$.

Finally, let us show that $\operatorname{Im} \partial_n^c = \operatorname{Ker} \varphi_{n-1}^*$, where φ_{n-1}^* is the induced map $\varphi_{n-1}^* : H_{n-1}(\mathcal{C}) \to H_{n-1}(\mathcal{D})$. Take $\gamma \in Z_n^{\mathcal{E}}$, $\beta \in \psi_n^{-1}(\gamma)$, and $\alpha = \varphi_{n-1}^{-1}(\partial_n \beta)$, so $\partial_n^c([\gamma]) = [\alpha]$. We have

$$\varphi_{n-1}^*([\alpha]) = [\varphi_{n-1}(\alpha)] = [\partial_n \beta] = 0,$$

and hence $\operatorname{Im} \partial_n^c \subseteq \operatorname{Ker} \varphi_{n-1}^*$.

On the other hand, take $[\alpha] \in \operatorname{Ker} \varphi_{n-1}^*$. We have $0 = \varphi_{n-1}^*([\alpha]) = [\varphi_{n-1}(\alpha)]$ and hence there exists $\beta \in D_n$, such that $\partial_n \beta = \varphi_{n-1}(\alpha)$. Set $\gamma := \psi_n(\beta)$. We have

$$\partial_n \gamma = \partial_n(\psi_n(\beta)) = \psi_{n-1}(\partial_n \beta) = \psi_{n-1}(\varphi_{n-1}(\alpha)) = 0,$$

and so $\gamma \in Z_n^{\mathcal{E}}$. By construction, $\partial_n^c([\gamma]) = [\alpha]$, and we obtain the reverse inclusion $\operatorname{Im} \partial_n^c \supseteq \operatorname{Ker} \varphi_{n-1}^*$. This finishes the entire proof. □

Exercises

(1) Let $\mathcal{C}$ and $\mathcal{D}$ be chain complexes, and let $f : \mathcal{C} \to \mathcal{D}$ be a chain map.
   (a) Show that a quotient of the mapping cylinder $\mathcal{C}yl(f)$ by its top copy of $\mathcal{C}$ gives the mapping cone $\mathcal{C}one(f)$.
   (b) Show furthermore that the quotient of $\mathcal{C}yl(f)$ by the bottom copy of $\mathcal{D}$ gives the shifted complex $\mathcal{C}[1]$.

(2) Show that when f is the inclusion map of chain complexes $f : \mathcal{C} \hookrightarrow \mathcal{D}$, the chain complex $\mathcal{C}one(f)$ has the same homology as $\mathcal{D}/\operatorname{Im}(f)$.

(3) Assume we are given a short exact sequence of abelian groups

$$0 \longrightarrow A \xrightarrow{\varphi} B \xrightarrow{\psi} C \longrightarrow 0\,. \tag{6.14}$$

   (a) Show that C is isomorphic to $B/\operatorname{Im}\varphi$.
   (b) Show that if the group C is free, then B is isomorphic to the direct sum $A \oplus C$.

(4) Given a short exact sequence

$$0 \longrightarrow \mathbb{Z} \longrightarrow \mathbb{Z} \longrightarrow B \longrightarrow 0,$$

what are the possibilities for B?

Chapter 7

Singular Homology

7.1. Definition of singular homology

Singular homology is easy to define formally and it is extremely useful when we want to talk about homology directly associated to *topological spaces*, as opposed to various combinatorial gluing schemes. Many difficult questions associated to the combinatorial constructions in Chapter 2, such as independence on the specific triangulation, are rendered irrelevant by virtue of the definition itself.

Furthermore, singular homology is the tool of choice whenever formal succinct proofs are required. On the other hand, the biggest disadvantage of using singular homology is that we can virtually never compute anything directly from the chain complex. This is why in applied topology one uses combinatorial homology theories, such as simplicial or cubical ones.

Definition 7.1. Let X be an arbitrary topological space. A *singular simplex* of dimension n is simply a continuous map $\sigma : \Delta^n \to X$ from the standard n-simplex to our space.

We let $C_n^{\text{sing}}(X)$ denote the free abelian group generated by the set of all singular n-simplices. This group is called the n*th singular chain group* of X.

A *singular* n*-chain* in X is any element of $C_n^{\text{sing}}(X)$. By definition of the free abelian group generated by a set, a singular n-chain is a finite linear combination of singular n-simplices with integer coefficients.

The singular homology is now defined in exactly the same way as the simplicial homology, albeit with the singular simplices replacing the simplicial ones.

Definition 7.2. Assume X is a topological space; we define the *singular boundary operator* $\partial_n^{\text{sing}} : C_n^{\text{sing}}(X) \to C_{n-1}^{\text{sing}}(X)$ as follows. When $\sigma : \Delta^n \to X$ is a singular n-simplex, we set

$$\partial_n^{\text{sing}}(\sigma) := \sum_{i=0}^{n} (-1)^i \sigma_i,$$

where σ_i is the restriction of σ to the $(n-1)$-dimensional boundary simplex of Δ^n obtained by deleting the ith vertex. We then extend ∂_n^{sing} to the entire group $C_n^{\text{sing}}(X)$ by linearity.

Assuming the vertices of Δ^n are $v_0, \dots, v_n$ (in that order), we have $\sigma_i = \sigma|_{[v_0,\dots,\hat{v}_i,\dots,v_n]}$. Furthermore, the linearity means that for an arbitrary singular n-chain $\sigma = c_1\alpha_1 + \cdots + c_t\alpha_t$ we set

$$\partial_n^{\text{sing}}(\sigma) := c_1\partial_n^{\text{sing}}(\alpha_1) + \cdots + c_t\partial_n^{\text{sing}}(\alpha_t).$$

Proposition 7.3. *Let X be an arbitrary topological space X, and let $(\partial_n^{\text{sing}})_{n\in\mathbb{Z}}$ be the associated family of singular boundary operators. Then, for all n, we have*

$$\partial_n^{\text{sing}} \circ \partial_{n+1}^{\text{sing}} = 0. \tag{7.1}$$

The proof of Proposition 7.3 is an elementary exercise; see Exercise (1). Just as before, Equation (7.1) can be equivalently reformulated as saying that $\operatorname{Im}\partial_{n+1}^{\text{sing}} \subseteq \operatorname{Ker}\partial_n^{\text{sing}}$, for all n. This fact paves the way for the next definition.

Definition 7.4. For an arbitrary topological space X, we set

$$H_n^{\text{sing}}(X) := \operatorname{Ker}\partial_n^{\text{sing}} / \operatorname{Im}\partial_{n+1}^{\text{sing}},$$

where ∂_n^{sing} and $\partial_{n+1}^{\text{sing}}$ are the singular boundary operators associated to X. The group $H_n^{\text{sing}}(X)$ is called the *nth singular homology group* of X.

Equation (7.1) means that we have a chain complex of free abelian groups

$$\cdots \xrightarrow{\partial_{n+2}^{\text{sing}}} C_{n+1}^{\text{sing}}(X) \xrightarrow{\partial_{n+1}^{\text{sing}}} C_n^{\text{sing}}(X) \xrightarrow{\partial_n^{\text{sing}}} C_{n-1}^{\text{sing}}(X) \xrightarrow{\partial_{n-1}^{\text{sing}}} \cdots,$$

which is called the *singular chain complex* of X and is denoted by $\mathcal{C}^{\text{sing}}(X)$. The singular homology groups of the topological space X are precisely the homology groups of this chain complex.

Calculating singular homology using its definition directly is in general a daunting task, and so it can be done for relatively few topological spaces; see Exercise (2). The only dimension in which it can be done efficiently is the dimension 0; see Exercise (3).

7.2. Singular homology as a functor

Assume now we are given topological spaces X and Y, and a continuous map $f : X \to Y$.

Definition 7.5. Given a singular n-simplex $\sigma : \Delta^n \to X$, we set

$$f_n^\sharp(\sigma) := f \circ \sigma : \quad \Delta^n \to X \to Y.$$

This is a continuous map from Δ^n to Y, so it can be interpreted as a singular n-simplex in Y. Extending linearly to the whole free abelian group $C_n^{\text{sing}}(X)$ we obtain group homomorphisms $f_n^\sharp : C_n^{\text{sing}}(X) \to C_n^{\text{sing}}(Y)$, for all n.

The maps $f_n^\sharp$ which we just defined are said to be *induced by* f, and one also writes $f^\sharp : \mathcal{C}^{\text{sing}}(X) \to \mathcal{C}^{\text{sing}}(Y)$ for their collection. The following properties hold for all n, and are immediate consequences of Definition 7.5:

(1) $(f \circ g)_n^\sharp = f_n^\sharp \circ g_n^\sharp$,

(2) $(\text{id}_X)_n^\sharp = \text{id}_{C_n^{\text{sing}}(X)}$.

Proposition 7.6. *Assume X and Y are topological spaces, and $f : X \to Y$ is a continuous map. The induced map $f^\sharp : \mathcal{C}^{\text{sing}}(X) \to \mathcal{C}^{\text{sing}}(Y)$ is a chain map.*

To prove this proposition, we just need to show that the maps $f_n^\sharp$ commute with the respective boundary operators. We leave this straightforward verification as an exercise; see Exercise (4). Since we know that any chain map will induce a map on homology, we have the following corollary.

Corollary 7.7. *A continuous map $f : X \to Y$ between topological spaces induces a family of group homomorphisms $f^* = (f_n^*)_{n\in\mathbb{Z}}$, $f_n^* : H_n^{\text{sing}}(X) \to H_n^{\text{sing}}(Y)$.*

The family f^* is also said to be induced by f, and for brevity we write $f^* : H_*^{\text{sing}}(X) \to H_*^{\text{sing}}(Y)$. It has the same properties as $f^\sharp$: for all n we have

(1) $(f \circ g)_n^* = f_n^* \circ g_n^*$,

(2) $(\text{id}_X)_n^* = \text{id}_{H_n^{\text{sing}}(X)}$.

These imply that a homeomorphism between topological spaces will induce isomorphisms between their homology groups. It turns out that this observation can be extended to homotopy equivalences.

Theorem 7.8. *Homotopic maps induce equal maps on the singular homology.*

Proof. Assume X and Y are topological spaces, and $f, g : X \to Y$ are continuous maps such that $f \simeq g$. Let $\Phi : X \times [0,1] \to Y$ be some homotopy between f and g. The full-blown argument would take us too far away from our goals, so let us stay with a non-technical sketch.

Take a singular n-simplex $\sigma : \Delta^n \to X$. The homotopy Φ yields a map from the *prism* $\Delta^n \times [0,1] \to Y$. At the top and the bottom base facets of the prism, this map restricts to the singular n-simplices $f^\sharp(\sigma)$ and $g^\sharp(\sigma)$. Take some simplicial subdivision of $\Delta^n \times [0,1]$. The technical details here are not important, for instance we could take the canonical subdivision of the direct product of two simplices; see [**Ko08**, Subsection 10.5.1]. Mapping the simplex σ to the sums of appropriately signed $(n+1)$-simplices in that subdivision will yield a chain homotopy between $f^\sharp$ and $g^\sharp$. The statement of our theorem then follows from Corollary 5.6. □

Corollary 7.9. *Homotopy equivalent spaces have isomorphic singular homology groups.*

Proof. Assume X and Y are homotopy equivalent topological spaces. Let $f : X \to Y$ and $g : Y \to X$ be some continuous maps such that $g \circ f \simeq \mathrm{id}_X$ and $f \circ g \simeq \mathrm{id}_Y$. Passing on to homology, for all n, we have

$$g_n^* \circ f_n^* = (g \circ f)_n^* = (\mathrm{id}_X)_n^* = \mathrm{id}_{H_n^{\mathrm{sing}}(X)},$$

and similary $f_n^* \circ g_n^* = \mathrm{id}_{H_n^{\mathrm{sing}}(Y)}$. It follows that, for all n, f_n^* and g_n^* are isomorphisms between the nth singular homology groups of X and Y. □

7.3. Simplicial approximation

While in general not all topological spaces are *triangulable*, that is, homeomorphic to the geometric realization of some simplicial complex, the vast majority of spaces we are interested in are triangulable. So for all ends and purposes we can restrict ourselves to such spaces. The next natural query which arises is whether the simplicial maps are sufficient to model the full richness of the family of continuous maps.

This is the main question which concerns us in this section, so assume that $\mathcal{K}$ and $\mathcal{M}$ are simplicial complexes, and $f : |\mathcal{K}| \to |\mathcal{M}|$ is a continuous map between their geometric realizations. We then ask whether we can find a *simplicial approximation* of f. What we would really want is to guarantee the existence of a simplicial map $\varphi : \mathcal{K} \to \mathcal{M}$, such that its geometric realization $|\varphi|$ is homotopic to f.

As a first step we would like to contemplate the notion of *being close* inside a simplicial complex. Let us take a point $x \in |\mathcal{K}|$. Let σ be the support simplex of x, denoted $\mathrm{supp}_{\mathcal{K}}\, x$, or simply $\mathrm{supp}\, x$. This is the unique minimal simplex which contains x; in particular, it must contain x in its interior.

We shall then say that x is close to the vertices of σ. In terms of barycentric coordinates: each point y of $|\mathcal{K}|$ can be expressed in barycentric coordinates, and it is close to those vertices of $|\mathcal{K}|$, which appear with a non-zero coefficient in the barycentric coordinate presentation of y.

Reversely, while each point of $|\mathcal{K}|$ is close to the vertices of its support simplex, there is a formal way to describe all the points close to a fixed vertex of $|\mathcal{K}|$. Namely, for a vertex $v \in \mathcal{K}$, we have defined its open star $\mathrm{st}^{\circ}_{\mathcal{K}} v$ as a set of all simplices which contain v as one of their vertices.[1] It is therefore logical to write $|\mathrm{st}^{\circ}_{\mathcal{K}} v|$ to denote the subset of $|\mathcal{K}|$ consisting of the interiors of the simplices from $\mathrm{st}^{\circ}_{\mathcal{K}} v$. These are precisely all the points of $|\mathcal{K}|$ which are close to v or, in other words, all the points of $|\mathcal{K}|$ whose barycentric coordinates contain v with a non-zero coefficient. We shall set

$$\mathcal{O}_{\mathcal{K}}(v) := |\mathrm{st}^{\circ}_{\mathcal{K}} v|,$$

and call it a *standard open neighborhood* of the vertex v in $|\mathcal{K}|$.

We now have the technical tools and the intuitive understanding to define the notion of a simplicial map φ approximating a continuous map f. The basic idea is to require that f maps the standard open neighborhood of v inside the standard open neighborhood of $\varphi(v)$.

Definition 7.10. Assume $\mathcal{K}$ and $\mathcal{M}$ are simplicial complexes, and $f : |\mathcal{K}| \to |\mathcal{M}|$ is a continuous map between their geometric realizations. A simplicial map $\varphi : \mathcal{K} \to \mathcal{M}$ is called a *simplicial approximation of* f if we have the inclusion

$$f(\mathcal{O}_{\mathcal{K}}(v)) \subseteq \mathcal{O}_{\mathcal{M}}(\varphi(v)), \tag{7.2}$$

for all vertices $v \in \mathcal{K}(0)$.

Given a continuous function $f : |\mathcal{K}| \to |\mathcal{M}|$, we may not be able to find any simplicial approximation at all; see Figure 7.1.

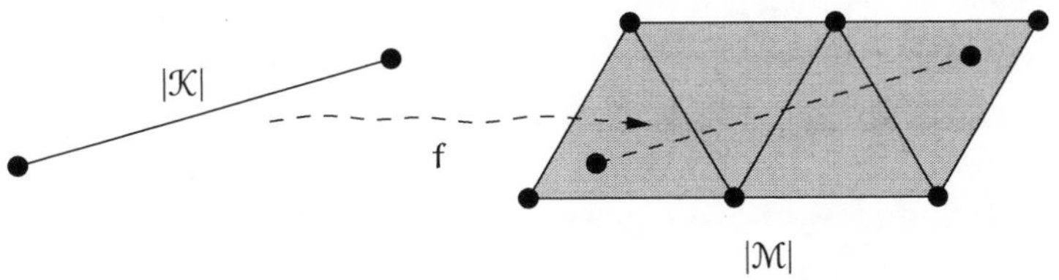

Figure 7.1. Continuous map without a simplicial approximation.

A useful way to think about inclusion (7.2) is as follows: if a vertex v appears with a non-zero coefficient among the barycentric coordinates of some point $x \in |\mathcal{K}|$, then the vertex $\varphi(v)$ appears with a non-zero coefficient

[1] To aid geometric intuition, one should really think about the interiors of those simplices.

among the barycentric coordinates of the point $f(x)$. For future reference we formally fix this observation.

Lemma 7.11. *Assume* $\mathcal{K}$ *and* $\mathcal{M}$ *are simplicial complexes,* $f : |\mathcal{K}| \to |\mathcal{M}|$ *is a continuous map, and* $\varphi : \mathcal{K}(0) \to \mathcal{M}(0)$ *is a function between the sets of vertices, such that condition* (7.2) *holds for all* v.

For any point $x \in |\mathcal{K}|$ *we have: whenever* v *is a vertex of* $\operatorname{supp}_{\mathcal{K}} x$*, its image* $\varphi(v)$ *is a vertex of* $\operatorname{supp}_{\mathcal{M}} f(x)$.

As a result we can see that any vertex map satisfying Equation (7.2) will yield a simplicial approximation.

Proposition 7.12. *Assume* $\mathcal{K}$ *and* $\mathcal{M}$ *are simplicial complexes, and* $f : |\mathcal{K}| \to |\mathcal{M}|$ *is a continuous map. There is a one-to-one correspondence, given by restriction, between simplicial approximations of* f*, and vertex set functions* $\varphi : \mathcal{K}(0) \to \mathcal{M}(0)$*, for which inclusion* (7.2) *holds for all* v.

Proof. All we need to show is that any vertex set function $\varphi : \mathcal{K}(0) \to \mathcal{M}(0)$, for which inclusion (7.2) holds for all v, can be uniquely extended to a simplicial approximation of f.

Take any simplex σ of $\mathcal{K}$, and let x be its barycenter. Clearly, $\operatorname{supp}_{\mathcal{K}} x = \sigma$. Let V denote the set of vertices of σ. By Lemma 7.11, we know that $\varphi(V)$ is contained in the set of vertices of $\operatorname{supp}_{\mathcal{M}} f(x)$. In particular, the set $\varphi(V)$ forms a simplex in $\mathcal{M}$: it is a subsimplex of $\operatorname{supp}_{\mathcal{M}} f(x)$, not necessarily proper. This shows that φ maps simplices of $\mathcal{K}$ to simplices of $\mathcal{M}$, so it extends to a simplicial map. □

Proposition 7.13. *Assume* $\mathcal{K}$ *and* $\mathcal{M}$ *are simplicial complexes,* $f : |\mathcal{K}| \to |\mathcal{M}|$ *is a continuous map, and* $\varphi : \mathcal{K} \to \mathcal{M}$ *is a simplicial approximation of* f. *Then the maps* f *and* $|\varphi| : |\mathcal{K}| \to |\mathcal{M}|$ *are homotopic.*

Proof. Take an arbitrary point $x \in |\mathcal{K}|$, and set $\sigma := \operatorname{supp} x$. The point $|\varphi|(x)$ is contained in $|\varphi|(\sigma)$, which by Lemma 7.11 is contained in $\operatorname{supp} f(x)$. Therefore, the geometric realization $|\mathcal{M}|$ contains an interval connecting $f(x)$ with $|\varphi|(x)$. We can therefore define a homotopy by simply letting $f(x)$ slide along this interval with constant speed towards the point $|\varphi|(x)$. This is called the linear homotopy and is given by the formula $\Phi(x, t) = (1 - t)f(x) + t|\varphi|(x)$. □

We now show that iterated use of the barycentric subdivision will force the existence of a simplicial approximation. In order to keep the presentation not too technical, we limit ourselves to the finite case.

Theorem 7.14 (The finite simplicial approximation theorem). *Assume* $\mathcal{K}$ *and* $\mathcal{M}$ *are finite simplicial complexes, and* $f : |\mathcal{K}| \to |\mathcal{M}|$ *is a continuous map.*

Then there exists an integer N, *and a simplicial map* $\psi : \mathrm{Bd}^N \mathcal{K} \to \mathcal{M}$, *such that* ψ *is a simplicial approximation of* $f : |\mathrm{Bd}^N \mathcal{K}| \to |\mathcal{M}|$.

Proof. Consider the set family $\mathcal{A} := (f^{-1}(\mathcal{O}(v)))_{v \in \mathcal{M}(0)}$. First, since each $\mathcal{O}(v)$ is an open set, and f is continuous, the sets $f^{-1}(\mathcal{O}(v))$ are also open. Furthermore, $|\mathcal{K}|$ is compact, and $\mathcal{A}$ provides an open set covering of $|\mathcal{K}|$.

It is a standard fact of set-theoretic topology that there exists a number λ, the so-called *Lebesgue number* of the covering $\mathcal{A}$, which satisfies the following condition: if $T \subseteq |\mathcal{K}|$ is an open set, whose diameter is less than λ, then there exists v such that $T \subseteq f^{-1}(\mathcal{O}(v))$.

It is a well-known fact, see Exercise (6), that repeated use of the barycentric subdivision will let the maximal diameter of a star go to 0. This means that there exists an integer N such that every star of a vertex of $\mathrm{Bd}^N \mathcal{K}$ has diameter which is smaller than λ. Therefore, whenever w is a vertex of $\mathrm{Bd}^N(\mathcal{K})$, we have $\mathcal{O}(w) \subseteq f^{-1}(\mathcal{O}(v))$, for some $v \in \mathcal{M}(0)$. Applying f to this inclusion, we obtain $f(\mathcal{O}(w)) \subseteq \mathcal{O}(v)$. We now set $\psi(w) := v$. By Proposition 7.12 this yields a simplicial approximation of f. □

Corollary 7.15. *Any continuous map* f *between geometric realizations of finite simplicial complexes* $\mathcal{K}$ *and* $\mathcal{M}$ *can, up to homotopy, be replaced by the continuous map induced by some simplicial map* $\varphi : \mathcal{K} \to \mathcal{M}$.

Proof. By Theorem 7.14, for some integer N, there exists a simplicial approximation of the map $f : |\mathrm{Bd}^N \mathcal{K}| \to |\mathcal{M}|$. This map is homotopic to φ, by Proposition 7.13. □

7.4. The 5-Lemma

In the next section we will sketch the proof of the fact that singular and simplicial homologies are isomorphic, when both are defined, and as a consequence the fact that simplicial homology does not depend on the specific triangulation.

Before we proceed with that, we do need a certain central result from homological algebra. Due to its universal utility we present it in a separate section.

Theorem 7.16 (5-Lemma). *Let* (7.3) *be a commutative diagram of abelian groups and group homomorphisms.*

$$
\begin{array}{ccccccccc}
A & \xrightarrow{i} & B & \xrightarrow{j} & C & \xrightarrow{k} & D & \xrightarrow{l} & E \\
\downarrow{\scriptstyle\alpha} & & \downarrow{\scriptstyle\beta} & & \downarrow{\scriptstyle\gamma} & & \downarrow{\scriptstyle\delta} & & \downarrow{\scriptstyle\varepsilon} \\
A' & \xrightarrow{i'} & B' & \xrightarrow{j'} & C' & \xrightarrow{k'} & D' & \xrightarrow{l'} & E'
\end{array}
\tag{7.3}
$$

Assume that both rows in (7.3) *are exact, and the maps* α, β, δ, *and* ε *are isomorphisms. Then* γ *is also an isomorphism.*

Proof. The proof is again by use of the so-called *diagram chasing.* Roughly speaking, one produces the proof by simply using whatever information is available at each step. If the statement is theoretical and stripped down to pure necessities, as this one is, the proof is easy to produce step-by-step.

Let us first show that γ is injective. Take $c \in C$ such that $\gamma(c) = 0$. Then $\delta(k(c)) = 0$. Since δ is an isomorphism, we have $k(c) = 0$. So $c \in \operatorname{Ker} k = \operatorname{Im} j$. Take $b \in B$ such that $j(b) = c$. Then $j'(\beta(b)) = 0$. Therefore $\beta(b) \in \operatorname{Ker} j' = \operatorname{Im} i'$. Take $a' \in A'$ such that $i'(a') = \beta(b)$. The map α is surjective, so we can find $a \in \alpha^{-1}(a')$. We have

$$\beta(i(a)) = i'(\alpha(a)) = i'(a') = \beta(b).$$

Since β is injective, it follows that $b = i(a)$. We then have $c = j(b) = j(i(a)) = 0$, which means that γ is injective.

Let us now show that γ is surjective. Pick $c' \in C'$, and set $d := \delta^{-1}(k'(c'))$. We have $\varepsilon(l(d)) = l'(\delta(d)) = l'(k'(c)) = 0$. Since ε is injective, we have $l(d) = 0$. Since $d \in \operatorname{Ker} l = \operatorname{Im} k$, we can choose $c \in C$, such that $k(c) = d$. By diagram commutativity, we have $k'(\gamma(c)) = \delta(k(c)) = \delta(d) = k'(c')$. In particular, $k'(c' - \gamma(c)) = 0$, so $c' - \gamma(c) \in \operatorname{Ker} k' = \operatorname{Im} j'$, so there exists $b' \in B'$ such that $j'(b') = c' - \gamma(c)$. Set $b := \beta^{-1}(b')$. We have

$$\gamma(j(b)) = j'(\beta(b)) = j'(b') = c' - \gamma(c).$$

In particular, we obtain $\gamma(c + j(b)) = \gamma(c) + (c' - \gamma(c)) = c'$, and so γ is surjective. □

Note that the proof of Theorem 7.16 has only used that α is surjective and that ε is injective, so if necessary the assumptions can be weakened accordingly.

7.5. Independence of simplicial homology of the triangulation

It is now time to show that the homology of a simplicial complex does not depend on the actual triangulation of the underlying topological space. To be precise, if some topological space is represented in two different ways as a geometric realization of a simplicial complex, the simplicial homology groups of these triangulations will be isomorphic.

The actual fact which we prove is that simplicial homology of a simplicial complex $\mathcal{K}$ is isomorphic to the singular homology of the topological space $|\mathcal{K}|$. In order not to get entangled in set-theoretical technicalities, we shall only prove this for a finite simplicial complex, and in fact our whole proof will be just a sketch, with some explicitely stated facts which we shall accept without a proof.

Specifically, we shall assume that when X is a topological space, Y is its subspace, and the embedding of Y into X is not too convoluted, the relative homology coincides with the homology of the quotient space, that is, we have isomorphisms

$$\widetilde{H}_n(X/Y) \approx H_n(X, Y), \text{ for all } n. \tag{7.4}$$

It is rather technical to explain what we mean by the embedding being not too convoluted. Let us just say that this holds for all the spaces which we care for here. In particular, it holds if X is a geometrical realizaton of a CW complex (including the simplicial complex), and Y is the geometric realization of a subcomplex of X. To do a rigorous proof one needs to show the so-called *excision* property, together with some technicalities concerning the topology of attaching a cell. These facts can be found in most algebraic topology textbooks; see for example [**Hat02**].

Assume now that $\mathcal{K}$ is a simplicial complex, and let $\mathcal{K} \cup e^d$ denote the simplicial complex obtained from $\mathcal{K}$ by adding a single maximal simplex of dimension d, whose boundary was already in $\mathcal{K}$. For the simplicial homology, we obviously have

$$H_n(\mathcal{K} \cup e^d, \mathcal{K}) \approx \begin{cases} \mathbb{Z}, & \text{if } d = n, \\ 0, & \text{otherwise.} \end{cases} \tag{7.5}$$

The geometric realization $|\mathcal{K} \cup e^d|$ is obtained from the topological space $|\mathcal{K}|$ by attaching a d-cell. Recall that for any index n, there is a natural map $\rho : C_n(\mathcal{K}) \to C_n^{\text{sing}}(|\mathcal{K}|)$, which takes each simplex σ to the associated characteristic map $\chi_\sigma : \Delta^n \to |\mathcal{K}|$. This collection of maps induces maps ρ_n^* on the corresponding homology groups.

We can see that Equation (7.5) holds for the singular homology as well. Indeed, the quotient space $|\mathcal{K} \cup e^d|/|\mathcal{K}|$ is homeomorphic to a d-sphere, and we can use the isomorphism (7.4). With a little bit of work, one can see that the isomorphisms $H_n(\mathcal{K} \cup e^d, \mathcal{K}) \approx H_n^{\text{sing}}(|\mathcal{K} \cup e^d|, |\mathcal{K}|)$ are induced by ρ_n^*, for all n.

Theorem 7.17. *Assume $\mathcal{K}$ is a finite simplicial complex. Then the homology map ρ^* defined above is an isomorphism.*

Proof. We use induction on the number of simplices in $\mathcal{K}$. The base is clear, since the statement obviously holds when $\mathcal{K}$ is 0-dimensional.

For the induction step, assume we are adding a simplex e^d to the simplicial complex $\mathcal{K}$. We have the commutative diagram in Figure 7.2, where both columns are exact.

$$
\begin{array}{ccc}
H_{n+1}(\mathcal{K} \cup e^d, \mathcal{K}) & \xrightarrow{\rho^*_{n+1}} & H_{n+1}(|\mathcal{K} \cup e^d|, |\mathcal{K}|) \\
\downarrow \partial^c & & \downarrow \partial^c \\
H_n(\mathcal{K}) & \xrightarrow{\rho^*_n} & H_n(|\mathcal{K}|) \\
\downarrow i & & \downarrow i \\
H_n(\mathcal{K} \cup e^d) & \xrightarrow{\rho^*_n} & H_n(|\mathcal{K} \cup e^d|) \\
\downarrow q & & \downarrow q \\
H_n(\mathcal{K} \cup e^d, \mathcal{K}) & \xrightarrow{\rho^*_n} & H_{n-1}(|\mathcal{K} \cup e^d|, |\mathcal{K}|) \\
\downarrow \partial^c & & \downarrow \partial^c \\
H_{n-1}(\mathcal{K}^{(d)}) & \xrightarrow{\rho^*_{n-1}} & H_n(|\mathcal{K}|)
\end{array}
$$

Figure 7.2. Commutative diagram in the proof of Theorem 7.17.

By Equation (7.5) and the induction assumptions, all the horizontal arrows, except for the middle one, are isomorphisms. Therefore the conditions of Theorem 7.16 are satisfied, and we can conclude that the map ρ is an isomorphism. □

Corollary 7.18. *Two simplicial complexes $\mathcal{K}$ and $\mathcal{L}$ with homeomorphic geometric realizations have isomorphic simplicial homology groups.*

Proof. The singular homology groups of $|\mathcal{K}|$ and $|\mathcal{L}|$ are isomorphic since the spaces are homeomorphic. On the other hand, by Theorem 7.17, we know that the singular homology of $|\mathcal{K}|$ is isomorphic to the simplicial homology of $\mathcal{K}$, and the same for $\mathcal{L}$. It then follows that the simplicial homology groups of $\mathcal{K}$ and $\mathcal{L}$ are isomorphic. □

Exercises

(1) Prove Proposition 7.3.

(2) Use the definition to directly calculate the singular homology groups of the topological space with finitely many points, equipped with discrete topology. What about the discrete topological spaces with an arbitrary number of points?

(3) Assume X is a topological space, and the set I indexes the path-connected components of X. Describe the group $H_0^{sing}(X)$ in terms of I.

(4) Prove Proposition 7.6.

(5) Show that the composition of simplicial approximations is a simplicial approximation of the composition.

(6) Let $\mathcal{K}$ be a finite simplicial complex of dimension n.
   (1) Let d denote the maximal diameter of a simplex of $|\mathcal{K}|$, and let $\tilde{d}$ denote the maximal diameter of a simplex of $|\operatorname{Bd}\mathcal{K}|$. Show that $\tilde{d} < \alpha d$, where $\alpha < 1$ is a constant depending only on n and not on $\mathcal{K}$;
   (2) let s denote the maximal diameter of a star of a vertex in $|\mathcal{K}|$, and let $\tilde{s}$ denote the maximal diameter of a star of a vertex in $|\operatorname{Bd}\mathcal{K}|$. Show that $\tilde{s} < \gamma s$, where again $\gamma < 1$ is a constant depending only on n and not on $\mathcal{K}$.

Chapter 8

Cellular Homology

CW complexes were defined in Subsection 3.3.2. Our task in this chapter is to give a definition of the homology groups of CW complexes defined inherently in terms of their cellular structure, the so-called *cellular homology*. As usual, the homology is defined using a certain chain complex, the so-called *cellular chain complex*.

While it is simple to define the cellular chain groups, defining the cellular boundary operator is somewhat tricky. There are two basic approaches. The first one, using the *winding numbers*, carries more geometric intuition and is more elementary. Its main disadvantage is that it is rather difficult to adapt for use in formal proofs. The alternative definition uses the connecting homomorphism from an appropriate long exact sequence. While more theoretical in nature, it provides a useful tool for writing rigorous arguments.

8.1. Winding number

We begin by defining a winding number of a continuous map between spheres of the same dimension. To start with, imagine we are considering a closed directed curve γ in the plane, together with a point $x \in \mathbb{R}^2$ which does not belong to the curve. We are interested in counting the "number of times γ winds around x." (See Figure 8.1.)

A good way to formalize this question is to view the curve γ as a continuous map from the circle S^1 to the plane, visualized by its image. Draw a unit circle C with x as the center. For each point $y \in \gamma$ let r_y be the ray starting in x and passing through y. Finally, let s_y be the intersection point of the circle C and the ray r_y. As y traces the curve γ, the point s_y moves continuously on the circle, eventually returning to its original position. Intuitively the winding number should count the number of ways the point goes around the circle, and the sign of the winding number should tell us the direction in which the point is moving. Of course, going once around the circle in one direction and then once in the opposite direction should cancel out. As a final building stone in this formalization we need the following definition.

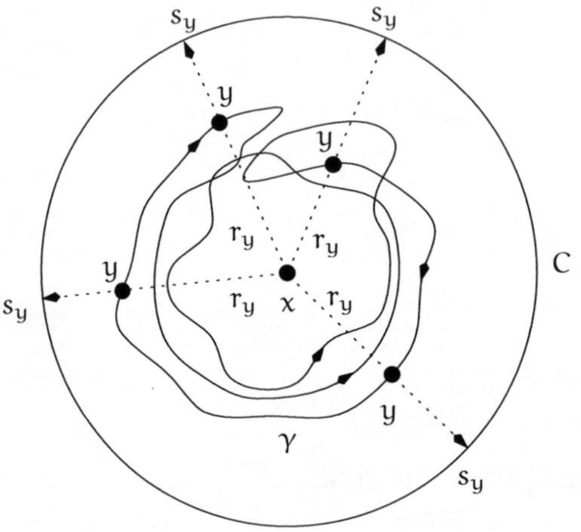

Figure 8.1. Winding number of a curve in the plane.

Definition 8.1. Assume $f : \mathbb{Z} \to \mathbb{Z}$ is a group homomorphism. Then there exists unique $k \in \mathbb{Z}$, such that $f(g) = kg$, for all $g \in \mathbb{Z}$. This number k is called the *degree of* f, and is denoted by $\deg f$.

Note that another way to define $\deg f$ is to simply set $\deg f := f(1)$. It is easy to list some elementary properties of $\deg f$.

Proposition 8.2. *The degree of an endomorphism of* $\mathbb{Z}$ *satisfies the following properties:*

(1) $\deg(f \circ g) = \deg f \cdot \deg g$,

(2) $\deg(\mathrm{id}_{\mathbb{Z}}) = 1$,

(3) f *is invertible if and only if* $\deg f = \pm 1$, *in which case we have* $\deg(f^{-1}) = \deg f$,

(4) f *is a* 0*-map if and only if* $\deg f = 0$.

Let us return to our curve γ and the point x. Since a curve is a continuous map from S^1 to the plane, the motion of the point s_y around the circle can be viewed as a continuous map f from a unit circle to itself. We know that the first homology group of S^1 is isomorphic to $\mathbb{Z}$, and that f induces the group homomorphism $f_* : H_1(S^1) \to H_1(S^1)$. The degree of f_* is defined and provides us with a formal way to define the number of times the curve γ winds around the point x.

Producing a geometric picture of the winding number of a surface winding around a point is not as simple. However, the advantage of having reformulated things homologically is that we do not need to do that, and we can easily generalize our observations to a higher dimension. The crucial point is that such a higher-dimensional surface, together with a point outside of that surface, will produce a continuous map from a higher-dimensional sphere to itself, which will suffice for our purposes.

Definition 8.3. Assume $n \geqslant 1$, and we have a continuous map $f : S^n \to S^n$. The *winding number* of f is defined to be the degree of the induced group homomorphism $f_* : H_n(S^n) \to H_n(S^n)$.

We extend the previous notations and let $\deg f$ also denote the winding number of f. Proposition 8.2 together with the standard facts about the induced maps imply the following properties of the winding number.

Proposition 8.4. *The winding number of a continuous map from the n-sphere to itself satisfies the following properties:*

(1) $\deg(f \circ g) = \deg f \cdot \deg g$,

(2) $\deg(\mathrm{id}_{S^n}) = 1$,

(3) *if* f *is homotopic to* g, *then* $\deg f = \deg g$,

(4) *when* f *is a reflection with respect to any hyperplane, we have* $\deg f = -1$,

(5) *when* f *is the antipodal map, we have* $\deg f = (-1)^{n+1}$.

Proof. The properties (1)–(3) are trivial. Property (4) follows from the fact that a reflection changes the orientation of the homology generator. Property (5) follows from the fact that an antipodal map in $\mathbb{R}^{n+1}$ is a composition of $n+1$ reflections. □

It turns out that having a non-trivial winding number has the following reasonably strong implication.

Proposition 8.5. *If* $\deg f \neq 0$, *then* f *is surjective.*

Proof. If f is not surjective, there exists $x \in S^n \setminus \operatorname{Im} f$. Consider the composition of maps

$$S^n \xrightarrow{\tilde{f}} S^n \setminus x \xrightarrow{i} S^n,$$

where $\tilde{f}$ is the restriction of f and i is the inclusion map. For homology, it induces the following composition:

$$H_n(S^n) \xrightarrow{\tilde{f}_*} H_n(S^n \setminus x) \xrightarrow{i_*} H_n(S^n).$$

The space $S^n \setminus x$ is contractible, so we have $H_n(S^n \setminus x) = 0$, which implies $i_* \circ \tilde{f}_* = 0$. On the other hand, $i_* \circ \tilde{f}_* = (i \circ \tilde{f})_* = f_*$. This implies $\deg f = 0$, yielding a contradiction. □

Definition 8.6. Let X be an arbitrary topological space. A function $f : X \to X$ is called *fixed-point free* if $f(x) \neq x$, for all $x \in X$.

An antipodal map of an n-sphere is a classical example of a fixed-point free map. A weaker reverse of this statement also holds.

Proposition 8.7. *Any fixed-point free map of an n-sphere to itself is homotopic to the antipodal map. In particular, the winding number of any fixed-point free map of S^n to itself is $(-1)^{n+1}$.*

Proof. Pick $x \in S^n$. We know that $f(x) \neq x$. This means that there exists a unique geodesic[1] curve γ_x connecting $f(x)$ with $-x$. Let α_n denote the antipodal map on S^n. We obtain a homotopy between f and α_n by simply letting each $f(x)$ slide along γ_x with a constant speed. □

8.2. Incidence numbers

In order to describe a cellular boundary operator we need to understand the relation between a d-cell and a $(d-1)$-cell on its boundary. In the simplicial case, that relation is simple. When a $(d-1)$-simplex τ belongs to the boundary of a d-simplex α, their orientations may or may not match. Accordingly τ is counted in the algebraic formula for the boundary of α with coefficient 1 or -1.

Unfortunately, the situation is not as simple in the CW case. Even in dimension $d = 1$, the 1-cell α can be attached to the same 0-cell τ with both ends, in which case τ should count with coefficient 0 in the boundary of α, or, to say it differently, it should not count at all. For higher dimensions the situation becomes even more convoluted. Fortunately, there is a formally clean way to calculate the coefficient of τ in the boundary of α, using the concept of the winding number.

In what follows, assume X is a CW complex. Let α be a d-cell, and let τ be a $(d-1)$-cell of X. Recall that X_{d-1} denotes the $(d-1)$th skeleton of X, which is the part obtained by gluing all the cells of dimension $d-1$ or less. Let $\rho_\alpha : S^{d-1} \to X_{d-1}$ be the attaching map of the cell α.

[1] Recall that the geodesic curve is any curve of shortest length between the chosen endpoints.

Consider the quotient space X_{d-1}/X_{d-2} and the canonical quotient map $q : X_{d-1} \to X_{d-1}/X_{d-2}$. Since X_{d-1} is obtained from X_{d-2} by simultaneously attaching a number of $(d-1)$-cells, the quotient X_{d-1}/X_{d-2} is homeomorphic to the wedge of $(d-1)$-spheres, indexed by the $(d-1)$-cells of X, i.e.,

$$X_{d-1}/X_{d-2} \cong \bigvee_{\gamma \in X(d-1)} S^{d-1}_{\gamma}.$$

Finally, let $s_\tau : X_{d-1}/X_{d-2} \to S^{d-1}_{\tau}$ denote the projection map which is equal to identity on the sphere S^{d-1}_{τ}, corresponding to the cell τ, but which shrinks every other sphere to a point.

Definition 8.8. Let X, α, and τ be as above, and consider the composition of the continuous maps

$$S^{d-1} \xrightarrow{\rho_\alpha} X_{d-1} \xrightarrow{q} X_{d-1}/X_{d-2} \xrightarrow{s_\tau} S^{d-1}_{\tau}.$$

We set $[\tau : \alpha]$ to be equal to the winding number of $s_\tau \circ q \circ \rho_\alpha$, and call this number the *incidence number* of α and τ.

In formula, we have $[\tau : \alpha] := \deg(s_\tau \circ q \circ \rho_\alpha)$.

8.3. Cellular chain complex

Equipped with the notion of the incidence number, we can now proceed to define the cellular boundary operator.

Definition 8.9. Let X be a CW complex, we define the cellular boundary operator ∂^{CW}_d by setting

$$\partial^{CW}_d(\alpha) := \sum_{\tau \in X(d-1)} [\tau : \alpha]\tau, \tag{8.1}$$

whenever α is a d-cell of X.

Of course, for ∂^{CW}_d to be a real boundary operator, the following property needs to be satisfied.

Theorem 8.10. *We have* $\partial^{CW}_d \circ \partial^{CW}_{d+1} = 0$, *for all* d.

While it is possible to prove Theorem 8.10 directly, we prefer to postpone the proof to the next section, where it will be done using a roundabout method: show that Definition 8.9 is equivalent to an alternative definition for which this identity is much easier to prove.

Definition 8.11. Assume X is a CW complex. The *cellular chain complex* of X is the sequence of abelian groups and group homomorphisms

$$\cdots \longrightarrow C^{CW}_{d+1}(X) \xrightarrow{\partial^{CW}_{d+1}} C^{CW}_d(X) \xrightarrow{\partial^{CW}_d} C^{CW}_{d-1}(X) \longrightarrow \cdots,$$

where, for each d, $C_d^{CW}(X)$ is the free abelian group generated by the set of all d-cells, and ∂_d^{CW} is the cellular boundary operator defined above.

We let $\mathcal{C}_*^{CW}(X)$ denote the cellular chain complex of X.

Definition 8.12. For a CW complex X, the *cellular homology* of X is defined by setting $H_d^{CW}(X) := H_d(\mathcal{C}_*^{CW}(X))$.

8.4. Alternative definition of the cellular boundary operator

To provide an alternative definition of the cellular boundary operator, we begin with the observation that cellular chain groups are isomorphic to the corresponding relative homology groups: $C_d^{CW}(X) \approx H_d(X_d, X_{d-1})$, for all d.

Definition 8.13. Let X be a CW complex. The cellular boundary operator $\tilde{\partial}_d^{CW} : C_d^{CW}(X) \to C_{d-1}^{CW}(X)$ is defined as the composition

$$H_d(X_d, X_{d-1}) \xrightarrow{\partial_d^c} H_{d-1}(X_{d-1}) \xrightarrow{j_*} H_{d-1}(X_{d-1}, X_{d-2}), \tag{8.2}$$

where ∂_d^c is the connecting homomorphism and j_* is the standard quotient map.

Proposition 8.14. *We have* $\tilde{\partial}_d^{CW} \circ \tilde{\partial}_{d+1}^{CW} = 0$, *for all* d.

Proof. Combining sequences (8.2) for consecutive values of d, we obtain the sequence

$$\begin{array}{ccccccc}
 & & H_{d+1}(X_{d+1}, X_d) & & & & \\
 & & \downarrow{\scriptstyle \partial_{d+1}^c} & & & & \\
\dashrightarrow H_d(X_d) & \xrightarrow{j_*} & H_d(X_d, X_{d-1}) & \xrightarrow{\partial_d^c} & H_{d-1}(X_{d-1}) & \dashrightarrow & \\
 & & & & \downarrow{\scriptstyle j_*} & & \\
 & & & & H_{d-1}(X_{d-1}, X_{d-2}) & &
\end{array}$$

The middle two homomorphisms can be embedded into the long exact sequence corresponding to the pair (X_d, X_{d-1}), as the dashed arrows indicate. Due to exactness, the composition $j_* \circ \partial_d^c$ is a zero map, hence so is the composition of all four arrows. □

Theorem 8.15. *The two definitions of the cellular boundary operator give the same map.*

Proof. Rather than giving a tedious formal proof, let us try to understand why the two definitions give the same answer. So assume X is a CW complex, α is a d-cell, and τ is a $(d-1)$-cell of X. We need to compare $\partial_d^{CW}(\alpha)$ with $\tilde{\partial}_d^{CW}(\alpha)$.

To start with, both obviously depend on the d-skeleton of X only, so we can assume that $\dim X = d$, and in fact, we can also assume α is the only d-cell of X as the other d-cells play no role in either of the definitions. Furthermore, we can also replace X with the quotient X/X_{d-2}. Indeed, in the definition of ∂_d^{CW} one takes the quotient with X_{d-2} anyway. In the definition for $\tilde{\partial}_d^{CW}$ one passes on to $H_{d-1}(X_{d-1}, X_{d-2})$, which, according to Equation (7.4), is the same as $H_{d-1}(X_{d-1}/X_{d-2})$.

All-in-all, we can assume that X is obtained by starting with a wedge of $(d-1)$-spheres, and then attaching a single d-cell α. The connecting homomorphism applied to the homology generator of $H_d(X_d, X_{d-1})$ indexed by α simply takes the boundary sphere of α and maps it to the wedge of $(d-1)$-spheres X_{d-1}. Following the definition of $\tilde{\partial}_d^{CW}$ we then project to the $(d-1)$-sphere indexed by τ. This is of course precisely the map whose winding number was used to define the incidence number $[\tau, \alpha]$. We conclude that the definitions yield the same boundary operator. □

Because of Theorem 8.15 we shall no longer use the notation $\tilde{\partial}_d^{CW}$, writing ∂_d^{CW} to denote either one of the cellular boundary operators.

Note that Theorem 8.10 is now clearly a consequence of Proposition 8.14 and Theorem 8.15.

8.5. Equivalence of singular and cellular homology

We are now ready to show that the singular and the cellular homology groups of a CW complex coincide.

Theorem 8.16. *Let* X *be a CW complex; we have* $H_d^{sing}(X) \approx H_d^{CW}(X)$.

Proof. Let X be a CW complex. For brevity, we shall just write $H_d(X)$ instead of $H_d^{sing}(X)$. Consider the quotient map $j_d : H_d(X_d) \to H_d(X_d, X_{d-1})$, while recalling that $H_d(X_d, X_{d-1}) = C_d^{CW}(X)$. We shall break our proof into four parts, showing the following four facts.

Fact 1. We have $\operatorname{Im} j_d \subseteq Z_d^{CW}(X) = \operatorname{Ker} \partial_d^{CW}$.

Combining the map j_d with the standard projection map $Z_d^{CW}(X) \to H_d^{CW}(X)$, we obtain a map $\tilde{j}_d : H_d(X_d) \to H_d^{CW}(X)$.

Fact 2. We have $\operatorname{Ker} \tilde{j}_d = \operatorname{Im} \partial_{d+1}^c$, where $\partial_{d+1}^c : H_{d+1}(X_{d+1}, X_d) \to H_d(X_d)$ is the corresponding connecting homomorphism.

Fact 3. The map $\tilde{j}_d$ is surjective.

It now follows that $H_d^{CW}(X) \approx H_d(X_d)/\operatorname{Im} \partial_{d+1}^c$.

Fact 4. We have $H_d(X_d)/\operatorname{Im}\partial^c_{d+1} \approx H_d(X)$.

This clearly implies the statement of the theorem. Let us now prove each of the four facts.

Proof of Fact 1. Consider the following diagram, where the horizontal row is an extract from the exact sequence of the pair (X_d, X_{d-1}):

$$\begin{array}{ccccccc} H_d(X_d) & \xrightarrow{j_d} & H_d(X_d, X_{d-1}) & \xrightarrow{\partial^c_d} & H_{d-1}(X_{d-1}) & \xrightarrow{i_{d-1}} & H_{d-1}(X_d) \\ & & & \searrow^{\partial^{CW}_d} & \downarrow{\scriptstyle j_{d-1}} & & \\ & & & & H_{d-1}(X_{d-1}, X_{d-2}) & & \end{array} \tag{8.3}$$

Due to exactness, the composition $\partial^c_d \circ j_d$ is a 0-map, so $\partial^{CW}_d \circ j_d = j_{d-1} \circ \partial^c_d \circ j_d$ must be a 0-map as well.

Proof of Fact 2. Let us first show that $\operatorname{Ker}\tilde{j}_d \supseteq \operatorname{Im}\partial^c_{d+1}$. Consider the diagram (8.3) one index higher:

$$\begin{array}{ccccccc} H_{d+1}(X_{d+1}) & \xrightarrow{j_{d+1}} & H_{d+1}(X_{d+1}, X_d) & \xrightarrow{\partial^c_{d+1}} & H_d(X_d) & \xrightarrow{i_d} & H_d(X_{d+1}) \\ & & & \searrow^{\partial^{CW}_{d+1}} & \downarrow{\scriptstyle j_d} & & \\ & & & & H_d(X_d, X_{d-1}) & & \end{array} \tag{8.4}$$

For $\alpha \in H_{d+1}(X_{d+1}, X_d)$, we have $j_d(\partial^c_{d+1}(\alpha)) = \partial^{CW}_{d+1}(\alpha) \in B^{CW}_d(X)$, hence $\tilde{j}_d(\partial^c_{d+1}(\alpha)) = 0$ in $H^{CW}_d(X)$, which shows $\partial^c_{d+1}(\alpha) \in \operatorname{Ker}\tilde{j}_d$.

Second, let us show that $\operatorname{Ker}\tilde{j}_d \subseteq \operatorname{Im}\partial^c_{d+1}$. Take $\alpha \in H_d(X)$, such that $\tilde{j}_d(\alpha) = 0$. This means that $[j_d(\alpha)] = 0$, which in turn means $j_d(\alpha) \in B^{CW}_d(X)$. Therefore, there exists $\beta \in H_{d+1}(X_{d+1}, X_d)$, such that $\partial^{CW}_{d+1}(\beta) = j_d(\alpha)$. However $\partial^{CW}_{d+1}(\beta) = j_d(\partial^c_{d+1}(\beta))$, so $j_d(\alpha - \partial^c_{d+1}(\beta)) = 0$. The injectivity of j_d implies that $\alpha = \partial^c_{d+1}(\beta)$, which is precisely what was to be demonstrated.

Proof of Fact 3. Take $[\alpha] \in H^{CW}_d(X)$. We have $\alpha \in C^{CW}_d(X) = H_d(X_d, X_{d-1})$, such that $\partial^{CW}_d(\alpha) = 0$. We have $\partial^{CW}_d(\alpha) = j_{d-1}(\partial^c_d(\alpha))$. Since the map j_{d-1} is injective, this implies $\partial^c_d(\alpha) = 0$. On the other hand, the horizontal row in diagram (8.3) is exact at $H_d(X_d, X_{d-1})$, so $\alpha \in \operatorname{Im} j_d$. So there exists $\beta \in H_d(X_d)$, such that $j_d(\beta) = \alpha$, which means $\tilde{j}_d(\beta) = [\alpha]$, and the statement is proved.

Proof of Fact 4. The horizontal row in diagram (8.4) is exact at $H_d(X_d)$. Furthermore, i_d is surjective, since $H_d(X_{d+1}, X_d) = 0$. This yields an isomorphism $H_d(X_{d+1}) \approx H_d(X_d)/\operatorname{Im} \partial^c_{d+1}$. However, we also have an isomorphism $H_d(X) \approx H_d(X_{d+1})$, so the fact is proved. $\square$

Exercises

(1) For an arbitrary continuous map $f : X \to Y$, let susp f denote the induced map on the corresponding suspensions susp f : susp $X \to$ susp Y. Assume $f : S^n \to S^n$ is a continuous map. Calculate the winding number of susp f in terms of $\deg f$.

(2) Fix a positive integer n. Show that any integer can be realized as the winding number of a map $f : S^n \to S^n$.

(3) Show that in the special case of simplicial complexes, the incidence numbers are ± 1 or 0, depending on mutual orientations of simplices and whether one belongs to the boundary of the other one.

(4) For the following topological spaces find an explicit CW decomposition and then use it to calculate cellular homology:
   (a) an n-sphere S^n;
   (b) real projective space $\mathbb{RP}^n$;
   (c) complex projective space $\mathbb{CP}^n$;
   (d) an n-torus T^n.

(5) Use the cellular homology approach to calculate by hand the homology groups of the infinite-dimensional sphere S^∞ and the infinite-dimensional projective space $\mathbb{RP}^\infty$.

Suggested further reading for Parts 1 and 2

In the first eight chapters of this book we have tried to provide the reader with the motivation and the first impression of algebraic topology. In our limited space, we could do not do more than to scratch the surface and to whet his or her appetite for more. Algebraic topology is a deep subject with many ramifications. In the remainder of the book we will concentrate on the subject of discrete Morse theory. To do a little bit of justice to the rest and to assist the reader in the quest of mastering this mathematical discipline, we have chosen to provide a few reading suggestions below. We split our recommendations in different subareas.

General texts on algebraic topology.

There are many excellent textbook style introductions to algebraic topology. For the reader primarily interested in homology theory we recommend the accessible text by Vick, [**Vi94**], as an entry point. A comprehensive, yet still equally accessible introduction can also be found in Munkres, [**Mu84**].

A modern treatment can be found in Hatcher, [**Hat02**]. This is a wonderful text, available freely online, whose graphic presentation remains an inspiration for this author to this day.

A reader who is looking for a broad approach combined with motivation and appealing intuitive pictures, may find the book by Fomenko, Fuchs, and Gutenmacher, [**FFG86**], indespensable.

The short *blue* book by May, [**May99**], is a gem in the rough for anybody willing to invest time in filling details, having the great benefit of getting much deeper insight into the subject than from a regular textbook alone.

Furthermore, there are a number of further beautiful texts, ranging from historically significant textbooks by Greenberg and Harper, [**GH81**], Spanier, [**Sp95**], and Switzer, [**Sw02**], to modern texts by Fulton, [**Fu95**], emphasizing the geometric approach, and Davis and Kirk, [**DK01**], which really provides a good introduction to many topics across the board, from obstruction theory to spectral sequences. These texts can each be used as the main source of study, but at the very least, they will be useful as complimentary literature in any serious course in algebraic topology.

As far as the specific topics of algebraic topology are concerned, we recommend Milnor, [**Mi63**], and Milnor and Stasheff, [**MS74**], for the classic introductions to Morse theory, and to the theory of characteristic classes. Finally, in the author's opinion, the book by McCleary, [**McC01**], still remains the best introduction to spectral sequences.

Homological algebra.

This author admittedly has a weak point for the amazing book by Gelfand and Manin, [**GM03**]. Although terse at times, it provides an unparalleled intution, combined with stunning vistas across the mathematical landscape.

A more traditional textbook approach can be found in another favourite: the book by Weibel, [**We94**]. That, or the book of Gelfand and Manin are our recommendation for the first foray into the world of homological algebra.

As further quality sources we recommend the historical texts by Hilton and Stammbach, [**HS97**], and Mac Lane, [**McL67**], as well as more modern texts by Osborne, [**Os00**], and Rotman, [**Ro09**].

Category theory.

While there are many good texts on category theory, in our opinion the book by Mac Lane, [**McL98**], stands out, and we recommend it as an entry point. Many aspects can also be found in the already mentioned [**GM03**], and, more humbly, in [**Ko08**].

Simplicial objects.

The thinking presented in our brief introduction to semisimplicial sets can be vastly generalized to other categories. For the classical introduction into *all things simplicial* we recommend the book by May, [**May92**].

Applied topology.

This is a growing subject, where other aspects of the theory, as well as different types of complexes, play a role. We recommend the book by Kaczynski, Mischaikow, and Mrozek, [**KMM04**], for computational aspects, where also the grid cubical complexes can be found.

The reader interested in branching into applications of topological methods in discrete mathematics and combinatorics may want to look at the first book by this author, [**Ko08**].

Part 3

Basic Discrete Morse Theory

Chapter 9

Simplicial Collapses

9.1. Collapses in abstract simplicial complexes

9.1.1. Elementary simplicial collapses. We have now arrived at the point in time when we would like to start investigating in some detail the notion of *simplicial collapse.* The prototypical example of such an operation is the removal of a leaf from a tree, or more generally, the removal of a vertex of valency 1 from any graph.

In general, an elementary simplicial collapse is the removal of a simplex together with one of its boundary simplices in such a way that the remaining structure is still an abstract simplicial complex. (See Figure 9.1.) This can be formalized as follows.

Definition 9.1. Let $\mathcal{K}$ be an abstract simplicial complex. Assume the simplices $\sigma, \tau \in \mathcal{K}$ satisfy the following two conditions:

(1) τ is a boundary simplex of σ of codimension 1, in other words, $\dim \tau = \dim \sigma - 1$;

(2) the only simplices of $\mathcal{K}$ which contain τ are σ and τ.

The removal of the simplices σ and τ from $\mathcal{K}$ is called an *elementary simplicial collapse.*

In this text we will mostly abbreviate this to just saying that we have a *simplicial collapse*, and reserve the term elementary simplicial collapse for the situations where it might be unclear what type of collapse we are using.

Note that the conditions of Definition 9.1 imply that σ must be a maximal simplex, since any simplex which contains σ would also contain τ.

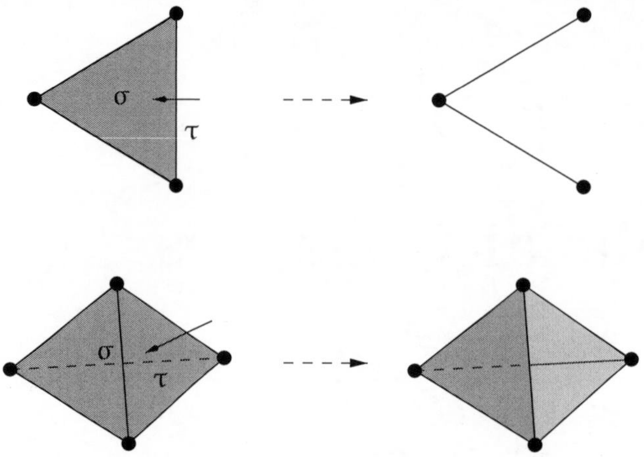

Figure 9.1. Examples of elementary simplicial collapses.

Proposition 9.2. *Let $\mathcal{K}$ be an abstract simplicial complex with the ground set S, and let σ and τ be simplices of $\mathcal{K}$ satisfying the conditions of Definition* 9.1. *Then the resulting set $\mathcal{K} \setminus \{\sigma, \tau\}$ is again an abstract simplicial complex.*[1]

Proof. Take an arbitrary simplex $\gamma \in \mathcal{K} \setminus \{\sigma, \tau\}$, and pick $\rho \subset \gamma$. We cannot have $\rho = \sigma$, since σ is a maximal simplex, while ρ is strictly contained in γ. Furthermore, we cannot have $\rho = \tau$, since the only simplex which strictly contains τ is σ, so we would have $\sigma = \gamma$, clearly contradicting our assumptions. We conclude that $\rho \in \mathcal{K} \setminus \{\sigma, \tau\}$. This verifies that $\mathcal{K} \setminus \{\sigma, \tau\}$ is again an abstract simplicial complex when the ground set is correctly adjusted. □

In the situation described in Definition 9.1 the simplex τ is called *free*. Clearly, if the given simplicial complex does not have any free simplices, then no simplicial collapses are possible.

As an example, let us consider the simplicial complex in the upper left corner of Figure 9.2. The free simplices are $\{1, 2\}$, $\{2, 3\}$, and $\{1, 3\}$. Two possible sequences of simplicial collapses are shown in Figure 9.2. These sequences lead to simplicial subcomplexes which are not isomorphic and which do not allow further elementary collapses. Even worse, it may happen that we start with a collapsible simplicial complex, but by following the "wrong" collapsing sequence end up with a non-collapsible one. This shows that the order in which the collapses are performed is of utmost importance.

Finally, let us spend a moment's thought on a somewhat degenerate case. Recall that almost always we include the empty set among the simplices of

[1] The ground set of $\mathcal{K} \setminus \{\sigma, \tau\}$ is S if $\dim \tau \geqslant 1$, it is $S \setminus \tau$ if $\dim \tau = 0$, and it is $\emptyset$ if $\dim \sigma = 0$.

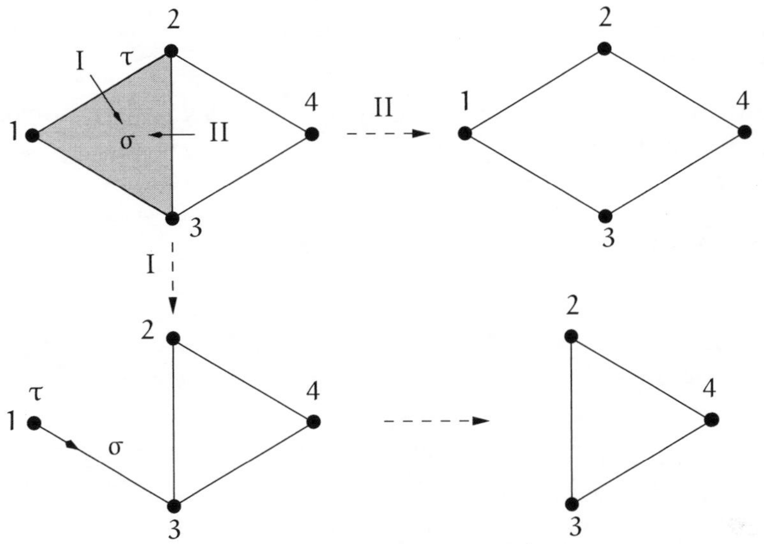

Figure 9.2. Two sequences of elementary simplicial collapses.

a simplicial complex. The only exception of this rule is the so-called void complex which has no simplices at all. There is exactly one situation in which the empty simplex is free: namely, if we consider the abstract simplicial complex which has exactly one vertex v. In that case, removing the simplices $\{v\}$ and $\emptyset$ is a valid simplicial collapse, and the resulting simplicial complex is the void one.

9.1.2. Collapsible simplicial complexes.

Once we start considering the simplicial collapses, it is only natural to look at those abstract simplicial complexes for which *all* the simplices can be successively removed in this manner.

Definition 9.3. An abstract simplicial complex $\mathcal{K}$ is called *collapsible* if there exists a sequence of simplicial collapses reducing $\mathcal{K}$ to the void simplicial complex.

Note that in particular the void simplicial complex, or the complex consisting of a single vertex are collapsible, whereas the empty simplicial complex is not collapsible.

As an alternative to Definition 9.3 one could also declare, as a basis, that all simplicial complexes with one vertex are collapsible, and then say that $\mathcal{K}$ is collapsible if it can be collapsed onto one of its vertices.[2] That definition would be fine as well for most purposes. From our point of view,

[2]As a matter of fact, in this case $\mathcal{K}$ can be collapsed to *any* of its vertices.

it has a slight disadvantage that the vertex to which the simplicial complex is collapsed is not in any way fixed canonically; instead it has to be chosen. Definition 9.3 avoids the necessity of making such a choice.

Definition 9.4. When an abstract simplicial complex $\mathcal{K}_2$ can be obtained from another abstract simplicial complex $\mathcal{K}_1$ via a sequence of elementary collapses, we say that $\mathcal{K}_1$ *can be collapsed to* $\mathcal{K}_2$. We then write $\mathcal{K}_1 \searrow \mathcal{K}_2$.

This is clearly a transitive relation: $\mathcal{K}_1 \searrow \mathcal{K}_2$ together with $\mathcal{K}_2 \searrow \mathcal{K}_3$ will imply $\mathcal{K}_1 \searrow \mathcal{K}_3$.

Proposition 9.5. *Assume that an abstract simplicial complex $\mathcal{K}_1$ can be collapsed to its subcomplex $\mathcal{K}_2$. Then the (reduced) Euler characteristic of $\mathcal{K}_1$ and $\mathcal{K}_2$ must be equal.*

In particular, the reduced Euler characteristic of a collapsible simplicial complex is always equal to 0.

Proof. Since $\mathcal{K}_2$ can be obtained from $\mathcal{K}_1$ by a sequence of simplicial collapses, it is enough to check that a single simplicial collapse does not change the Euler characteristic.

Note that as a result of a simplicial collapse, the simplices are removed in pairs. The two simplices which form such a pair must have different parities, so their total contribution to the Euler characteristic is 0. Clearly, removing such a pair will not change the Euler characteristic.

The last statement of the proposition follows from the fact that a collapsible abstract simplicial complex can be collapsed to the void complex. The latter has the reduced Euler characteristic equal to 0. □

When we have abstract simplicial complexes $\mathcal{K}_1$ and $\mathcal{K}_2$ such that $\mathcal{K}_1 \searrow \mathcal{K}_2$, then we can talk about various *collapsing sequences* from $\mathcal{K}_1$ to $\mathcal{K}_2$. In particular, when $\mathcal{K}_1$ is collapsible, we can take $\mathcal{K}_2$ to be the void complex and talk about *collapsing sequences for* $\mathcal{K}_1$.

9.2. Collapses and topology

9.2.1. Deformation retracts. Let us start by recalling some standard terminology from point-set topology.

Definition 9.6. Let X be a topological space, let $A \subseteq X$, and let $i : A \to X$ be the inclusion map. A continuous map $f : X \to A$ is called

- a *retraction* if $f|_A = \mathrm{id}_A$;
- a *deformation retraction* if $i \circ f : X \to X$ is homotopic to the identity map id_X;

- a *strong deformation retraction* if there exists a homotopy $F : X \times I \to X$ between $i \circ f$ and id_X, which is constant on A, i.e., $F(a, t) = a$, for all $t \in I$ and $a \in A$.

Correspondingly, A is called a *retract*, a *deformation retract*, or a *strong deformation retract* of X. The situation is illustrated in Figure 9.3.

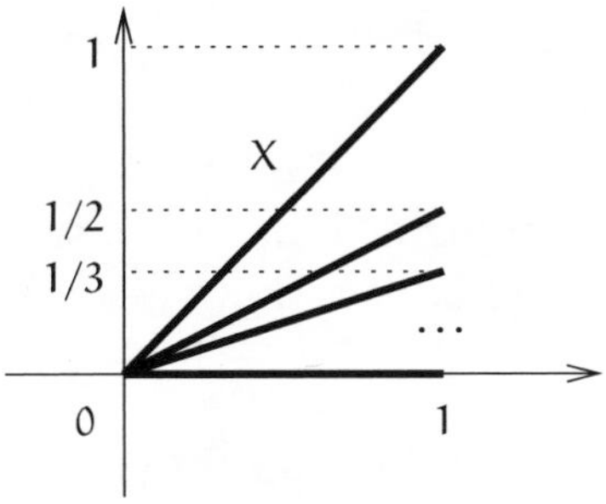

Figure 9.3. The interval $[0, 1]$ on the horizontal axis is a deformation retract of the space X, but it is not a strong deformation retract of X.

The notion of homotopy equivalence can be completely understood by means of strong deformation retracts, because of the following convenient fact.

Proposition 9.7. *Assume we are given topological spaces* X *and* Y, *and a continuous map* $f : X \to Y$. *The map* f *induces a homotopy equivalence if and only if the space* $X \times \{0\}$ *is a strong deformation retract of the mapping cylinder* $\mathrm{Cyl}(f)$.

Proof. One direction of this statement is simple. Assume the space $X \times \{0\}$ is a strong deformation retract of the mapping cylinder $\mathrm{Cyl}(f)$, and let $\varphi : \mathrm{Cyl}(f) \to X \times \{0\}$ be the corresponding strong deformation retraction. We set $g : Y \to X$ to be the composition

$$Y \xrightarrow{j} \mathrm{Cyl}(f) \xrightarrow{\varphi} X \times \{0\} \xrightarrow{p} X,$$

where $j : Y \hookrightarrow \mathrm{Cyl}(f)$ is the standard inclusion map, and $p : X \times \{0\} \to X$ is the forgetful map.

Proving the other direction is a bit technical. It would have to rely on the fact that the embedding of X into the mapping cylinder $\mathrm{Cyl}(f)$ as the copy $X \times \{0\}$ is what is called a *cofibration*. This would distract too much from our main subject of study. We therefore refer our reader to a standard text in algebraic topology, such as [**Hat02**], where this statement is proved as Corollary 0.21. □

Proposition 9.7 immediately implies the following neat statement.

Theorem 9.8. *Two topological spaces* X *and* Y *are homotopy equivalent if and only if there exists a third topological space which contains both* X *and* Y *as strong deformation retracts.*

Proof. Indeed, if X and Y are homotopy equivalent, then the mapping cylinder Cyl(f) of the corresponding homotopy equivalence f is this third space. Its base space is homeomorphic to Y, and it is the strong deformation retract of Cyl(f), as is the case for all mapping cylinders. On the other hand, by Proposition 9.7, the space Cyl(f) contains a strong deformation retract which is homeomorphic to X.

Reversely, since each strong deformation retraction is also a homotopy equivalence, the existence of such a third space will of course imply that $X \simeq Y$. □

9.2.2. Collapses and strong deformation retracts. Simplicial collapses provide a useful example of a strong deformation retraction.

Proposition 9.9. *An elementary simplicial collapse, removing simplices* σ *and* τ*, such that* $\dim \sigma = \dim \tau + 1 \geqslant 1$*, yields a strong deformation retraction of the geometric realizations of the corresponding abstract simplicial complexes.*

Proof. Assume we have an abstract simplicial complex $\mathcal{K}$, with simplices σ and τ such that τ is in the boundary of σ, $\dim \tau \geqslant 0$, and removing τ and σ yields an elementary collapse. Let X denote the geometric realization of $\mathcal{K}$, and let A denote the geometric realization of $\mathcal{K} \setminus \{\sigma, \tau\}$. Finally, let $i : A \to X$ denote the obvious inclusion map. Our goal is to define a continuous map $f : X \to A$, together with a homotopy $F : X \times I \to X$ between $i \circ f$ and id_X, which is constant on A.

Let d denote the dimension of σ. Assume $\sigma = \{v_0, \dots, v_d\}$, and assume $v_0 \notin \tau$; in other words, $\tau = \{v_1, \dots, v_d\}$. Pick an arbitrary point $x \in \sigma \subseteq |\mathcal{K}|$, and represent it in barycentric coordinates, say $x = \alpha_0 v_0 + \dots + \alpha_d v_d$, where $\alpha_0 + \dots + \alpha_d = 1$, and $0 \leqslant \alpha_i \leqslant 1$, for all $0 \leqslant i \leqslant d$. Set $\alpha := \min_{1 \leqslant i \leqslant d} \alpha_i$, and define

$$f(x) := (\alpha_0 + d\alpha)v_0 + (\alpha_1 - \alpha)v_1 + \dots + (\alpha_d - \alpha)v_d.$$

We can examine the coefficients to see that this map is well-defined. Since α is chosen to be the minimum of $\alpha_1, \dots, \alpha_d$, all the coefficients will be nonnegative. Obviously the sum of the coefficients is equal to 1. Furthermore, one of the coefficients $\alpha_1 - \alpha, \dots, \alpha_d - \alpha$ *must be* equal to 0, again because of the way α was chosen. This means precisely that $f(x) \in A$, and of course f is continuous. It can be extended to a continuous function $f : X \to A$ by setting it to be the identity outside of the (closed) simplex σ.

Next, we can define the homotopy $F : X \times I \to X$ as follows. For arbitrary $x \in \sigma$ and $0 \leqslant t \leqslant 1$, we set

$$F(x,t) := (\alpha_0 + td\alpha)v_0 + (\alpha_1 - t\alpha)v_1 + \cdots + (\alpha_d - t\alpha)v_d.$$

It is immediate that this is well-defined, continuous, and $F(x,0) = x$, while $F(x,1) = f(x)$. For $a \in A$, we have $\alpha = 0$, hence $F(a,t) = a$, for all t, and so f is a strong deformation retraction. □

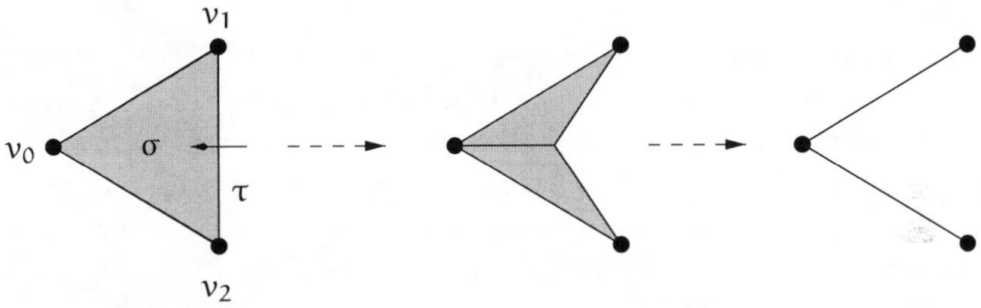

Figure 9.4. The homotopy corresponding to an elementary collapse.

Figure 9.4 provides a geometric illustration of the homotopy described in the proof of Proposition 9.9. This homotopy can be visualized as follows: connect by a piece of cord the vertex v_0 and the barycenter of the simplex τ; as time runs from 0 to 1 pull the barycenter towards v_0 so that it reaches it precisely at the time $t = 1$; let the rest of the simplex follow in linear fashion. More precisely, we take the stellar subdivision of the simplex τ, which induces the subdivision of σ into d smaller simplices; these simplices are then deformed linearly as the barycenter approaches v_0.

9.3. More on collapses

9.3.1. 1-dimensional simplicial complexes. Clearly, the case of 0-dimensional complexes is trivial: only the single vertex complex is collapsible. The case of 1-dimensional complexes is only slightly more complicated. Recall that a vertex whose valency is 1 is called a *leaf*. Clearly, elementary collapses where the free simplex has dimension 0 are precisely removals of leaves. Simplicial complexes which are not connected cannot be collapsible. In fact, simplicial collapses preserve the number of connected components. For this reason, it is enough to look at the connected complexes.

The following proposition provides the equivalence between various topological concepts in the case of 1-dimensional complexes.

Proposition 9.10. *Let G be a 1-dimensional abstract simplicial complex. The following statements are equivalent:*

(1) G *is collapsible;*

(2) G *is contractible;*

(3) *the groups* $\widetilde{H}_n(G;\mathbb{Z})$ *are trivial for all* n*;*

(4) G *is a tree.*

Proof. To start with, the implications (1) ⇒ (2) ⇒ (3) are simply true for all simplicial complexes. On the other hand, assume the groups $\widetilde{H}_0(G;\mathbb{Z})$ and $\widetilde{H}_1(G;\mathbb{Z})$ are trivial. The first assumption says that G is connected. The second assumption says that G does not have any cycles, so then G is a tree, and we have (3) ⇒ (4).

Now let G be a tree with n vertices, where $n \geqslant 2$. It is well known that G must have a leaf. Removing this leaf again gives a tree, and continuing in this matter we will collapse G to a vertex. In fact, we can collapse it to any vertex which is chosen a priori. Simply declare this vertex to be a root and collapse all the edges towards that vertex. This shows that trees are collapsible, i.e., (4) ⇒ (1), and we have proved the whole equivalence statement. □

Definition 9.11. We say that a graph G is *leafless* if all its vertices have valency at least 2.

When G is a graph, and H a subgraph, we say that H is a *leafless subgraph* of G if any vertex of H is adjacent to at least two edges of H.

For example, cycles in a graph are leafless subgraphs. In general, we can see that a connected graph G does not have any leafless subgraphs if and only if it is a tree. Indeed, if G is a tree, then any of its subgraphs is a forest, hence has leaves. Reversely, if a connected graph G does not have any leafless subgraphs, it cannot have cycles, as these are leafless. Therefore, it must be a tree.

Clearly, the union of any two leafless subgraphs of a graph is again a leafless subgraph. This justifies the following definition.

Definition 9.12. Given a graph G, we let Core(G) denote the union of all leafless subgraphs of G.

By what is said above, the graph Core(G) is the unique maximal leafless subgraph of G. Furthermore, since Core(G) itself is leafless, we have Core(Core(G)) = Core(G).

The following simple observation provides the crucial link to simplicial collapses.

Proposition 9.13. *Assume a graph* G *can be collapsed to* H*, and assume* K *is a leafless subgraph of* G*. Then* K *is contained in* H.

Proof. If K is not contained in H, then a part of it was collapsed when we went from G to H. Let ν be the first vertex of K which was collapsed in this process. The valency of ν in K is at least 2, hence at the time when ν was collapsed, its valency in what is left of G at this point is also at least 2, yielding a contradiction. □

In particular, we see that no matter how much we collapse in G, we can never collapse any part of Core(G).

Corollary 9.14. *Assume* G *is an arbitrary connected graph, which is not a tree. The following statements are true:*

(1) G *can be collapsed to* Core(G).

(2) *If* G *can be collapsed to* H, *then* Core(G) = Core(H).

Proof. To show (1) assume that G was collapsed to a subgraph H, which cannot be collapsed any further. Since G is connected, so must be H. Furthermore, G is not a tree, so H is not an isolated vertex. We conclude that all of the vertices have valency at least 2 in H. We know that H contains Core(G), by Proposition 9.13. The argument above shows that Core(G) contains H, so H = Core(G).

To see (2), note that any leafless subgraph of H is also a leafless subgraph of G, so Core(G) must contain Core(H). On the other hand, Core(G) is contained in H and is leafless in H, so Core(H) must contain Core(G). □

We have now seen that any graph G contains a special subgraph Core(G), such that no matter how we proceed in collapsing G eventually we will end up with Core(G), at which point we will have to stop.

We have defined Core(G) as the union of all leafless subgraphs of G. Alternatively, this subgraph can be defined directly, using the following terminology.

Definition 9.15. Assume that G is an arbitrary connected graph. An edge e of G is called a *tree-bridge* if

(1) it is a bridge, in other words, the graph obtained from G by removal of e, called $G \setminus e$, consists of two connected components;

(2) one of these connected components is a tree.

Let NTB(G) denote the subgraph of G whose edges are all the edges of G which are *not* tree-bridges, and whose vertices are all the vertices of G which are adjacent to one of these edges.

Proposition 9.16. *Let* G *be an arbitrary connected graph. Then, the subgraphs* Core(G) *and* NTB(G) *are equal.*

Proof. First, let e be an edge of G, such that e is a tree-bridge. Let $G \setminus e$ consist of two connected components A and B, where B is a tree. Let v denote the vertex of e contained in B. Taking v as a root of B, we can collapse B to v, after which we can collapse e. This means that e cannot be contained in $\text{Core}(G)$, so we have shown that $\text{Core}(G)$ is contained in $\text{NTB}(G)$.

On the other hand, assume e is not a tree-bridge. If the graph $G \setminus e$ is connected, then e is contained in a cycle, and hence e is contained in $\text{Core}(G)$. Otherwise, $G \setminus e$ has two connected components A and B, none of which is a tree. Let C be a cycle contained in A, let D be a cycle contained in B, and let P be any path connecting an arbitrary vertex in C to an arbitrary vertex in D. By what is said above, this path must contain e. On the other hand, the union of A, B, and P is clearly a leafless subgraph of G. It contains e, so e is contained in $\text{Core}(G)$. This means that $\text{NTB}(G)$ is contained in $\text{Core}(G)$. □

As a final remark in this section, let us say a few words about collapsing sequences in simplicial complexes of dimension 2 or higher. Indeed, in this case things get much more complicated, and no analog of Proposition 9.10 or Corollary 9.14 can possibly hold. For instance, as Figure 9.2 illustrates, it is no longer true that each simplicial complex has some sort of unique backbone, into which it can be collapsed. In fact, more than that, starting from dimension 3, we need to begin to distinguish between the notions of collapsible complexes and *sustainably* collapsible complexes. The latter notion will be introduced in Subsection 9.3.3.

9.3.2. The compound collapses.

There is a natural generalization of the notion of the elementary simplicial collapse in which the dimension gap between the two simplices defining the collapse is more than one.

Definition 9.17. Let $\mathcal{K}$ be an abstract simplicial complex, and let σ and τ be some simplices of $\mathcal{K}$, such that the following conditions are satisfied:

(1) $\tau \subset \sigma$, in particular, $\dim \tau < \dim \sigma$;

(2) all simplices containing τ must be contained in σ.

A *compound simplicial collapse* of $\mathcal{K}$ is the removal of all simplices γ, such that $\tau \subseteq \gamma \subseteq \sigma$.

For brevity, we shall say that the pair (σ, τ) itself *is* a compound simplicial collapse.

As a curious special case we note that when the simplicial complex $\mathcal{K}$ is just a simplex, there is a compound collapse which removes *all simplices* of $\mathcal{K}$ in one move. The empty simplex is removed as well, so with just one compound collapse, the complex $\mathcal{K}$ is reduced to the void simplicial complex.

Obviously, any elementary simplicial collapse is also a compound simplicial collapse in the sense of Definition 9.17. On the other hand, any compound simplicial collapse can be represented by a sequence of elementary simplicial collapses, as the next proposition shows.

Proposition 9.18. *Let $\mathcal{K}$ be an abstract simplicial complex, and let σ and τ be some simplices of $\mathcal{K}$, such that (σ, τ) is a compound simplicial collapse. Set $d := \dim \sigma - \dim \tau$, and let Σ be the $(d-1)$-simplex, whose set of vertices is identified with $\sigma \setminus \tau$.*

Now let $((\rho_1, \gamma_1), \dots, (\rho_t, \gamma_t))$ be an arbitrary collapsing sequence of Σ, with the last step removing some vertex together with the empty simplex.[3] Then, $((\rho_1 \cup \tau, \gamma_1 \cup \tau), \dots, (\rho_t \cup \tau, \gamma_t \cup \tau))$ is a collapsing sequence resulting in the compound collapse (σ, τ).

Proof. Assume the contrary, and let k be the minimal index such that $(\rho_k \cup \tau, \gamma_k \cup \tau)$ is not a valid elementary collapse. This can only happen if there is a simplex η, such that $\eta \supset \gamma_k \cup \tau$ and $\eta \neq \rho_k \cup \tau$. Since (σ, τ) is a compound simplicial collapse, and $\eta \supset \tau$, we must have $\eta \subseteq \sigma$. But then there exists i, such that $\eta = \rho_i \cup \tau$ or $\eta = \gamma_i \cup \tau$. Since $((\rho_1, \gamma_1), \dots, (\rho_t, \gamma_t))$ is a valid collapsing sequence, and $\eta \setminus \tau \supset \gamma_k$, we must have $i < k$, leading to a contradiction, since this means that $\eta \setminus \tau \in \{\rho_1, \dots, \rho_{k-1}, \gamma_1, \dots, \gamma_{k-1}\}$, so η has already been removed. □

It is easy to produce a specific sequence of elementary collapses emulating the compound collapse (σ, τ). To do that, fix some vertex v which belongs to σ, but not to τ. Take all the simplices in σ which contain $\tau \cup \{v\}$ and arrange them so that the dimension does not increase. Let us assume this gives the sequence of simplices of $\mathcal{K}$, which we call $\rho_1, \dots, \rho_t$. Then the sequence $(\rho_1, \rho_1 \setminus v), \dots, (\rho_t, \rho_t \setminus v)$ is the desired sequence of elementary collapses.

In general, let sc_n denote the number of the collapsing sequences of an n-simplex. The magnitude of that number is investigated in Exercise (5) of this chapter.

Corollary 9.19. *A sequence of compound collapses from an abstract simplicial complex $\mathcal{K}_1$ to an abstract simplicial complex $\mathcal{K}_2$ yields a strong deformation retraction, and hence also a homotopy equivalence between the corresponding geometric realizations $|\mathcal{K}_1|$ and $|\mathcal{K}_2|$.*

In particular, the geometric realization of a collapsible abstract simplicial complex is contractible.

[3] Clearly, $t = 2^{d-1}$, but we do not need that here.

Proof. Any compound collapse is a sequence of elementary ones, so all the statements follow immediately by repeated application of Proposition 9.9. □

9.3.3. Sustainably collapsible simplicial complexes. From a constructive point of view, when we know that an abstract simplicial complex $\mathcal{K}$ is collapsible, we may try to find a collapsing sequence by first finding some collapse which can be performed in $\mathcal{K}$, and then continuing the collapsing procedure with whatever collapses are available. Unfortunately, it may very well happen that, even when starting with a collapsible simplicial complex, by choosing an unfortunate initial sequence of collapses, we could arrive at a subcomplex where no further collapses are possible. This phenomenon is formally managed by the following definition.

Definition 9.20. An abstract simplicial complex $\mathcal{K}$ is called *sustainably collapsible* if any simplicial complex obtained from $\mathcal{K}$ by a sequence of simplicial collapses is itself collapsible.

Note that it does not matter for Definition 9.20 whether or not we allow compound collapses.

Here is a very rough sketch of how a collapsible abstract simplicial complex which is *not* sustainably collapsible can be obtained. Take a simplicial subdivision of the Dunce hat. Say we get a 2-dimensional simplicial complex $\mathcal{K}$. Take the cylinder $\mathcal{K} \times [0, 1]$. There is a standard way to subdivide this cylinder so that on one hand the obtained simplicial complex $\mathcal{H}$ can be collapsed to $\mathcal{K}$ (this part is easy), and on the other hand $\mathcal{H}$ is collapsible (this is more difficult, and needs to use specific structure of the Dunce hat). We omit the technical details.

Definition 9.21. Assume $\mathcal{K}$ is an abstract simplicial complex, and $\mathcal{H}$ is a subcomplex. We say that $\mathcal{K}$ is *sustainably collapsible to* $\mathcal{H}$ if any simplicial complex, which is obtained from $\mathcal{K}$ by a sequence of collapses, and contains $\mathcal{H}$, can then be further collapsed to $\mathcal{H}$.

When $\mathcal{K}$ is sustainably collapsible to $\mathcal{H}$ we shall write $\mathcal{K} \searrow_s \mathcal{H}$. The careful reader should note at this point that $\mathcal{K}_1 \searrow_s \mathcal{K}_2$ and $\mathcal{K}_2 \searrow_s \mathcal{K}_3$ will not necessarily imply that $\mathcal{K}_1 \searrow_s \mathcal{K}_3$. We leave it as an exercise.

On the positive side, in the 1-dimensional case, an examination of our proof of Corollary 9.14 reveals that we have actually proved that G is sustainably collapsible to Core(G).

Above we have mentioned an example of a 3-dimensional collapsible, but not sustainable collapsible, simplicial complex. The next proposition shows that this example has the minimal possible dimension.

Proposition 9.22. *Let $\mathcal{K}$ be a 2-dimensional collapsible simplicial complex. Then $\mathcal{K}$ is also sustainably collapsible.*

Proof. Assume this is not the case, and let $\mathcal{H}$ be a subcomplex of $\mathcal{K}$, such that $\mathcal{K}$ can be collapsed to $\mathcal{H}$, but no further collapses are possible in $\mathcal{H}$.

First, assume that $\mathcal{H}$ has dimension 2. Consider an arbitrary collapsing sequence of $\mathcal{K}$, and let σ be the first one among the 2-simplices of $\mathcal{H}$ which is collapsed using this sequence. Let us say the corresponding collapse is (σ, e), where e is some edge of σ. Since we cannot collapse (σ, e) in $\mathcal{H}$, we know that e must belong to at least two 2-simplices of $\mathcal{H}$. By our choice, this other simplex occurs later in the fixed collapsing sequence of $\mathcal{K}$. This means that e is not a free edge yet, so the collapse (σ, e) cannot be performed, and we arrive at a contradiction.

Assume now that $\mathcal{H}$ has dimension 1. Since $\mathcal{H}$ is not collapsible, by Proposition 9.10, it is also not contractible. This, however, is impossible, since $\mathcal{K}$ was collapsed to $\mathcal{H}$, $\mathcal{K}$ is contractible, and collapses are strong deformation retractions. This yields a contradiction, and we have shown that such a subcomplex $\mathcal{H}$ cannot exist. □

9.4. Collapses and chain homotopy

Let us now visualize an elementary simplicial collapse as a chain homotopy. Assume $\mathcal{K}$ is an abstract simplicial complex and (σ, τ) is an elementary collapse, such that $d = \dim \tau \geqslant 0$. We work with the integer coefficients. Changing orientations if necessary we can assume, without loss of generality, that τ is contained in the boundary of σ with coefficient 1. Let us now define a chain map $f : \mathcal{C}(\mathcal{K}) \to \mathcal{C}(\mathcal{K})$ by setting

$$\begin{aligned} f(\tau) &:= \tau - \partial\sigma, \\ f(\sigma) &:= 0, \\ f(\gamma) &:= \gamma, \text{ if } \gamma \neq \sigma, \tau, \end{aligned}$$

for simplices, and then extending linearly.

Define furthermore a sequence of maps $\Phi = (\Phi_i)_i$, where $\Phi_i : C_i(\mathcal{K}) \to C_{i+1}(\mathcal{K})$, for all i, by setting, again for simplices,

$$\begin{aligned} \Phi_d(\tau) &:= \sigma, \\ \Phi_i(\gamma) &:= 0, \text{ if } \gamma \neq \tau. \end{aligned}$$

Proposition 9.23. *The sequence of maps Φ is a chain homotopy between the chain map f and the identity map $\mathrm{id}_{\mathcal{C}(\mathcal{K})}$.*

Proof. Set $g := \mathrm{id}_{\mathcal{C}(\mathcal{K})}$. We verify the statement of the proposition by a direct calculation. First, for the map $g - f$, we obtain

$$(g - f)(\tau) = \tau - (\tau - \partial\sigma) = \partial\sigma,$$
$$(g - f)(\sigma) = \sigma,$$
$$(g - f)(\gamma) = 0, \text{ if } \gamma \neq \sigma, \tau.$$

Second, we have

$$(\partial \circ \Phi)(\tau) = \partial\sigma,$$
$$(\partial \circ \Phi)(\gamma) = 0, \text{ if } \gamma \neq \tau.$$

And finally, we have

$$(\Phi \circ \partial)(\sigma) = \sigma,$$
$$(\Phi \circ \partial)(\gamma) = 0, \text{ if } \gamma \neq \sigma,$$

where the last two equalities use the fact that (σ, τ) is an elementary collapse, so τ is contained in $\partial\gamma$, if and only if $\gamma = \sigma$. Combining these calculations, we see that $\partial \circ \Phi + \Phi \circ \partial = g - f$, thus proving our proposition. □

9.5. A glimpse of simple homotopy theory

As we have already seen, the converse of the second statement of Corollary 9.19 is not true: there are abstract simplicial complexes which are not collapsible, yet their geometric realizations are contractible. However, it turns out that the following weaker statement is true.

Theorem 9.24. *A geometric realization of a finite abstract simplicial complex $\mathcal{K}$ is contractible if and only if there exists an abstract simplicial complex $\widetilde{\mathcal{K}}$ such that*

(1) *$\mathcal{K}$ is a simplicial subcomplex of $\widetilde{\mathcal{K}}$, and $\widetilde{\mathcal{K}}$ can be collapsed to $\mathcal{K}$;*

(2) *$\widetilde{\mathcal{K}}$ is collapsible.*

The proof of Theorem 9.24 is by no means straighforward. It requires a substantial theoretical build-up, and will not be presented here. Let us just mention at this point that a statement closely related to Theorem 9.24 is called the *Zeeman Conjecture* and it implies in particular the famous *Poincaré Conjecture.*

Theorem 9.24 motivates the introduction of further terminology.

Definition 9.25. Assume $\mathcal{K}$ is a simplicial complex and $\mathcal{K}'$ is obtained from $\mathcal{K}$ via an elementary simplicial collapse. Then we say that $\mathcal{K}$ is obtained from $\mathcal{K}'$ via an *elementary simplicial expansion* or just an elementary expansion.

Furthermore, we say that an abstract simplicial complex $\mathcal{K}$ is obtained from $\mathcal{K}'$ via a simplicial expansion if and only if $\mathcal{K}'$ is obtained from $\mathcal{K}$ via a simplicial collapse.[4]

As before, a simplicial expansion can be decomposed as a sequence of elementary simplicial expansions.

Theorem 9.24 can now be reformulated as saying that whenever a geometric realization of a finite abstract simplicial complex is contractible, there exists a sequence of simplicial collapses and simplicial expansions leading from $\mathcal{K}$ to a vertex.

More generally, one benefits from the following definition.

Definition 9.26. Two abstract simplicial complexes are said to have the same *simple homotopy type* if there exists a sequence of elementary collapses and expansions leading from one to the other. Such a sequence is called a *formal deformation.*

One can easily see that collapses and expansions commute in the following weak sense.

Proposition 9.27. *Assume $\mathcal{K}$ is a simplicial complex, where we first collapse and then expand. Then we could also do expansion first, followed by the collapse, with the same final result.*

Proposition 9.27 means that any sequence of elementary collapses and expansions can be replaced with a sequence of expansions followed by a sequence of collapses. Hence we have the following statement.

Proposition 9.28. *Two simplicial complexes have the same simple homotopy type if and only if there exists a third complex which collapses to each one of them.*

Let us look at an example of how Proposition 9.28 might work. Let us show that a barycentric subdivision of any abstract simplicial complex $\mathcal{K}$ has the same simple homotopy type as $\mathcal{K}$.

Proposition 9.29. *Let $|\mathcal{K}|$ be the geometric realization of an arbitrary finite abstract simplicial complex $\mathcal{K}$. Then there exists a formal deformation from $|\mathcal{K}|$ to $|\mathrm{Bd}\,\mathcal{K}|$.*

Proof. To start with, since the barycentric subdivision can be represented as a sequence of stellar subdivisions, see Subsection 2.7.8, it is enough to find a formal deformation leading from $|\mathcal{K}|$ to $|\mathrm{sd}(\mathcal{K},\sigma)|$, for an arbitrary

[4] Alternatively, the simplicial expansions are sometimes called *anti-collapses.*

simplex $\sigma \in \mathcal{K}$. One choice of such a deformation is a concatenation of two steps.

Step 1. Add a cone over $\mathrm{st}_{\mathcal{K}}\,\sigma$. More precisely, consider a new simplicial complex $\mathcal{K}'$, such that $V(\mathcal{K}') = V(\mathcal{K}) \cup \{v\}$, $\mathcal{K}$ is an induced subcomplex of $\mathcal{K}'$, and $\mathrm{lk}_{\mathcal{K}'}\,v = \mathrm{st}_{\mathcal{K}}\,\sigma$.

Step 2. Delete from $\mathcal{K}'$ all the simplices containing σ.

Since $\mathrm{st}_{\mathcal{K}}\,\sigma$ is a cone, in particular collapsible, Step 1 can be performed as a sequence of elementary expansions. Furthermore, Step 2 can be performed as a sequence of elementary collapses as follows. The set of the simplices which are to be deleted can be written as a disjoint union of sets A and B, where B is the set of all simplices which contain both σ and v. Clearly, adding v to a simplex is a bijection $\mu : A \to B$. Let $\tau_1 \dots, \tau_t$ be a reverse linear extension order on A, then $((\tau_1, \mu(\tau_1)), \dots, (\tau_t, \mu(\tau_t)))$ is an elementary collapsing sequence. Finally, we see that performing Steps 1 and 2, in this order, will yield a stellar subdivision of $|\mathcal{K}|$ at σ, and therefore our description is completed. □

Theorem 9.24 leads to a natural question: if the geometric realizations of two abstract simplicial complexes are homotopy equivalent, can we conclude that the abstract simplicial complexes themselves have the same simple homotopy type?

Theorem 9.8 tells us that if two topological spaces X and Y are homotopy equivalent, then there exists a third topological space which contains both X and Y as strong deformation retracts. Therefore, to positively answer the previous question, it would be enough to show that a strong deformation retraction preserves the simple homotopy type.

Unfortunately, this is not the case. The simple homotopy type is a much more fine invariant than the mere homotopy type. A sophisticated obstruction, called *Whitehead torsion*, will prevent homotopy equivalent spaces from having the same simple homotopy type. Still, this obstruction lives in the group algebra associated to the fundamental group of the spaces in question, so on the positive side, we have the following result.

Theorem 9.30. *Two simply connected finite abstract simplicial complexes are homotopy equivalent if and only if they have the same simple homotopy type.*

Exercises

(1) Show that a non-void collapsible simplicial complex can be collapsed to any of its vertices.

(2) Let T be a tree with n edges, and let $c(T)$ denote the number of ways T can be collapsed to a point.

(a) Calculate the value $c(T)$ for all trees T with at most 5 edges.

(b) Show that

$$2n! \geqslant c(T) \geqslant 2^n. \tag{9.1}$$

(c) Give a complete description of the sets of trees for which the bounds of Equation (9.1) are attained.

(3) (a) Assume T is a tree with n edges, $n \geqslant 3$, which contains a vertex of valency $\geqslant 3$. Show that

$$c(T) \geqslant 2!(2^n - 2).$$

Characterize the family of trees for which this bound is achieved.

(b) Assume T contains a vertex of valency $d \geqslant 4$. Show that

$$c(T) \geqslant 3!(2^n - 2n).$$

Characterize the family of trees for which this bound is achieved.

(c) Assume T contains a vertex of valency $d \geqslant 5$. Show that

$$c(T) \geqslant 4!(2^n - n^2 + n - 2).$$

Characterize the family of trees for which this bound is achieved.

(d) In the general case, show that

$$c(T) \geqslant (d-1)! \sum_{i=0}^{n-d+1} \binom{n-1}{i},$$

where d is the maximal vertex valency in T.

(4) For an arbitrary integer $n \geqslant 3$, let U_n denote the 2-dimensional simplicial complex obtained as a cone over a cycle with n edges. Alternatively, U_n can be obtained as a stellar triangulation of an n-gon. The simplicial complex U_n has $n+1$ vertices, $2n$ edges, and n triangles, with all triangles sharing a common vertex. It is clearly collapsible, and we let uc_n denote the number of its collapsing sequences.

(a) Calculate uc_3, and use it to enumerate all collapsing sequences of a 3-simplex.

(b) Calculate uc_4.

(5) Let sc_n denote the number of the collapsing sequences of an n-simplex, e.g., $\mathrm{sc}_1 = 2$, $\mathrm{sc}_2 = 12$.
   (a) Calculate sc_3.
   (b) Show that
$$\mathrm{sc}_n \geqslant (n+1)\prod_{k=1}^{n-1}\binom{n}{k}!.$$
   (c) Derive that $\log\log \mathrm{sc}_n = \Omega(n)$.

(6) Complete the proof of Proposition 9.7.

(7) Let $\mathcal{K}$ be an abstract simplicial complex. Describe a simplicial subdivision $\mathcal{H}$ of the cylinder $\mathcal{K} \times [0,1]$ such that the bottom copy $\mathcal{K} \times \{0\}$ is not further subdivided, and $\mathcal{H}$ can be collapsed to $\mathcal{K} \times \{0\}$.[5]

(8) Find a collapsible simplicial complex $\mathcal{K}$, such that there exists an elementary simplicial collapse of $\mathcal{K}$ producing a simplicial complex which is not collapsible.

(9) Define cubical collapses. Formulate and prove the cubical analogs of the main theorems of this chapter. What about polyhedral collapses?

(10) Find abstract simplicial complexes $\mathcal{K}$, $\mathcal{L}$, and $\mathcal{M}$, such that $\mathcal{K} \searrow_s \mathcal{L}$ and $\mathcal{L} \searrow_s \mathcal{M}$ are true, but $\mathcal{K} \searrow_s \mathcal{M}$ is false.

[5]This exercise assumes that you are familiar with the concept of arbitrary simplicial subdivisions.

Chapter 10

Organizing Collapsing Sequences

10.1. Face poset of an abstract simplicial complex

In order to learn how to keep track of various collapsing sequences, it is useful to introduce some combinatorial notions which encode the simplicial structure.

Definition 10.1. Let $\mathcal{K}$ be an arbitrary abstract simplicial complex. The *face poset* of $\mathcal{K}$ is a partially ordered set, which we denote by $\mathsf{F}(\mathcal{K})$, defined by the following:

- the elements of $\mathsf{F}(\mathcal{K})$ are all the simplices of $\mathcal{K}$, including the empty one;
- the partial order is given by the inclusion relation on the simplices, in other words, we set $\sigma \geqslant \tau$ as elements of $\mathsf{F}(\mathcal{K})$ if and only if $\sigma \supseteq \tau$ as simplices.

Note that sometimes one defines the face poset as the partially ordered set of all *non-empty* simplices. There are advantages to both conventions. When used to record collapses, it is handy to have the empty simplex included.

As an example, when $\mathcal{K}$ is the n-simplex, whose set of vertices is $[n]$, we obtain the partially ordered set consisting of all the subsets of $[n]$. This partially ordered set is called the *Boolean algebra*.

The next definition describes a procedure which in some sense is the reverse of taking the face poset. For this, recall that in a partially ordered

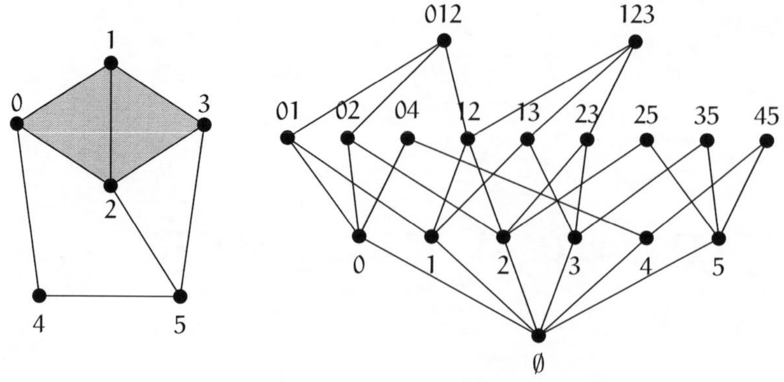

Figure 10.1. An abstract simplicial complex and its face poset.

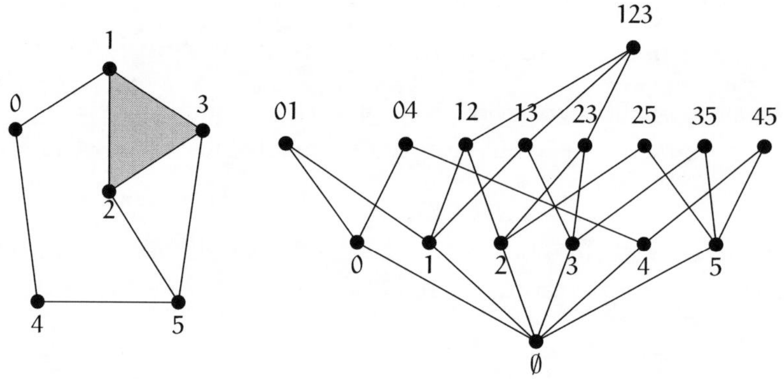

Figure 10.2. The effect of an elementary simplicial collapse $(\{0,1,2\},\{0,2\})$ on the face poset of the corresponding abstract simplicial complex.

set, a *chain* is a subset of elements which is totally ordered. In particular, a set consisting of a single element of P is a chain, and so is the empty set.

Definition 10.2. Let P be a partially ordered set. Its *order complex* is an abstract simplicial complex, which we denote by $\Delta(\mathsf{P})$, defined as follows:

- we take the elements of P as the vertices of $\Delta(\mathsf{P})$;
- the simplices of $\Delta(\mathsf{P})$ are precisely all the finite chains of P.

The next proposition describes the precise manner in which the constructions described in Definitions 10.1 and 10.2 interact. Before that, just a piece of notation: for any abstract simplicial complex $\mathcal{K}$, we denote the minimal element of $\mathsf{F}(\mathcal{K})$ by $\hat{0}$; it corresponds to the empty simplex.

Proposition 10.3.

(1) *Assume* $\mathcal{K}$ *is an abstract simplicial complex; then* $\Delta(\mathsf{F}(\mathcal{K}) \setminus \{\hat{0}\})$ *is the barycentric subdivision of* $\mathcal{K}$.

(2) *Assume* P *is a partially ordered set; then the poset* $\mathsf{F}((\Delta(\mathsf{P}))$ *is the poset of chains of* P*, including the empty one.*

Proof. Assume first that we have an abstract simplicial complex $\mathcal{K}$. Unwinding the definitions we see that the non-empty simplices of $\Delta(\mathsf{F}(\mathcal{K}) \setminus \{\hat{0}\})$ are all the totally ordered sets of non-empty simplices of $\mathcal{K}$. These, of course, are exactly the chains of $\mathsf{F}(\mathcal{K}) \setminus \{\hat{0}\}$, so comparing this with the description of the simplicial structure given in Definition 2.41 we arrive at the desired conclusion.

The second part involving the partially ordered set P is immediate as well, once the definitions of F and Δ have been unwinded. □

Most of the combinatorial constructions involving abstract simplicial complexes have their poset interpretation. Figure 10.2 shows the effect of an elementary simplicial collapse. Figures 10.3 and 10.4 show the meaning of the deletion and the link in the face poset.

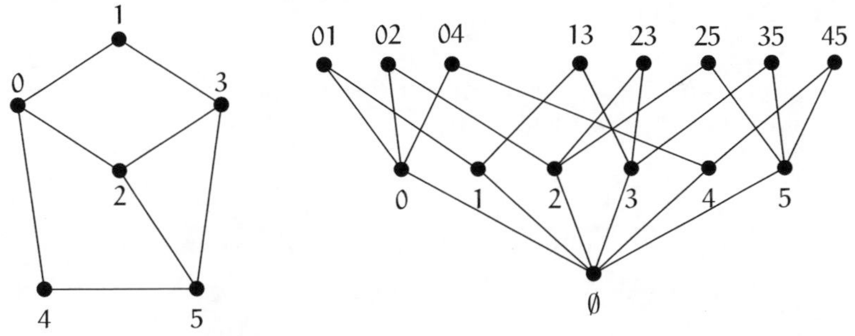

Figure 10.3. Deletion of the simplex $\{1, 2\}$ from the simplicial complex in Figure 10.1 and the corresponding face poset.

Figure 10.5 illustrates the case of the stellar subdivision. When passing from the face poset of an abstract simplicial complex to the face poset of its stellar subdivision one needs to perform the so-called *combinatorial blowup*. Before we proceed with the definition, recall the following terminology.

Let P be a poset, and choose a subset $\mathsf{A} \subseteq \mathsf{P}$. Consider the set S of all *lower bounds* for A, i.e., $\mathsf{S} := \{z \,|\, z \leqslant x,\ \forall x \in \mathsf{A}\}$. If the set S has a unique maximal element, then it is called the *meet* of A, and is denoted by $\bigwedge_{\mathsf{P}} \mathsf{A}$, or simply $\bigwedge \mathsf{A}$. The poset P is called a *meet-semilattice*, or simply a *semilattice*, if it has a meet for any non-empty finite subset.

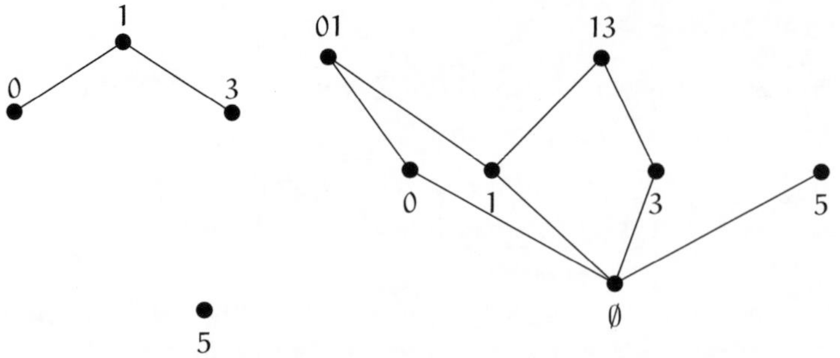

Figure 10.4. Link of the simplex {2} in the simplicial complex in Figure 10.1 and the corresponding face poset.

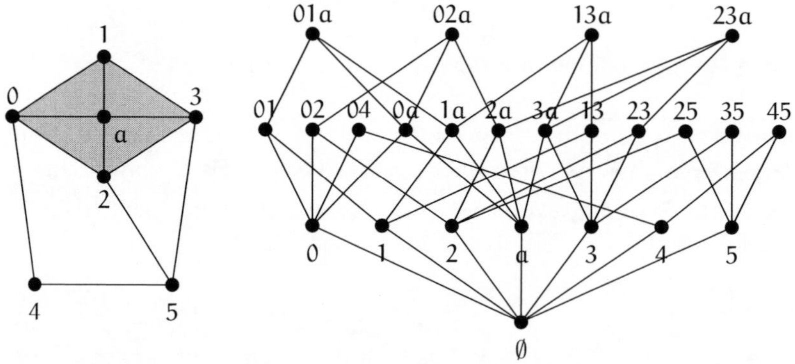

Figure 10.5. Stellar subdivision of the simplex {1, 2} in the simplicial complex in Figure 10.1 and the corresponding face poset.

When A consists of two elements, $A = \{x, y\}$, the meet of A is called the meet of x and y, and is denoted by $x \wedge_P y$, or simply by $x \wedge y$.

Dually, for a subset $A \subseteq P$. Consider the set S of all *upper bounds* for A, i.e., $S := \{z \mid z \geqslant x, \ \forall x \in A\}$. If the set S has a unique minimal element, then it is called the *join* of A, and is denoted by $\vee_P A$, or simply $\vee A$. For $A = \{x, y\}$ we write $x \vee_P y$, or simply $x \vee y$.

Definition 10.4. For a semilattice L and an element $a \in L$, $a \neq \hat{0}$,[1] we define a poset $\mathrm{Bl}_a L$, the *combinatorial blowup* of L at a, as follows. The elements of $\mathrm{Bl}_a L$ are given by

(1) $y \in L$, such that $y \not\geqslant a$;

(2) $\langle a, y \rangle$, for $y \in L$, such that $y \not\geqslant a$ and $y \vee_L a$ exists (in particular, $\left\langle a, \hat{0} \right\rangle$ can be thought of as the result of blowing up a).

The order relations in $\mathrm{Bl}_a L$ are given by

[1] Here, $\hat{0}$ denotes the unique minimal element of L.

(1) $y > z$ in $\mathrm{Bl}_a L$ if $y > z$ in L;

(2) $\langle a, y\rangle > \langle a, z\rangle$ in $\mathrm{Bl}_a L$ if $y > z$ in L;

(3) $\langle a, y\rangle > z$ in $\mathrm{Bl}_a L$ if $y \geqslant z$ in L,

where in all three cases $y, z \not\geqslant a$.

As a special case, we can easily describe the combinatorics of the simplicial complex obtained by taking an n-simplex, and taking the stellar subdivision of one of its simplices. Let $\mathcal{K}$ denote the n-simplex whose set of vertices is $[n]$. Pick $S \subseteq [n]$, and let σ be the corresponding simplex of $\mathcal{K}$. Then, the set of all the simplices of $\mathrm{Sd}_{\mathcal{K}}(\sigma)$ is given by

$$\{T \mid T \not\supseteq S\} \cup \{\langle a, T\rangle \mid T \not\supseteq S\},$$

where a is the symbol corresponding to the barycenter of σ. Note that the actual new vertex at the barycenter of σ is denoted by $\langle a, \emptyset\rangle$. The simplex inclusion rules are then simply

(1) the simplex indexed by T_1 contains the simplex indexed by T_2 if and only if $T_1 \supseteq T_2$;

(2) $\langle a, T_1\rangle$ contains $\langle a, T_2\rangle$ if and only if $T_1 \supseteq T_2$;

(3) $\langle a, T_1\rangle$ strictly contains T_2 if and only if $T_1 \supseteq T_2$,

where in all three cases $T_1, T_2 \not\supseteq S$.

10.2. Acyclic matchings

Matching is the combinatorial notion for the face posets corresponding to elementary simplicial collapses. Let us recall this concept from graph theory.

Definition 10.5. Let G be a graph whose set of vertices is V and whose set of edges is E. A *partial matching* in G is a set of edges $\{\{a_1, b_1\}, \dots, \{a_t, b_t\}\}$ such that all the vertices $\{a_1, \dots, a_t, b_1, \dots, b_t\}$ are distinct.

Our notion of the partial matching is flexible, in the sense that it includes the case where *all* the vertices are matched. This makes writing arguments easier. However, often it is useful to specifically point out that all the vertices have really been matched, in which case we may also call such a matching *a complete matching*. In this text, we shall never drop the adjective "complete", so when we simply say "matching", we shall always mean the partial matching.

It is often convenient to think of a matching in a formal way: namely, as a function $\mu : M \to M$, where M is a subset of the set of vertices of G. This function must satisfy the following two conditions:

- for all $v \in M$, the vertices v and $\mu(v)$ are connected by an edge, called the *matching edge*;

- for all $v \in M$, we have $\mu(\mu(v)) = v$.

The correspondence with the matchings is easy: M is the set of matched vertices, and each vertex $v \in M$ is matched to the vertex $\mu(v)$.

Matching theory is an extensive branch of graph theory, with many methods developed to find new matchings and to improve existing ones. We refer the reader to [**Lo86**] as a possible point of entry.

In general, there are many constructions which associate a graph to a poset P. The one we need here takes the set of vertices of P as the set of vertices of that graph, and then connects two elements by an edge if and only if one of these elements covers the other one. To this end, recall that for $x, y \in P$ we say that x *covers* y, and write $x \succ y$, if $x > y$ and there exists no $z \in P$, such that $x > z > y$. The obtained graph is called the *underlying graph of the Hasse diagram of* P.

Definition 10.6. A *partial matching* in a poset P is a partial matching in the underlying graph of the Hasse diagram of P. In other words, it is a subset $M \subseteq P$, together with a bijection $\mu : M \to M$, such that for all $v \in M$, the following two conditions are satisfied:

- either v covers $\mu(v)$, or vice versa;
- $\mu(\mu(v)) = v$.

We shall think about the set M as being a part of the information provided by the the function μ, so we shall simply say things like "assume we have a matching μ."

Given a bijection $\mu : M \to M$ as in Definition 10.6, for future reference, we introduce the following notation:

- $M^{\uparrow}$ is the subset of all $v \in M$, such that $\mu(v)$ is covered by v;
- $M^{\downarrow}$ is the subset of all $v \in M$, such that $\mu(v)$ covers v;
- $R(\mu)$ is the complement of M, i.e., $R(\mu) := P \setminus M$.

Note that $M^{\uparrow} \cup M^{\downarrow} = M$, the union is disjoint, and the maps $\mu : M^{\uparrow} \to M^{\downarrow}$ and $\mu : M^{\downarrow} \to M^{\uparrow}$ are well-defined bijections, which are inverses of each other. When μ is clear, we shall simply write R instead of $R(\mu)$.

As a more precise piece of notation, we write $\mu_{-}(v)$ instead of just $\mu(v)$ if v covers $\mu(v)$. Symmetrically, we write $\mu_{+}(v)$ instead of $\mu(v)$ if $\mu(v)$ covers v.

An elementary simplicial collapse in an abstract simplicial complex $\mathcal{K}$ is now encoded as the matching of two vertices in the face poset $F(\mathcal{K})$, subject to further conditions. These vertices correspond to the two simplices σ and τ which are removed during the collapse, and the fact that they are connected by an edge is ensured by the conditions $\sigma \supset \tau$ and $\dim \tau + 1 = \dim \sigma$.

Accordingly, a set of elementary simplicial collapses is described by a matching consisting of a collection of pairs of simplices (σ, τ), such that σ contains τ, and $\dim \sigma = \dim \tau + 1$. It is a simple, but crucial observation, that not every matching of this type can be turned into a collapsing sequence. For example, no order can be chosen in the matching on the right of Figure 10.6, which would correspond to an allowed collapsing sequence.

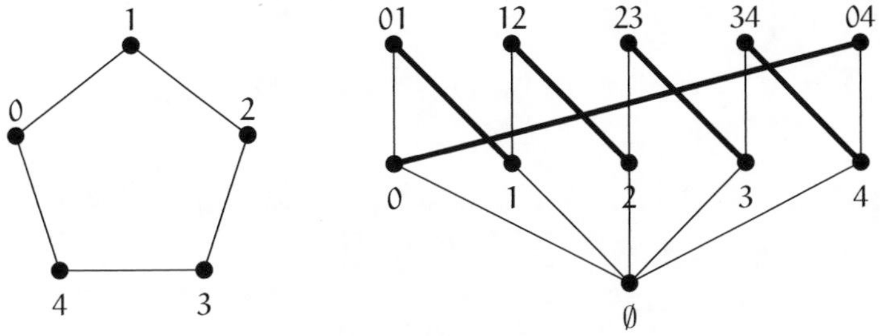

Figure 10.6. A cycle and a matching in its face poset.

Here is what goes wrong in this example: the prospective collapses are all "hooked up" with each other in a cyclic pattern, so that any suggested collapsing sequence would have one of these edges from the cycle occurring before the other ones, clearly contradicting the conditions for being an elementary collapse. This simple observation leads to the following formalization.

Definition 10.7. Assume we are given a partially ordered set P, and a partial matching $\mu : M \to M$ on P. This matching is called *acyclic* if there does not exist a cycle of the following form:

$$b_1 \succ \mu(b_1) \prec b_2 \succ \mu(b_2) \prec \cdots \prec b_n \succ \mu(b_n) \prec b_1, \tag{10.1}$$

with $n \geqslant 2$ and all $b_i \in M$ being distinct.

A graphic way to reformulate condition (10.1) of Definition 10.7 is as follows. Given a poset P, we start by orienting all edges in the underlying graph of the Hasse diagram of P, so that each one points from the larger element to the smaller one. This graph is obviously acyclic.[2] Now, assume we are given a partial matching $\mu : M \to M$. For each $v \in M$, such that v is covered by $\mu(v)$, change the orientation of the edge $(\mu(v), v)$ to the opposite one. The condition in question now says that the directed graph, obtained in this fashion, has no cycles.

Let us next formulate a proposition which provides yet another alternative reformulation of Definition 10.7. Consider first the following general construction. Assume P is a poset, and the element set of P is partitioned

[2]A graph is called *acyclic* if it does not have any cycles.

into non-empty disjoint sets $\{A_i\}_{i \in Q}$. We define a partial order on the index set Q using the following two rules:

(1) for $i, j \in Q$, we write $i \succ j$ if there exist $x \in A_i$ and $y \in A_j$, such that $x > y$;

(2) for $i, j \in Q$, we write $i >_Q j$ if there exists a finite sequence $i_1, \dots, i_t \in Q$, $t \geqslant 2$, such that $i_1 = i$, $i_t = j$, and $i_k \succ i_{k+1}$, for all $k = 1, \dots, t-1$.

The resulting partial order on Q is said to be *induced by* P. It may or may not be well-defined.

Proposition 10.8. *Assume* P *is a poset equipped with a partial matching* μ. *Let* $\{A_i\}_{i \in Q}$ *be the partition of* P *induced by that matching, where matched pairs of elements form 2-sets and non-matched elements give singletons.*

The matching μ *is acyclic if and only if the partial order on* Q *induced by* P *is well-defined.*

The proof of Proposition 10.8 is straightforward and is best left to the interested reader. From the point of view of universal constructions the thinking along the lines of Proposition 10.8 is rather fruitful. We will return to this topic in the context of the universality of the colimit of a matching in Theorem 16.5, where more details will be provided.

10.3. Collapsing sequences vs acyclic matchings: Theorem A

The next theorem is the first, and the simplest, of the central results of discrete Morse theory. In essence, it states that acyclic matchings provide a perfect language for saying that one abstract simplicial complex collapses to another one.

Theorem 10.9 (Theorem A). *Assume* $\mathcal{K}$ *is an abstract simplicial complex, and assume* $\mathcal{K}'$ *is a simplicial subcomplex of* $\mathcal{K}$, *such that* $\mathcal{K} \setminus \mathcal{K}'$ *is finite. The following statements are equivalent:*

(1) *there exists a sequence of elementary collapses leading from* $\mathcal{K}$ *to* $\mathcal{K}'$;

(2) *there exists a complete acyclic matching*[3] *on the set of all simplices of* $\mathcal{K}$ *which are not contained in* $\mathcal{K}'$.

Proof. Let us first show that (1) implies (2). Fix some sequence of elementary simplicial collapses leading from $\mathcal{K}$ to $\mathcal{K}'$, and take the matching μ on the set of simplices of $\mathcal{K} \setminus \mathcal{K}'$, which corresponds to this sequence.

[3]By this we mean *matching on the underlying graph of the Hasse diagram of the face poset of* $\mathcal{K}$.

Assume that this matching is not acyclic. Then, by definition, there must exist a cycle of the form

$$b_1 \succ \mu(b_1) \prec b_2 \succ \mu(b_2) \prec \cdots \prec b_n \succ \mu(b_n) \prec b_1,$$

for some distinct elements $b_1, \dots, b_n \in \mathcal{K} \setminus \mathcal{K}'$.

Consider the sequence $(b_1, \mu(b_1)), \dots, (b_n, \mu(b_n))$ of elementary collapses. Without loss of generality, we can assume that in the sequence of elementary collapses leading from $\mathcal{K}$ to $\mathcal{K}'$, the elementary collapse $(b_1, \mu(b_1))$ occurs before all the other elementary collapses from this set. Clearly, this contradicts the fact that $\mu(b_1) \prec b_2$, since then $\mu(b_1)$ is properly contained in at least two simplices, namely in b_1 and in b_2, both of which are present in the complex when we attempt to perform the elementary collapse $(b_1, \mu(b_1))$.

Let us now show the reverse direction, that is, that (2) implies (1). Consider a complete acyclic matching on the set of simplices $\mathcal{K} \setminus \mathcal{K}'$. We shall show that there exists a collapsing sequence from $\mathcal{K}$ to $\mathcal{K}'$ using induction on $|\mathcal{K} \setminus \mathcal{K}'|$. When $|\mathcal{K} \setminus \mathcal{K}'| = 1$, the statement is trivial, and we take it as the basis for induction.

For the induction step, assume $|\mathcal{K} \setminus \mathcal{K}'| \geqslant 2$. We construct a directed graph G as follows. As vertices of G we take the elements of $\mathcal{K} \setminus \mathcal{K}'$. We let edges be defined by the containment relations, that is, (σ, τ) is an edge if $\sigma \supset \tau$ as simplices. Finally, whenever $\sigma \supset \tau$, we orient the edge (σ, τ) *from* σ *to* τ, unless $\tau = \mu_-(\sigma)$, in which case we orient the edge *from* τ *to* σ instead. As already mentioned above, the fact that the matching is acyclic is equivalent to saying that the obtained directed graph is acyclic, i.e., does not have any *oriented* cycles.

It is a standard fact of graph theory that an acyclic directed graph contains at least one *source*, which is a vertex v such all the edges adjacent to v are oriented away from v. Let $\tau \in \mathcal{K} \setminus \mathcal{K}'$ denote such a source. There cannot exist $\sigma \in \mathcal{K} \setminus \mathcal{K}'$ such that $\tau = \mu_+(\sigma)$, because then the edge (σ, τ) would be oriented from σ to τ, contradicting the assumption that τ is a source. Since the matching is complete, we must instead have some $\sigma \in \mathcal{K} \setminus \mathcal{K}'$, such that $\tau = \mu_-(\sigma)$.

We now claim that (σ, τ) corresponds to an elementary simplicial collapse in $\mathcal{K}$. Indeed, since τ is a source, there exists no vertex γ with an edge towards τ, which means that there exists no simplex $\gamma \neq \sigma$ which properly contains τ. On the other hand, the simplex τ is of course a boundary simplex of σ of codimension 1, since these two simplices are matched, thus yielding a contradiction.

Set $\widetilde{\mathcal{K}} := \mathcal{K} \setminus \{\sigma, \tau\}$. Clearly, the simplicial complex $\mathcal{K}'$ is a subcomplex of $\widetilde{\mathcal{K}}$, since we have removed two simplices outside of $\mathcal{K}'$. The acyclic matching above gives a complete acyclic matching on $\widetilde{\mathcal{K}} \setminus \mathcal{K}'$. This matching has one edge less, so by induction hypothesis, there exists a collapsing sequence from $\widetilde{\mathcal{K}}$ to $\mathcal{K}'$. Concatenating this sequence with the elementary collapse (σ, τ) will give the desired collapsing sequence from $\mathcal{K}$ to $\mathcal{K}'$. □

10.4. Collapsing sequences and cones

10.4.1. Canonical way to collapse cones. Let $\mathcal{K}$ be a finite abstract simplicial complex, and let $\mathcal{L}$ be a cone over $\mathcal{K}$ with an apex a. There is a canonical way to collapse this cone. Before getting into the description of the collapsing procedure, we introduce a notation which will come in handy in many situations.

Definition 10.10. Assume we have a set A, a subset $B \subseteq A$, and an element $v \in A$; then we set

$$B \,\mathrm{XOR}\, v := \begin{cases} B \cup v, & \text{if } v \notin B; \\ B \setminus v, & \text{otherwise.} \end{cases}$$

The operation XOR is called *exclusive OR*.

We note the following useful identity:

$$(B \,\mathrm{XOR}\, v) \,\mathrm{XOR}\, v = B, \tag{10.2}$$

which is valid for all v and B. We also have $|B \,\mathrm{XOR}\, v| = |B| \pm 1$.

Any cone can now be collapsed by taking the exclusive OR with its apex.

Proposition 10.11. *The abstract simplicial complex $\mathcal{L}$ described above is collapsible.*

Proof. Consider the matching $\mu : \mathcal{L} \to \mathcal{L}$ on the set of simplices of $\mathcal{L}$, given by the rule

$$\mu(\sigma) := \sigma \,\mathrm{XOR}\, a.$$

Since the vertex a can be added to any simplex $\sigma \in \mathcal{K}$, the function μ is well-defined, and Equation (10.2) tells us that $\mu(\mu(\sigma)) = \sigma$. Furthermore, for all σ, $\dim \mu(\sigma) = \dim \sigma \pm 1$, and either $\mu(\sigma)$ is contained in σ or vice versa. This means that μ is actually a matching. It is also clearly complete.

Assume now μ is not acyclic, and take a cycle

$$b_1 \succ \mu(b_1) \prec b_2 \succ \mu(b_2) \prec \cdots \prec b_n \succ \mu(b_n) \prec b_1,$$

where $n \geqslant 2$, and all the simplices are distinct. By definition of μ we have $a \in b_1$, $a \in b_2$, and $a \notin \mu(b_1)$. This means $b_1 = \mu(b_1) \cup a = b_2$, yielding a contradiction. □

10.4.2. Stellar and barycentric subdivisions of a simplex. Let n be a positive integer, and let $\mathcal{K}$ be an n-simplex. Let $\mathcal{L}$ be the stellar subdivision of $\mathcal{K}$ with respect to the top-dimensional simplex. By definition, the set of vertices of $\mathcal{L}$ is $\{v_1, \dots, v_{n+1}, a\}$, where $\{v_1, \dots, v_{n+1}\}$ are the vertices of $\mathcal{K}$, and a is the new vertex added at the barycenter of the top-dimensional simplex. The simplices of $\mathcal{L}$ are given by the set

$$\{\sigma \,|\, \sigma \in \mathcal{K},\ \sigma \neq (v_1, \dots, v_{n+1})\} \cup \{a \cup \sigma \,|\, \sigma \in \mathcal{K},\ \sigma \neq (v_1, \dots, v_{n+1})\},$$

where in both sets σ is allowed to be empty.

It is obvious from this description that $\mathcal{L}$ can be obtained by starting from the $(n+1)$-simplex, and then performing an elementary collapse.

The complex $\mathcal{L}$ is a cone over $\mathcal{K} \setminus (v_1, \dots, v_{n+1})$ with apex at a, so it follows from Proposition 10.11 that $\mathcal{L}$ is collapsible.

As another example, we can take the barycentric subdivision of the simplex $\mathcal{K}$. We have seen that this subdivision is a cone with apex at the vertex indexed with the maximal simplex of $\mathcal{K}$, hence, again by Proposition 10.11 we know that it is collapsible.

10.4.3. Removing a simplex whose link is collapsible. One of the first things one can do to simplify the abstract simplicial complex at hand is to remove all the simplices whose links are collapsible themselves. As the first simple, but instructive, case, let us see how to remove a simplex whose link is actually a cone.

Proposition 10.12. *Assume $\mathcal{K}$ is a finite abstract simplicial complex, and assume σ is a simplex of $\mathcal{K}$, such that $\operatorname{lk}_{\mathcal{K}}(\sigma)$ is a cone. Then, we have $\mathcal{K} \searrow \operatorname{dl}_{\mathcal{K}}(\sigma)$.*

Proof. The argument is a modification of the proof of Proposition 10.11. Let b denote the apex of the cone $\operatorname{lk}_{\mathcal{K}}(\sigma)$. For an arbitrary simplex τ, which lies in the open star of σ, we set

$$\mu(\tau) := \tau \,\mathrm{XOR}\, b.$$

The same way as in the proof of Proposition 10.11 we see that μ is an acyclic matching. This matching is complete on the set of simplices in the open star of σ, which of course are precisely the simplices of the difference $\mathcal{K} \setminus \operatorname{dl}_{\mathcal{K}}(\sigma)$. The result then follows from Theorem 10.9. □

Let us now slightly upgrade our argument to deal with the general case.

Proposition 10.13. *Assume $\mathcal{K}$ is an abstract simplicial complex, and assume σ is a simplex of $\mathcal{K}$, such that $\operatorname{lk}_{\mathcal{K}}(\sigma)$ is collapsible. Then, again, we have $\mathcal{K} \searrow \operatorname{dl}_{\mathcal{K}}(\sigma)$.*

Proof. By Theorem 10.9 collapsibility of the complex $\mathrm{lk}_{\mathcal{K}}(\sigma)$ implies that there exists a complete acyclic matching on the set of the simplices of $\mathrm{lk}_{\mathcal{K}}(\sigma)$. Let ν denote this matching. For arbitrary simplex $\tau \in \mathcal{K}$ which lies in the open star of σ, we set

$$\mu(\tau) := \nu(\tau \setminus \sigma) \cup \sigma.$$

Assume this matching is not acyclic, and pick a cycle

$$b_1 \succ \mu(b_1) \prec b_2 \succ \mu(b_2) \prec \cdots \prec b_n \succ \mu(b_n) \prec b_1, \text{ where } n \geqslant 2. \tag{10.3}$$

The simplices $b_1, \dots, b_n$ belong to the open star of σ, which means that $\sigma \subseteq b_i$, for all $i = 1, \dots, n$. Write $b_1 = a_1 \cup \sigma, \dots, b_n = a_n \cup \sigma$. Then the cycle in Equation (10.3) becomes

$$a_1 \cup \sigma \succ \nu(a_1) \cup \sigma \prec a_2 \cup \sigma \succ \nu(a_2) \cup \sigma \prec \cdots \prec a_n \cup \sigma \succ \nu(a_n) \cup \sigma \prec a_1 \cup \sigma,$$

and deleting σ everywhere we obtain

$$a_1 \succ \nu(a_1) \prec a_2 \succ \nu(a_2) \prec \cdots \prec a_n \succ \nu(a_n) \prec a_1. \tag{10.4}$$

The existence of the cycle shown by Equation (10.4) contradicts our assumption that ν is an acyclic matching. Thus, assuming that μ was not acyclic was wrong. The statement of the proposition then again follows from Theorem 10.9. □

10.5. Standard subdivisions of collapsible complexes

10.5.1. Stellar subdivision of a collapsible simplicial complex. Next, let us consider a slightly more complicated example. We have seen that the stellar subdivision of a simplex is collapsible. In fact, the following generalization of this fact is true.

Theorem 10.14. *Assume $\mathcal{K}$ is a collapsible abstract simplicial complex, and let α be an arbitrary simplex of $\mathcal{K}$. Then, the abstract simplicial complex $Sd_{\mathcal{K}}(\alpha)$ is collapsible as well.*

The proof of Theorem 10.14 depends on the following lemma.

Lemma 10.15. *Assume n is a positive integer, and $\mathcal{K}$ is an n-simplex, with vertices indexed by the set $[n]$, and let $\mathcal{L}$ be the subcomplex of $\mathcal{K}$ consisting of all simplices except for $[n]$ and $[n-1]$. Let σ be an arbitrary simplex of $\mathcal{K}$. Then we have*

$$\begin{cases} \mathrm{Sd}_{\mathcal{K}}(\sigma) \searrow \mathrm{Sd}_{\mathcal{L}}(\sigma), & \textit{if } \sigma \neq [n-1], [n]; \\ \mathrm{Sd}_{\mathcal{K}}(\sigma) \searrow \mathcal{L}, & \textit{otherwise}. \end{cases} \tag{10.5}$$

Proof. We shall only show the first line of (10.5), leaving the cases $\sigma = [n-1]$ and $\sigma = [n]$ for the exercises.

The simplicial structure of $\mathrm{Sd}_{\mathcal{K}}(\sigma)$ was described in the discussion following Definition 10.4. As was done there, let a denote the barycenter of σ, so the set of the simplices of $\mathrm{Sd}_{\mathcal{K}}(\sigma)$ is the union of the sets $\{\langle a,\tau\rangle \mid \tau \not\supseteq \sigma\}$, and $\{\tau \mid \tau \not\supseteq \sigma\}$.

We need to distinguish two cases. Assume first that $\sigma \subset [n-1]$. Then, we have

$$\mathrm{Sd}_{\mathcal{K}}(\sigma) \setminus \mathrm{Sd}_{\mathcal{L}}(\sigma) = \{\langle a,\tau\rangle \mid \tau \supseteq [n-1]\setminus\sigma,\ \tau \not\supseteq \sigma\}.$$

This is precisely the open star of the simplex $\langle a, [n-1]\setminus\sigma\rangle$. The link of this simplex is a cone with apex at n. It is collapsible, using the matching given by the operation XOR n. It can then be checked directly that his gives the desired collapsing sequence $\mathrm{Sd}_{\mathcal{K}}(\sigma) \searrow \mathrm{Sd}_{\mathcal{L}}(\sigma)$. Alternatively, we can apply Proposition 10.13.

Assume now that n is a vertex of σ, but $\sigma \neq [n]$. In this case, we have

$$\mathrm{Sd}_{\mathcal{K}}(\sigma) \setminus \mathrm{Sd}_{\mathcal{L}}(\sigma) = \{\langle a,\tau\rangle \mid \tau \supseteq [n]\setminus\sigma,\ \tau \not\supseteq \sigma\} \cup \{[n-1]\}.$$

We now start by collapsing the pair $(\langle a, [n-1]\rangle, [n-1])$. This is a legal elementary collapse, as no other simplex of $\mathrm{Sd}_{\mathcal{K}}(\sigma)$ can contain $[n-1]$. After this we just need to collapse the open star of the simplex $\langle a, [n]\setminus\sigma\rangle$. Again, the link of that simplex is a cone with apex at n (it is actually isomorphic to the boundary of a $(\dim\sigma)$-simplex with one top-dimensional simplex removed), so we apply Proposition 10.13 as we did in the previous case. □

Proof of Theorem 10.14. In order to obtain a collapsing sequence for the simplicial complex $\mathrm{Sd}_{\mathcal{K}}(\alpha)$, we start with the collapsing sequence for $\mathcal{K}$, taking it as a blueprint. Then, every time we would have a collapse (σ,τ), in $\mathcal{K}$, such that $\alpha \subseteq \sigma$, we simply replace it with the collapsing sequence either for $\mathrm{Sd}_{\mathcal{K}}(\alpha) \searrow \mathrm{Sd}_{\mathcal{L}}(\sigma)$ or $\mathrm{Sd}_{\mathcal{K}}(\alpha) \searrow \mathcal{L}$, whichever is appropriate, where $\mathcal{L} = \mathcal{K}\setminus\{\tau,\sigma\}$. The existence of the latter collapsing sequence is guaranteed by Lemma 10.15. □

10.5.2. Barycentric subdivision of a collapsible simplicial complex.

In general, it is interesting to know which constructions preserve collapsibility. The next theorem tells us that taking barycentric subdivision is one of these constructions.

Theorem 10.16. *Assume $\mathcal{K}$ is a collapsible abstract simplicial complex. Then, the abstract simplicial complex* $\mathrm{Bd}\,\mathcal{K}$ *is collapsible as well.*

More generally, if $\mathcal{K}$ is an abstract simplicial complex and $\mathcal{L}$ its subcomplex such that $\mathcal{K} \searrow \mathcal{L}$, then $\mathrm{Bd}\,\mathcal{K} \searrow \mathrm{Bd}\,\mathcal{L}$.

Corollary 10.17. *The iterated barycentric subdivision of a simplex* $\mathrm{Bd}^t(\Delta^n)$ *is collapsible.*

Before we proceed with the proof of Theorem 10.16 we need the following notion.

Definition 10.18. Assume $\mathcal{K}$ is an abstract simplicial complex. For a simplex $\alpha \in \mathrm{Bd}\,\mathcal{K}$, $\alpha = \{\sigma_1, \dots, \sigma_t\}$, such that $\sigma_1 \subset \dots \subset \sigma_t$, we shall use the notation $\alpha = (\sigma_1 \subset \dots \subset \sigma_t)$. Furthermore, we call $\sigma_t \in \mathcal{K}$ the *support* of α, and write $\mathrm{supp}\,\alpha = \sigma_t$.

The following lemma is the analog of Lemma 10.15; it plays the crucial role in the proof of Theorem 10.16.

Lemma 10.19. *Assume* n *is a positive integer, and* $\mathcal{K}$ *is an* n*-simplex, with vertices indexed by the set* $[n]$*. Let* $\mathcal{L}$ *be the subcomplex of* $\mathcal{K}$ *consisting of all simplices except for* $[n]$ *and* $[n-1]$*. Then we have* $\mathrm{Bd}\,\mathcal{K} \searrow \mathrm{Bd}\,\mathcal{L}$*.*

Proof. Note that $\mathrm{Bd}\,\mathcal{L}$ is the subcomplex of $\mathrm{Bd}\,\mathcal{K}$ consisting of all simplices except for those whose support is $[n]$ or $[n-1]$. Let C denote the set of simplices $\mathrm{Bd}\,\mathcal{K} \setminus \mathrm{Bd}\,\mathcal{L}$. We define the matching $\mu : C \to C$ as follows. The first partial rule says

$$\mu(\sigma_1 \subset \dots \subset \sigma_k) := \begin{cases} \sigma_1 \subset \dots \subset \sigma_k \subset [n], & \text{if } \sigma_k = [n-1]; \\ \sigma_1 \subset \dots \subset \sigma_{k-1}, & \text{if } \sigma_{k-1} = [n-1]. \end{cases} \tag{10.6}$$

For the last line note that when $\sigma_{k-1} = [n-1]$, we automatically have $\sigma_k = [n]$. This will match completely all simplices α in C which have $\mathrm{supp}\,\alpha = [n-1]$ with those which have $\mathrm{supp}\,\alpha = [n]$ and $\sigma_{k-1} = [n-1]$.

What remains are the simplices $\alpha = (\sigma_1 \subset \dots \subset \sigma_k)$ for which $\sigma_k = [n]$ and $\sigma_{k-1} \neq [n-1]$. Assume α is such a simplex, and let $h(\alpha)$ be the maximal index $1 \leqslant h(\alpha) \leqslant k$ such that $n \notin \sigma_{h(\alpha)}$. If $n \in \sigma_i$ for all $1 \leqslant i \leqslant k$, then we set $h(\alpha) := 0$ and use $\sigma_0 = \emptyset$ as a default value.

The next rule completes our definition of μ:

$$\mu(\sigma_1 \subset \dots \subset \sigma_k)$$
$$:= \begin{cases} \sigma_1 \subset \dots \subset \sigma_{h(\alpha)} \subset \sigma_{h(\alpha)} \cup n \subset \dots \subset \sigma_k, & \text{if } |\sigma_{h(\alpha)+1}| \geqslant |\sigma_{h(\alpha)}| + 2; \\ \sigma_1 \subset \dots \subset \sigma_{h(\alpha)} \subset \sigma_{h(\alpha)+2} \subset \dots \subset \sigma_k, & \text{if } |\sigma_{h(\alpha)+1}| = |\sigma_{h(\alpha)}| + 1. \end{cases}$$

It is clear that μ is a complete matching on the set C. Before proceeding, we make the following observations:

- by definition of μ, we have $\mathrm{supp}\,b = [n]$ for all $b \in M^{\uparrow}(C)$;
- for all $b \in C$, we have $h(\mu(b)) = h(b)$, since μ adds or deletes a set containing n;
- if $b \prec c$ in $\mathrm{Bd}\,\mathcal{K}$, then $h(b) \leqslant h(c)$.

Let us now show that μ is acyclic. Assume it is not, and take a cycle

$$b_1 \succ \mu(b_1) \prec b_2 \succ \mu(b_2) \prec \cdots \prec b_t \succ \mu(b_t) \prec b_1,$$

where $n \geqslant 2$, and all the simplices are distinct. By what is said above, we have

$$h(b_1) = h(\mu(b_1)) \leqslant h(b_2) = h(\mu(b_2)) \leqslant \cdots \leqslant h(b_t) = h(\mu(b_t)) \leqslant h(b_1),$$

which of course implies

$$h(b_1) = h(\mu(b_1)) = h(b_2) = h(\mu(b_2)) = \cdots = h(b_t) = h(\mu(b_t)) = h(b_1).$$

To start with, assume that all of the matched pairs $(b_1, \mu(b_1)), \dots, (b_t, \mu(b_t))$ are of the first type, as defined in Equation (10.6); in other words, $\operatorname{supp} \mu(b_1) = \cdots = \operatorname{supp} \mu(b_t) = [n-1]$. Let us say $\mu(b_1) = (\sigma_1 \subset \cdots \subset \sigma_{d-1} \subset [n-1])$. Since $\operatorname{supp} b_1 = \cdots = \operatorname{supp} b_t = [n]$, we get

$$b_1 = (\sigma_1 \subset \cdots \subset \sigma_{d-1} \subset [n-1] \subset [n]) = b_2,$$

which obviously is a contradiction.

We can therefore assume without loss of generality that $\operatorname{supp} \mu(b_1) \neq [n-1]$, which of course implies $\operatorname{supp} \mu(b_1) = [n]$. Since $\mu(b_1) \in M^{\downarrow}(C)$, assuming $\mu(b_1) = (\sigma_1 \subset \cdots \subset \sigma_d)$, we must have

$$b_1 = (\sigma_1 \subset \cdots \subset \sigma_h \subset \sigma_h \cup n \subset \sigma_{h+1} \subset \cdots \subset \sigma_d),$$

where $h = h(\mu(b_1))$. We furthermore have assumed that $b_1 \succ \mu(b_t)$ and derived $h(b_1) = h(\mu(b_t))$. This forces us to conclude that

$$\mu(b_t) = (\sigma_1 \subset \cdots \subset \sigma_h \subset \sigma_h \cup n \subset \sigma_{h+1} \subset \cdots \subset \sigma_{j-1} \subset \sigma_{j+1} \subset \cdots \subset \sigma_d),$$

for some $h + 1 \leqslant j \leqslant d$. However, this means that $\mu(b_t) \in M^{\uparrow}(C)$, again yielding a contradiction.

All in all, we can conclude that the matching μ is acyclic. The result now follows from Theorem 10.9. □

Proof of Theorem 10.16. We shall show the second statement. Assume $\mathcal{K}$ is an abstract simplicial complex and $\mathcal{L}$ its subcomplex such that $\mathcal{K} \searrow \mathcal{L}$. Take some sequence of elementary collapses $(\sigma_1, \tau_1), \dots, (\sigma_t, \tau_t)$ leading from $\mathcal{K}$ to $\mathcal{L}$. During the elementary collapse (σ_k, τ_k) for some $1 \leqslant k \leqslant t$ we remove two simplices: σ_k and τ_k. Passing on to the barycentric subdivisions, we would like to come from $\operatorname{Bd} \mathcal{K}$ to $\operatorname{Bd} \mathcal{L}$ using essentially the same collapsing steps. The difference is that now instead of removing σ_k and τ_k we would like to delete the whole set of simplices $\operatorname{Bd} \sigma_k \cup \operatorname{Bd} \tau_k$. Here $\operatorname{Bd} \sigma_k$ denotes the set of simplices of $\operatorname{Bd} \mathcal{K}$ whose support is equal to σ_k, and similarly for $\operatorname{Bd} \tau_k$. Fortunately, this is precisely the statement of Lemma 10.19, so we are done. □

10.6. Standard chromatic subdivision

10.6.1. Standard chromatic subdivision of a simplex. Let n be a natural number, and again let Δ^n be the standard n-simplex. The abstract simplicial complex $\chi(\Delta^n)$ is a pure n-dimensional abstract simplicial complex defined as follows:

- the vertices of $\chi(\Delta^n)$ are indexed by all pairs (p, V), such that $V \subseteq [n]$, and $p \in V$;
- the n-dimensional simplices of $\chi(\mathcal{K})$ are formed by all sets of vertices $\{(0, V_0), (1, V_1), \dots, (n, V_n)\}$ satisfying the following axioms:
  (i) for all $i, j \in [n]$, we have either $V_i \subseteq V_j$ or $V_j \subseteq V_i$;
  (ii) for all $i, j \in [n]$, if $i \in V_j$, then $V_i \subseteq V_j$.

In particular, note that $\chi(\Delta^n)$ has $2^n(n+1)$ vertices in total.

Definition 10.20. The abstract simplicial complex $\chi(\Delta^n)$ is called the *standard chromatic subdivision* of Δ^n.

The standard chromatic subdivision of a simplicial complex is similar to the barycentric subdivision. Yet, there is a crucial difference, which also explains the etymology of the term. Imagine that we are interested in coloring the vertices of a simplicial complex $\mathcal{K}$, so that if two vertices are connected by an edge, they must get different colors. Clearly, we will need at least $\dim \mathcal{K} + 1$ colors, since all the vertices of any simplex of maximal dimension will need to be covered differently. However, if we did succeed to color $\mathcal{K}$ with $\dim \mathcal{K} + 1$ colors, taking the barycentric subdivision will ruin it, since the color assigned to the barycenter of any top-dimensional simplex σ cannot be any of the old ones, as this barycenter is connected to all the vertices of σ. This is not the case for the standard chromatic subdivision. On the contrary, given a valid coloring of the vertices of $\mathcal{K}$, the vertices of the simplicial complex $\chi(\mathcal{K})$ can be colored using the same of colors.

It is useful to obtain an alternative combinatorial description of the entire simplicial structure of $\chi(\Delta^n)$, including the boundary operator.

Definition 10.21. A *partial ordered set partition* of the set $[n]$ is a pair of ordered set partitions of non-empty subsets of $[n]$, $\sigma = ((A_1, \dots, A_t), (B_1, \dots, B_t))$, which have the same number of parts and are subject to the following additional conditions:

- for all $1 \leqslant i \leqslant t$, we have $B_i \subseteq A_i$;
- the sets A_i are disjoint.

Given such a partial ordered set partition σ, we introduce the following terminology.

- The union $A_1 \cup \cdots \cup A_t$ is called the *carrier set* of σ, and is denoted by $R(\sigma)$.
- The union $B_1 \cup \cdots \cup B_t$ is called the *color set* of σ, and is denoted by $C(\sigma)$.
- The *dimension* of σ is defined to be $|C(\sigma)|-1$, and is denoted $\dim \sigma$.

When appropriate, we shall also write

$$\sigma = \begin{array}{|c|c|c|}\hline A_1 & \dots & A_t \\ \hline B_1 & \dots & B_t \\ \hline \end{array}, \tag{10.7}$$

which we shall call the *table form* of σ.

We note that both nodes (A, x), for $A \subseteq [n]$, as well as ordered set partitions of $[n]$ are special cases of partial ordered set partitions of $[n]$. Indeed, a node (A, x), such that $A \subseteq [n]$, corresponds to the somewhat degenerate partial ordered set partition of $[n]$,

$$\sigma = \begin{array}{|c|}\hline A \\ \hline x \\ \hline \end{array},$$

whereas an ordered set partition $(A_1, \dots, A_t)$ corresponds to the partial ordered set partition of $[n]$,

$$\sigma = \begin{array}{|c|c|c|}\hline A_1 & \dots & A_t \\ \hline A_1 & \dots & A_t \\ \hline \end{array},$$

i.e., any partial ordered set partition $((A_1, \dots A_t), (B_1, \dots, B_t))$, such that $A_i = B_i$ for all i, and $A_1 \cup \cdots \cup A_t = [n]$.

Each partial ordered set partition has a non-empty color set, which in turn is contained in its carrier set. The nodes correspond to the partial ordered set partitions with minimal color set, consisting of just one element, and ordered set partitions correspond to the partial ordered set partitions with maximal color set, namely the whole set $[n]$.

Definition 10.22. Assume we are given a partial ordered set partition of the set $[n]$, say $\sigma = ((A_1, \dots, A_t), (B_1, \dots, B_t))$, such that $\dim \sigma \geqslant 1$, and we are also given an element $x \in C(\sigma)$, say $x \in B_k$, for some $1 \leqslant k \leqslant t$. To define the *deletion of* x *from* σ we consider three different cases.

Case 1. If $|B_k| \geqslant 2$, then the deletion of x from σ is set to be

$$((A_1, \dots, A_t), (B_1, \dots, B_{k-1}, B_k \setminus x, B_{k+1}, \dots, B_t)).$$

Case 2. If $|B_k| = 1$ and $k \leqslant t-1$, then the deletion of x from σ is set to be

$$((A_1, \dots, A_{k-1}, A_k \cup A_{k+1}, \dots, A_t), (B_1, \dots, B_{k-1}, B_{k+1}, \dots, B_t)).$$

Case 3. If $|B_k| = 1$ and $k = t$, then the deletion of x from σ is set to be

$$((A_1, \dots, A_{t-1}), (B_1, \dots, B_{t-1})).$$

We denote the deletion of x from σ by $\mathrm{dl}(\sigma, x)$.

The deletion of an element corresponds to the boundary relation in the standard chromatic subdivision. (See Figure 10.7.)

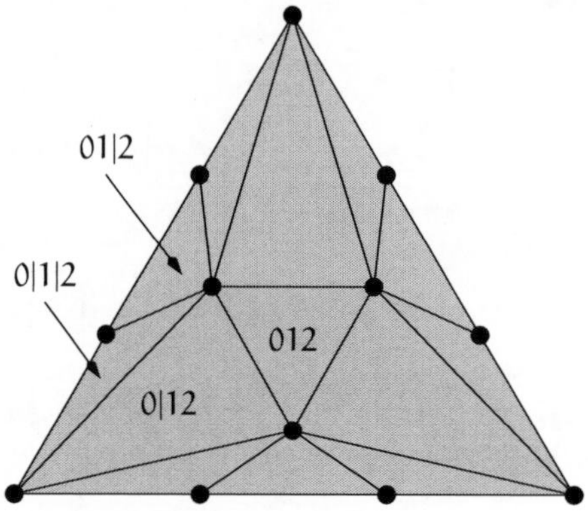

Figure 10.7. Standard chromatic subdivision of a triangle.

Theorem 10.23. *The standard chromatic subdivision of a simplex is collapsible.*

Proof. Consider an n-simplex $\mathcal{K}$, whose set of vertices is indexed by $[n]$. Let B be the set of all simplices

$$\sigma = \begin{array}{|c|c|c|}\hline A_1 & \dots & A_t \\ \hline A_1 & \dots & A_t \\ \hline\end{array},$$

such that $C(\sigma) = A_1 \cup \dots \cup A_t \neq [n]$. For each $\sigma \in B$, set

$$\lambda(\sigma) := \begin{array}{|c|c|c|c|}\hline A_1 & \dots & A_t & [n] \setminus C(\sigma) \\ \hline A_1 & \dots & A_t & [n] \setminus C(\sigma) \\ \hline\end{array}.$$

It is then easy to see that the face poset of $\chi(\mathcal{K})$ decomposes as a disjoint union of intervals $[\sigma, \lambda(\sigma)]$, where $\sigma \in B$. Each such interval corresponds to a (possibly non-elementary) collapse. The collapses can be performed in any order, so that the cardinality of $C(\sigma)$ does not decrease. □

10.6.2. Standard chromatic subdivision of a collapsible simplicial complex.

Definition 10.24. Let $\mathcal{K}$ be an arbitrary abstract simplicial complex. A new simplicial complex $\chi(\mathcal{K})$, called the *standard chromatic subdivision* of $\mathcal{K}$, is defined as follows:

- the simplices of $\chi(\mathcal{K})$ are indexed by all partial ordered set partitions
$$\sigma = \begin{array}{|c|c|c|}\hline A_1 & \dots & A_t \\ \hline B_1 & \dots & B_t \\ \hline\end{array},$$
such that $A_1 \cup \dots \cup A_t$ is a simplex of $\mathcal{K}$;
- the boundary relation is encoded by the deletion of elements, as described in Definition 10.22.

Theorem 10.25. *If $\mathcal{K}$ is an abstract simplicial complex and $\mathcal{L}$ its subcomplex such that $\mathcal{K} \searrow \mathcal{L}$, then $\chi(\mathcal{K}) \searrow \chi(\mathcal{L})$. In particular, the standard chromatic subdivision of a collapsible simplicial complex is collapsible.*

In line with our previous arguments, the collapsing sequence required in Theorem 10.25 can be obtained by an iterated application of the following lemma.

Lemma 10.26. *Let $\mathcal{K}$ denote the n-simplex, with the vertex set $[n]$, and let Λ denote the subcomplex of $\mathcal{K}$ obtained by an elementary collapse $([n],[n-1])$. Then, we have $\chi(\mathcal{K}) \searrow \chi(\Lambda)$.*

Proof. The proof proceeds in three stages. First, we perform all the collapses
$$\left(\begin{array}{|c|c|c|c|}\hline A_1 & \dots & A_t & [n]\setminus(A_1\cup\dots\cup A_t) \\ \hline B_1 & \dots & B_t & n \\ \hline\end{array}, \begin{array}{|c|c|c|}\hline A_1 & \dots & A_t \\ \hline B_1 & \dots & B_t \\ \hline\end{array}\right),$$
where $n \notin A_1 \cup \dots \cup A_t$.

Second, collapse the open star of the vertex $([n], n)$, using Propoition 10.13.

Finally, arrange the remaining simplices $([n], S)$, where $S \subseteq [n-1]$, in such an order that the cardinality of S does not increase, and use Proposition 10.13 again to delete the open stars of these simplices in this chosen order. Details are left as an exercise. □

Proof. Given a collapsing sequence leading from $\mathcal{K}$ to $\mathcal{L}$, we simply replace each elementary collapse in $\mathcal{K}$ by the corresponding sequence of elementary collapses in $\chi(\mathcal{K})$, whose existence is guaranteed by Lemma 10.26. □

Corollary 10.27. *The iterated standard chromatic subdivision of a simplex $\chi^t(\Delta^n)$ is collapsible.*

Proof. By Theorem 10.23 the standard chromatic subdivision of a simplex is collapsible. Now, repeated application of the second statement of Theorem 10.25 yields the result. □

10.7. Combinatorial collapsing sequences

10.7.1. Closure operators in posets. Let us now describe a framework which is classical in combinatorial topology, and which yields a sequence of simplicial collapses.

Definition 10.28. Let P be a partially ordered set. A *closure operator* on P is a poset map $\varphi : P \to P$ satisfying the following conditions:

(1) $\varphi(x) \geqslant x$, for all $x \in P$;

(2) $\varphi^2 = \varphi$.

Assume $\varphi : P \to P$ is a closure operator, and let $\varphi(P)$ denote its image $\{\varphi(x) \,|\, x \in P\}$. This is of course a partially ordered set as well, with the partial order induced by that of P. Furthermore, by condition (2) in Definition 10.28, the restriction of φ to the poset $\varphi(P)$ is simply the identity map. Moreover, we obtain the following implication:

$$\begin{cases} x \in P \\ y \in \varphi(P) \\ x \leqslant y \end{cases} \implies \varphi(x) \leqslant y. \tag{10.8}$$

Indeed, since φ is a poset map, the inequality $x \leqslant y$ implies the inequality $\varphi(x) \leqslant \varphi(y)$. On the other hand, $\varphi(y) = y$, since $y \in \varphi(P)$, so we obtain $\varphi(x) \leqslant y$.

The following theorem provides a connection between closure operators and simplicial collapsing sequences.

Theorem 10.29. *Let P be a finite partially ordered set, and let $\varphi : P \to P$ be a closure operator. Then there exists a collapsing sequence from the order complex $\Delta(P)$ to the order complex $\Delta(\varphi(P))$.*

Proof. Clearly, the simplicial complex $\Delta(\varphi(P))$ is a subcomplex of $\Delta(P)$. Let us define an acyclic matching on the simplices of $\Delta(P)$ such that the set of critical simplices is precisely $\Delta(\varphi(P))$.

Recall that simplices of $\Delta(P)$ are chains $c = (x_1 < \dots < x_t)$. Assume that c is not a chain in $\varphi(P)$, and let k be the largest index between 1 and t, such that $x_k \notin \varphi(P)$. Note that if $k \leqslant t-1$, then $x_{k+1} \in \varphi(P)$, so, by Equation (10.8), we have $x_k < \varphi(x_k) \leqslant \varphi(x_{k+1})$.

We now define a matching by setting

$$\mu(c) := c \,\mathrm{XOR}\, \varphi(x_k),$$

where XOR is the *exclusive OR* operation defined in Definition 10.10.

Let us see that μ is an acyclic matching. Consider a cycle

$$b_1 \prec \mu(b_1) \succ b_2 \prec \mu(b_2) \succ \dots \succ b_n \prec \mu(b_n) \succ b_1.$$

For a chain $c = (x_1 < \cdots < x_t)$ in P, let $h(b)$ denote the number of x_i's which belong to the image $\varphi(P)$. On one hand, we have $h(\mu(b_i)) = h(b_i) + 1$, for $i = 1, \dots, n$, since when the matching operation adds an element, it adds an element from the image of φ. On the other hand, $h(\mu(b_i)) - 1 \leqslant h(b_{i+1})$, for $i = 1, \dots, n$,[4] simply because when passing from $\mu(b_i)$ to b_{i+1}, we may delete at most one element from the image of φ. So, in total, we have

$$h(b_1) = h(\mu(b_1)) - 1 \leqslant h(b_2) = \cdots \leqslant h(b_n) = h(\mu(b_n)) - 1 \leqslant h(b_1).$$

We then have $h(b_1) = \cdots = h(b_n)$. Assume $\mu(b_1) = b_1 \cup \varphi(x_k)$. When passing from $\mu(b_1)$ to b_2 we must delete an element from the image of φ, so we cannot delete x_k. But then x_k is still the largest element of b_2 which lies outside of the image of φ, so $\mu(b_2) = b_2 \cup \varphi(x_k)$. This, of course, is impossible, since $b_1 \neq b_2$, so $\varphi(x_k) \in b_2$.

We conclude that μ is acyclic. Clearly, the set of those simplices which are not matched by μ coincides with the set of simplices of $\Delta(\varphi(P))$, so the proposition follows from Theorem 10.9. □

10.7.2. Order complexes of posets with a join-transversal.

Definition 10.30. An element α of P is called a *join-transversal* if for any other element $x \in P$ the join of x and α exists.

There is an easy way to produce a poset with a join-transversal. Start with any poset P and an element $\alpha \in P$, and then simply delete all $x \in P$ such that the join of α and x does not exist. It is an easy exercise to see that α will be a join-transversal in the resulting poset.

Theorem 10.31. *Assume P is a poset possessing a join-transversal; then the order complex of P is collapsible.*

Proof. This is a simple corollary of Theorem 10.29. Specifically, assume $\alpha \in P$ is a join-transversal. We define $\varphi : P \to P$ by setting $\varphi(x) := x \vee \alpha$. Obviously it is a poset map and $\varphi(x) \geqslant x$. Also $(x \vee \alpha) \vee \alpha = x \vee \alpha$, so $\varphi(\varphi(\alpha)) = \varphi(\alpha)$, making φ a closure operator. The image $\varphi(P)$ is precisely $P_{\geqslant \alpha}$, since, on one hand $x \vee \alpha \geqslant \alpha$, for all $x \in P$, and on the other hand, $x \vee \alpha = x$, whenever $x \geqslant \alpha$, so each element of $P_{\geqslant \alpha}$ lies in $\varphi(P)$.

By Theorem 10.29 this means that there exists a collapsing sequence from $\Delta(P)$ to $\Delta(P_{\geqslant \alpha})$. However, the simplicial complex $\Delta(P_{\geqslant \alpha})$ is a cone with apex at α, which is collapsible. Therefore $\Delta(P)$ is collapsible as well. □

[4] As usual, we use the convention $b_{n+1} = b_1$.

10.7.3. Removing dominating vertices in independence complexes.

Recall that a set of vertices of a graph is called *independent* if no two of them are connected by an edge. Now, given a graph G, its *independence complex* $\mathrm{Ind}(G)$ has vertices of G as vertices, and independent sets of G as simplices.

Definition 10.32. Assume we are given a graph G and two vertices of G, say v and w. We say that w *dominates* v if any vertex which is adjacent to v is also adjacent to w.[5]

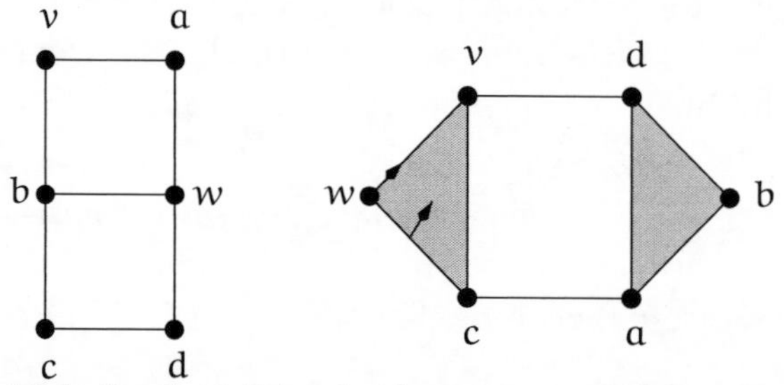

Figure 10.8. On the left-hand side we see a graph G with vertex w dominating the vertex v. On the right-hand side we see the independence complex $\mathrm{Ind}(G)$ and the collapsing sequence used in the proof of Proposition 10.33.

Proposition 10.33. *Assume we are given a graph* G *and two vertices* v *and* w *such that* w *dominates* v*; then there is a sequence of simplicial collapses reducing* $\mathrm{Ind}(G)$ *to* $\mathrm{Ind}(G \setminus w)$.

Proof. The following observation is crucial for defining the collapsing sequence: *if* A *is an independent set in* G*, and* $w \in A$*, then also* $A \cup v$ *is an independent set in* G. Indeed, if $A \cup v$ is not an independent set, then there exists $x \in A$, such that the edge (x, v) belongs to G. Since w dominates v, also the edge (x, w) must be an edge of G, contradicting the fact that A is an independent set.

Equipped with this fact, we simply define the matching $\mu(A) := A \,\mathrm{XOR}\, v$, for all $A \in \mathrm{Ind}(G)$, such that $w \in A$. This is well-defined and obviously acyclic. Figure 10.8 illustrates our argument. □

Proposition 10.33 can be effectively used to reduce independence complexes of graphs to independence complexes of potentially much smaller graphs. For example, when G is a path of n vertices, as in Exercise (2), then Proposition 10.33 allows us to obtain very extensive information on $\mathrm{Ind}(G)$.

---

[5] When the vertices are persons, and edges record who knows whom, w dominates v if it knows everybody whom v knows.

10.7.4. Complexes of disconnected graphs and the order complex of the partition lattice. There is a standard way to associate a family of simplicial complexes to any graph property Λ which is closed under the deletion of edges. In other words, if G has property Λ and e is an arbitrary edge of G, then also $G \setminus e$ will have the property Λ.

Definition 10.34. Let Λ be a graph property closed under the deletion of edges, and let n be an arbitrary integer, $n \geqslant 2$. We define a simplicial complex $GP_n(\Lambda)$ as follows:

(1) The vertices of $GP_n(\Lambda)$ are indexed by all ordered pairs (i, j), where $1 \leqslant i < j \leqslant n$; there are $\binom{n}{2}$ vertices.

(2) Given a set σ of vertices of $GP_n(\Lambda)$, we can construct a graph G_σ, whose vertices are indexed $1, \dots, n$, and edges are listed in σ. We now say that σ is a simplex of $GP_n(\Lambda)$ if and only if the graph G_σ has the property Λ.

Varying n, we get an infinite family of abstract simplicial complexes.

Colloquially we shall refer to the simplicial complexes $GP_n(\Lambda)$ as *complexes of all graphs with the property* Λ. In principle, one can take any graph property which is closed under the deletion of edges, such as planarity, or colorability with a certain number of colors. In general however, the resulting simplicial complexes can be hard to analyze.

Remark 10.35.

(1) Definition 10.34 can be easily modified to describe abstract simplicial complexes associated to those graph properties of *directed graphs*, which are closed under edge deletion.

(2) Another possible generalization of Definition 10.34 is to consider *hypergraphs* instead of graphs.

Here, we consider the simplicial complexes of disconnected graphs. These are of course well-defined, since a deletion of an edge from a disconnected graph again yields a disconnected graph. For brevity we shall let Disc_n denote the abstract simplicial complex of all disconnected graphs on n vertices. For $n = 2$, this simplicial complex is empty. For $n = 3$ it consists of 3 isolated vertices. The example $n = 4$ is shown in Figure 10.9. This simplicial complex can be visualized as taking every other triangle in an octahedron and then connecting the 3 pairs of opposite vertices by edges. It has the homotopy type of a wedge of 6 circles.

The case $n = 5$ is slightly more difficult. The simplicial complex Disc_5 has dimension 5. It has 5 maximal simplices of dimension 5 and 10 maximal simplices of dimension 3. With a little bit of extra effort one can figure out that Disc_5 is homotopy equivalent to a wedge of 24 spheres of dimension 2.

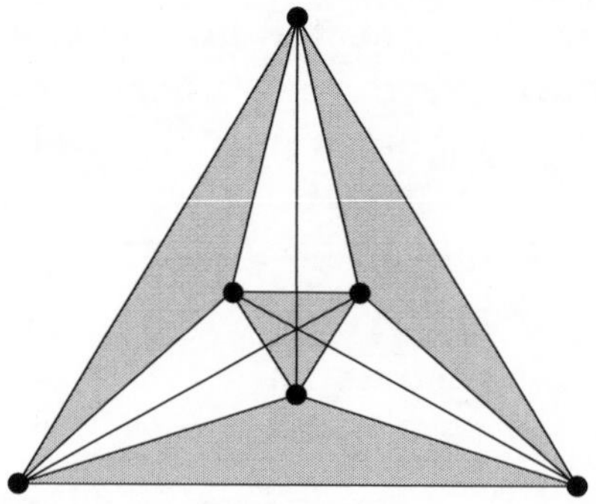

Figure 10.9. The complex of disconnected graphs on 4 vertices.

The observations made for the lower values of n carry over to the higher-dimensional case. The maximal simplices of Disc_n are indexed by partitions of the set $\{1, \ldots, n\}$ into two non-empty subsets. Accordingly, when these parts have cardinalities k and $n-k$, the corresponding simplex has dimension $\binom{k}{2} + \binom{n-k}{2} - 1$, so the dimension of Disc_n is equal to $\binom{n-1}{2} - 1$.

As a contrast, its homology is concentrated in a much lower dimension. As a matter of fact, it turns out that the simplicial complex Disc_n is homotopy equivalent to the wedge of $(n-1)!$ spheres of dimension $n-3$. We will see this in Chapter 11, however the fact that the homology in higher dimensions is trivial can be shown using collapsing sequences. In order to do this, we need another object, frequently met in combinatorial topology, which we now proceed to introduce.

Definition 10.36. Let n be an integer, $n \geqslant 3$. The *partition lattice* Π_n is the poset whose elements are all set partitions of the set $\{1, \ldots, n\}$, with the partial order given by refinement. (See Figure 10.10.)

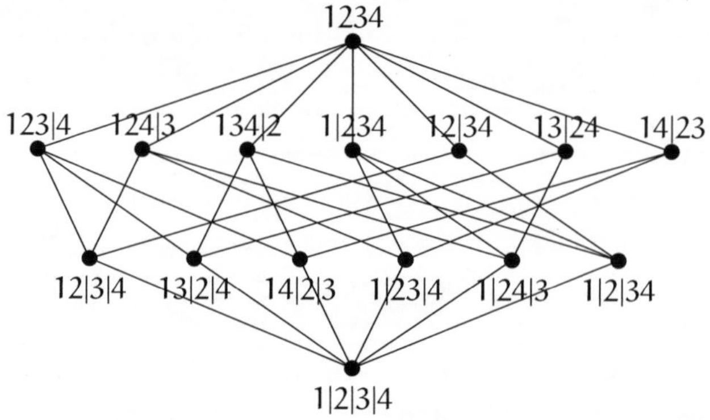

Figure 10.10. The partition lattice Π_4.

The idea behind Definition 10.36 is to encode the combinatorics of coincidences. For example, the Euclidean space $\mathbb{R}^n$ consists of all n-tuples of real numbers. We can stratify this space by geometric locuses of points with various sets of coordinates coinciding. Geometrically this is known as the *braid arrangement* and the stratification poset is precisely the partition lattice. More generally, the partition lattice describes the combinatorics of the standard stratification of the ordered configuration space of n points in an arbitrary topological space.

The partition lattice Π_n has a maximal element corresponding to the partition consisting of a single block $(1, \dots, n)$, and a minimal element corresponding to the partition $(1) \dots (n)$ consisting of singletons[6] only.

In general, we said that $\hat{0}$ should denote the minimal element in a poset, so it is close at hand to extend this notation, and let $\hat{1}$ stand for the maximal element. In many natural situations, as is the case for the partition lattice, the considered poset will have both the maximal and the minimal elements. When considering the associated complex, it is useful to exclude both, so as to avoid the double cone, which we would get otherwise. This makes the next definition natural.

Definition 10.37. Assume P is a partially ordered set, having both the minimal element $\hat{0}$, as well as the maximal element $\hat{1}$. We call the order complex $\Delta(P \setminus \{\hat{0}, \hat{1}\})$ the *reduced order complex* of P, and denote it by $\widetilde{\Delta}(P)$.

The following proposition provides a relation between the complex of disconnected graphs with the reduced order complex of partition lattice.

Proposition 10.38. *For every $n \geqslant 2$, there exists a collapsing sequence leading from the barycentric subdivision of the simplicial complex of all disconnected graphs on n vertices to the reduced order complex of the partition lattice Π_n, i.e., we have*

$$\mathrm{Bd}\,\mathrm{Disc}_n \searrow \widetilde{\Delta}(\Pi_n).$$

Proof. Let P be the face poset of Disc_n, and let $\varphi : P \to P$ map each graph to its transitive closure. The graphs in the image of φ all consist of disjoint unions of complete graphs, which are in a clear one-to-one correspondence with partitions of the vertex set. Since the elements of P encode disconnected graphs, we will never get the partition consisting of a single block, so we stay within $\Pi_n \setminus \{\hat{1}\}$. The statement now follows from Theorem 10.29. Figure 10.11 illustrates our argument. □

[6]Recall that *singletons* is the short term used for sets consisting of one element.

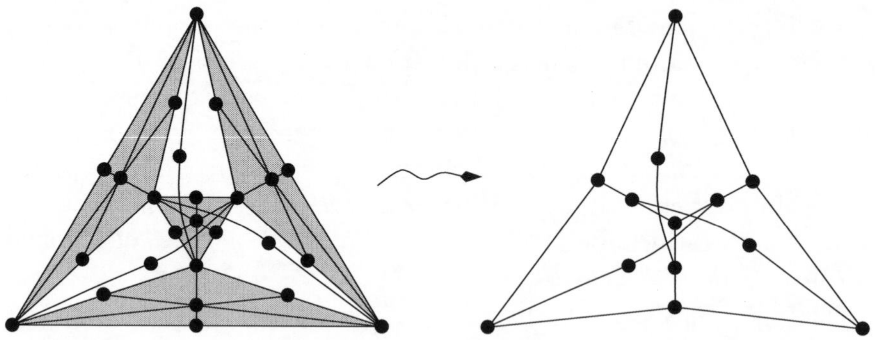

Figure 10.11. Collapsing the barycentric subdivision of the complex of disconnected graphs on 4 vertices to $\Delta(\Pi_4)$.

Exercises

(1) Prove Proposition 10.8.

(2) Compute the homotopy type of independence graphs of paths. Do the same for cycles.

(3) Characterize all graphs such that the iterative removal of dominating vertices gives a disjoint union of isolated vertices or edges. Use this to compute the homotopy type of the corresponding independence complexes.

(4) A finite abstract simplicial complex $\mathcal{K}$ is called *nonevasive* if it is either a point or contains a vertex v such that both the deletion of v as well as the link of v are non-evasive.

  (a) Show that the reduced Euler characteristic of a non-evasive simplicial complex is equal to 0.

  (b) Show that a non-evasive simplicial complex is collapsible.

  (c) Can you find a collapsible simplicial complex which is evasive (i.e., not non-evasive)?

(5) Assume $\mathcal{K}$ and $\mathcal{M}$ are abstract simplicial complexes. Let $d_{\text{coll}}(\mathcal{K}, \mathcal{M})$ denote the minimal number of elementary simplicial collapses and expansions which are needed to transform $\mathcal{K}$ to $\mathcal{M}$. We call $d_{\text{coll}}(\mathcal{K}, \mathcal{M})$ the *collapsing distance* between $\mathcal{K}$ and $\mathcal{M}$.

  (a) Show that d_{coll} is a metric.

  (b) For any $k \geqslant 3$, let C_k denote the cyclic graph with k edges. Assume $n \geqslant m \geqslant 3$. Show that $d_{\text{coll}}(C_m, C_n) = 3(n-m)$.

  (c) Assume $k, m \geqslant 3$. Let X_k be the *star graph* with k edges: its set of vertices is $[k]$, and its set of edges is $\{(0, v) \mid 1 \leqslant v \leqslant k\}$. Let P_m be the path graph with m edges: its set of vertices is $[m]$, and its set of edges is $\{(v, v+1) \mid 0 \leqslant v \leqslant m-1\}$. Derive a formula for $d_{coll}(X_k, P_m)$.

(6) Let a group G act on an abstract simplicial complex $\mathcal{K}$. Assume that removing a pair of simplices (σ, τ) is a simplicial collapse. Assume furthermore that we have the inclusion of stabilizers $\operatorname{stab} \sigma \subseteq \operatorname{stab} \tau$, and consider the set of pairs $S = \{(g\sigma, g\tau) \mid g \in G\}$.

Show that removing each element of S is a simplicial collapse, and that these simplicial collapses are disjoint and can be performed in an arbitrary order, independently of each other.

In a situation like this, we say that removing the entire set S is an *equivariant simplicial collapse.*

(7) Assume $\mathcal{K}$ is a finite abstract simplicial complex, and the group G acts on $\mathcal{K}$. The complex $\mathcal{K}$ is called *equivariantly collapsible* if there exists a sequence of equivariant collapses (defined in Exercise (6)), with respect to this G-action, resulting in a void simplicial complex.

(a) Assume $n \geqslant 2$. Show that the stellar subdivision of an n-simplex is equivariantly collapsible with respect to the natural vertex permutation action by S_{n+1}.

(b) Show that the barycentric subdivision of an n-simplex is equivariantly collapsible with respect to the same action.

(c) Show that the chromatic subdivision of an n-simplex is equivariantly collapsible with respect to the same action.

(8) Show the second line in Equation (10.5).

(9) Complete the proof of Lemma 10.26 by checking the correctness of the described collapsing sequence.

Chapter 11

Internal Collapses and Discrete Morse Theory

11.1. Replacing the simplicial complex with a smaller cellular complex: Theorem B

Assume $\mathcal{K}$ is an abstract simplicial complex. In Chapter 9 we have considered the situation where one chooses a simplicial subcomplex $\mathcal{L}$, and then matches all the simplices in the difference $\mathcal{K} \setminus \mathcal{L}$, using the so-called *acyclic matching*. In the simplicial picture, this leads to a collapsing sequence, whereas in the topological picture this leads to a strong deformation retraction, both of which are quite definitive conclusions.

Our next and in many respects primary goal is to relax that condition and to consider arbitrary acyclic matchings in the face poset $\mathsf{F}(\mathcal{K})$. Fortunately, in many specific situations, one can still achieve a rather satisfactory topological conclusion or, at the very least, say something meaningful about algebraic invariants of the underlying topological space.

Our basic setting will be as follows:

- We have an abstract simplicial complex $\mathcal{K}$.
- We let M be some fixed set of non-empty simplices of $\mathcal{K}$.
- We have an acyclic matching $\mu : \mathsf{M} \to \mathsf{M}$.

The central role will be played by those simplices which are not matched.

Definition 11.1. The non-empty simplices of $\mathcal{K}$ which do not belong to M are called *critical*.

Recall that, given a matching $\mu : \mathsf{M} \to \mathsf{M}$, we let $\mathsf{R}(\mu)$ denote the set of critical cells with respect to μ.

Theorem 11.2 (Theorem B). *Assume $\mathcal{K}$ is an abstract simplicial complex, M is some set of simplices of $\mathcal{K}$, and $\mu : \mathsf{M} \to \mathsf{M}$ is an acyclic matching. Then there exists a CW complex $\mathcal{X}$ such that*

(1) *for each dimension d, the number of d-cells in $\mathcal{X}$ is equal to the number of d-simplices in $\mathcal{K}$, which are critical with respect to μ,*

(2) *we have a homotopy equivalence $\mathcal{K} \simeq \mathcal{X}$.*

Before we can prove Theorem 11.2 we need to develop some terminology involving attachment maps, and to understand how varying these maps up to homotopy influences the topology of the space.

Still, we can already point out the following useful consequences of that theorem. In what follows, we will especially appreciate those acyclic matchings, which have no critical simplices in neighboring dimensions.

Definition 11.3. Let $\mathcal{K}$ be an abstract simplicial complex, and let C be some subset of the set of non-empty simplices of $\mathcal{K}$. The set C is called *sparse* if it does not contain a pair of simplices σ and τ in neighboring dimensions, that is, such that $|\dim \sigma - \dim \tau| = 1$.

The next corollary shows that the acyclic matchings with sparse sets of critical simplices are well-behaved.

Corollary 11.4. *Assume that as above $\mathcal{K}$ is an abstract simplicial complex, M is some subset of simplices of $\mathcal{K}$, and $\mu : \mathsf{M} \to \mathsf{M}$ is an acyclic matching. Assume furthermore the set $\mathsf{R}(\mu)$ is sparse. Then*

- *the integer homology groups of $\mathcal{K}$ are free,*
- *in each dimension d, the dth Betti number of $\mathcal{K}$ is equal to the number of critical d-simplices.*

Proof. Theorem 11.2 tells us that up to homotopy equivalence, the simplicial complex $\mathcal{K}$ can be replaced with the CW complex $\mathcal{X}$, with as many cells in each dimension as there are critical simplices. The fact that $\mathsf{R}(\mu)$ is sparse tells us that $\mathcal{X}$ does not have cells in neighboring dimensions. The homological conclusion then follows, since we know that the homology groups of CW complexes may be computed using the cellular chain complex. Of course, if a CW complex lacks cells in neighboring dimensions, all of the cellular boundary maps are zero, and its homology coincides with the cellular chain groups. □

Corollary 11.5. *If all the critical simplices are in the same dimension, then $\mathcal{K}$ is homotopy equivalent to a wedge of spheres. Specifically, we have*

$$\mathcal{K} \simeq \vee_{\sigma \in R(\mu)} S^{\dim \sigma}.$$

Proof. Continuing the argument of Corollary 11.4 we see that $\mathcal{X}$ has one cell in dimension 0, and all other cells have the same dimension, say d. There is however only one such CW complex, as all the gluing must be trivial. This complex is a wedge of d-spheres, and the number of spheres is equal to the number of d-cells. □

As a simple example of applying Corollary 11.5 let us consider a skeleton of a simplex. So let us assume $n \geqslant 1$ and $n \geqslant d \geqslant 0$.

Proposition 11.6. *The d-skeleton of an n-simplex is homotopy equivalent to a wedge of $\binom{n}{d+1}$ copies of d-dimensional spheres.*

Proof. Let $\mathcal{K}$ denote the d-skeleton of an n-simplex, and consider its face poset $F(\mathcal{K})$. In the standard combinatorial setting, the elements of this poset (i.e., the simplices of $\mathcal{K}$) are indexed by all subsets $A \subseteq [n]$, such that $|A| \leqslant d+1$.

Consider the matching $\mu : A \to A \operatorname{XOR} n$, where as before XOR denotes *exclusive OR*. In other words, we set

$$\mu(A) := \begin{cases} A \cup \{n\}, & \text{if } n \notin A, \\ A \setminus \{n\}, & \text{otherwise.} \end{cases}$$

It is easy to check that there is one critical 0-simplex, namely $\{n\}$, and there are $\binom{n}{d+1}$ critical d-simplices, indexed by the sets $\{x_0, \dots, x_d\}$, for all $0 \leqslant x_0 < \dots < x_d \leqslant n-1$.

Furthermore, the matching μ is acyclic. This is because in any cycle $b_1 \succ \mu_-(b_1) \prec b_2 \succ \dots$, we would have $\mu_-(b_1) = b_1 \setminus \{n\}$ and $n \in b_2$, hence $b_2 = \mu_-(b_1) \cup \{n\} = b_1$, yielding a contradiction.

The result then follows from Corollary 11.5. □

More examples will follow in Section 11.5.

11.2. Internal collapses and attachment maps

Let us now develop some intuition and machinery to prove Theorem 11.2. If the quintessential example of the elementary collapse in Chapter 9 was the removing of a leaf from a tree, the quintessential example of what we call an *internal collapse* here is the shrinking of an edge *inside* a graph.

Accordingly, let us start by considering a cycle with 4 vertices, thought of as a 1-dimensional simplicial complex. The complex does not have any free simplex, as any vertex is adjacent to two edges. Hence, no elementary collapse can be performed, and the methods described in Chapter 9 cannot be used. It is however possible to let one of the edges shrink, to form a cycle c with three vertices. This will not change the topology while reducing the total number of vertices and edges; see Figure 11.1.

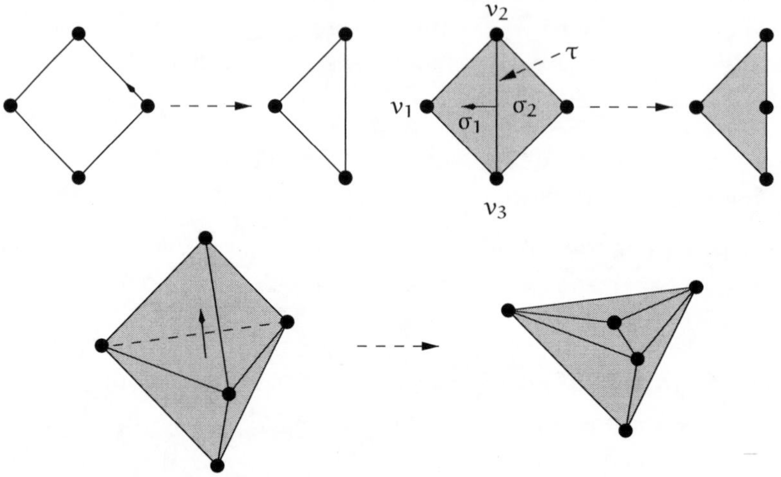

Figure 11.1. Various internal collapses.

A slight problem with this approach is to decide how to proceed with the cycle c. One way forward is to allow graphs with multiple edges. In this case, we can still shrink an edge in c to obtain a graph with 2 vertices and a double edge. If we allow loops on top of that, we can shrink again, to end up with a graph consisting of a single vertex and a loop. This is then in a certain sense the optimal, most compact presentation of the topology of the graph which we have had at the beginning.

As far as the connected graphs are concerned, the situation is simple. We can always shrink some edges one after the other to end up with a graph consisting of a single vertex and a bunch of loops. This can be done in an organized fashion by first choosing the so-called spanning tree, as described in Subsection 2.7.3. It is not difficult to adapt this to the case of disconnected graphs. For each graph, simply do this procedure in each connected component and end up with a graph which has only loops.

Things will get more complex once we go one up in the dimension. Consider the simplicial complex in the upper right corner of Figure 11.1. It consists of two triangles σ_1 and σ_2 sharing an edge τ. The edge τ is not free, so it cannot be removed using any elementary collapse. On the other hand, there is a clear geometric procedure of removing that edge together with the triangle σ_1. It can be visualized in the same way as we did for the elementary collapses. Envision a piece of cord connecting the vertex v_1 to the barycenter of τ, and let the cord shrink, while keeping v_1 fixed. It will eventually let σ_1 vanish completely, with σ_2 filling in and becoming a rectangle. The edge τ will also vanish, merging into the edges $\{v_1, v_2\}$ and $\{v_1, v_3\}$.

An alternative way to think of this is in terms of the attaching maps; see Definition 3.9. If we did not have the triangle σ_2 to start with, then we would be looking at the deformation associated to an elementary collapse, as we explained in Chapter 9. So let us think of the whole space as being obtained from a base space which does not include σ_2. Here that would be just the triangle σ_1, by *attaching* σ_2 using some continuous map. Then we could imagine just doing the elementary collapse on the base space, and then reattaching σ_2 to the result. Following this thinking, we would need to trace what happens to that attachment map, when the elementary collapse on the base space is performed.

The first and immediate problem which we then have is that, unlike in the graph situation, we must leave the world of simplicial complexes at once. Most internal collapses will destroy the simplicial structure. There are two ways to deal with this problem. One option would be to switch to the more general category of CW complexes. This allows for a more flexible work. The downside is clearly that the gluing procedure for the complex is not given anymore using purely combinatorial data. Instead, we need to specify continuous attachment maps: something which in many practical contexts may be rather prohibitive. We pursue the approach using CW complexes in Chapter 17.

Another option would be to work in the broader context of chain complexes. This turns out to be very fruitful and will be done in Section 15.1.

11.3. Attaching cells to homotopy equivalent spaces

Let us show the following standard fact concerning adjunction spaces which will be of major importance in our proof of Theorem 11.2.

Theorem 11.7. *Assume* X_1 *and* X_2 *are two homotopy equivalent topological spaces, and let* $h : X_1 \to X_2$ *be a homotopy equivalence. Let* σ *be a cell with attachment maps* $f_1 : \partial\sigma \to X_1$ *and* $f_2 : \partial\sigma \to X_2$*, such that* $h \circ f_1$ *is homotopic to* f_2*. Then the space* $X_1 \cup_{f_1} \sigma$ *is homotopy equivalent to the space* $X_2 \cup_{f_2} \sigma$*.*

An example of attaching over homotopy equivalent spaces is shown in Figure 11.2. A 2-dimensional disc is attached to a Möbius band over its boundary. The Möbius band is homotopy equivalent to a circle, so we might as well attach to the circle, yielding a projective plane.

Proof of Theorem 11.7. The homotopy equivalence in Theorem 11.7 can be described by giving an explicit map $f : X_1 \cup_{f_1} \sigma \to X_2 \cup_{f_2} \sigma$. This map is induced by the map h, and by the homotopy $H : \partial\sigma \times I \to X_2$ satisfying $H(\partial\sigma, 0) = f_2$, $H(\partial\sigma, 1) = h \circ f_1$. To describe f, we identify σ with the unit disc D^n, and $\partial\sigma$ with the bounding unit sphere S^{n-1}. Then we set

$$f(x) := h(x), \qquad \text{for } x \in X_1,$$

$$f(t\mathbf{v}) := \begin{cases} 2t\mathbf{v}, & \text{for } 0 \leqslant t \leqslant 1/2, \quad \mathbf{v} \in S^{n-1}, \\ H(\mathbf{v}, 2t-1), & \text{for } 1/2 \leqslant t \leqslant 1, \quad \mathbf{v} \in S^{n-1}. \end{cases}$$

We leave the verification of the details to the reader; see Exercise (6). □

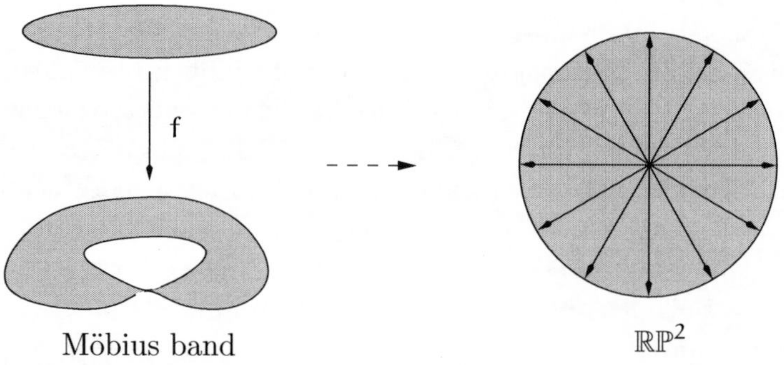

Figure 11.2. Attaching a disc to the Möbius band produces the projective plane.

The following two special cases of Theorem 11.7 are often distinguished as those of particular importance.

Case 1. $X_1 = X_2$ *and* $h = \mathrm{id}_{X_1}$.

This special case is used for example when justifying the fact that the homotopy type of a CW complex does not change when the attachment maps are replaced by the homotopic ones. Figure 11.3 shows an example of such a situation. On the right we see the attachment map from S^1 to S^1 which wraps around 3 times: twice in one direction, and then once in the opposite direction. The resulting adjunction space is the so-called *Dunce hat.* However, this attachment map is clearly homotopic to the trivial one. Replacing the map with the homotopic one will yield the adjunction space which is just a 2-dimensional disc. This space is contractible, hence the original Dunce hat is contractible as well.

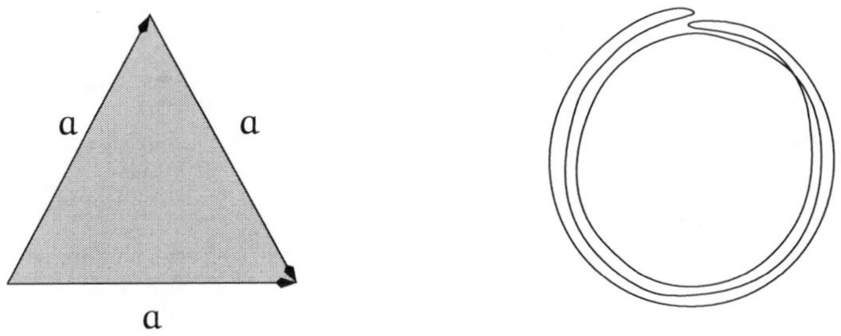

Figure 11.3. Changing the attachment map by a homotopy can show that the Dunce hat is contractible.

Case 2. $h \circ f_1 = f_2$.

In fact, if $h \circ f_1 = f_2$, then it is much simpler to describe the homotopy equivalence map $f : X_1 \cup_{f_1} \sigma \to X_2 \cup_{f_2} \sigma$. Specifically, we set

$$f(x) := \begin{cases} h(x), & \text{for } x \in X_1; \\ x, & \text{for } x \in \operatorname{Int} \sigma. \end{cases} \tag{11.1}$$

11.4. Organizing internal collapses

We shall find that a fruitful alternative to actually carrying out internal collapses geometrically and to tracing the evolution of the attachment maps, as we did in the previous section, will be to restrict ourselves to merely keeping records of which internal collapses were performed.

Under this approach, we could stay within the realm of abstract simplicial complexes. However, we would need to deal with the additional complication that some of the pairs of simplices are already marked as *internally collapsed.* (See Figure 11.4.) Any further internal collapses would need to take into account the existence of these previous ones.

Fortunately, the technical tool needed to express these conditions has already been introduced. As the formulation of Theorem 11.2 indicates, all we need to do is to restrict ourselves to acyclic matchings only.

As a warm-up, let us show that when μ is an acyclic matching in a nonempty abstract simplicial complex $\mathcal{K}$, we can always find a critical simplex in dimension 0. Indeed, if $\dim \mathcal{K} = 0$, then all the 0-simplices are critical. Otherwise, let $\dim \mathcal{K} \geqslant 1$ and assume there are no critical 0-simplices. This means that μ is defined on the entire set $\mathcal{K}(0)$. Consider a bipartite graph G, whose set of vertices is $\mathcal{K}(0) \cup \mathcal{K}(1)$. The edges between simplices are defined as above. Two simplices are connected by an edge if and only if one of them contains the other one. The orientation of edges between two matched simplices is towards the simplex of dimension 1, while the orientation of the other edges is towards the simplex of dimension 0.

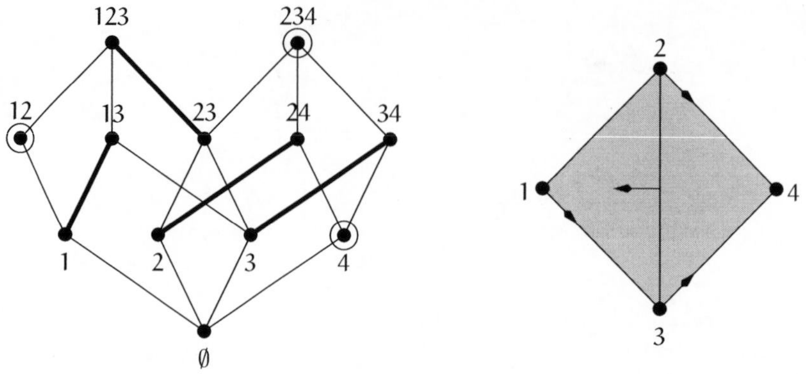

Figure 11.4. An acyclic matching and the corresponding sequence of internal collapses.

As was already mentioned, acyclicity of the matching implies that the graph G is acyclic. We know from graph theory that a finite acyclic directed graph will have at least one *sink*, a vertex with no outgoing edges. To find this sink, simply start from any vertex and follow the outgoing edges as long as you can: you will either find a sink or a cycle. If this sink is a simplex of dimension 0, we get a contradiction, as each one must have the outgoing edge corresponding to the matching. If, on the other hand, this sink is a simplex of dimension 1, we get a contradiction again, and since each simplex of dimension 1 has two adjacent edges, at least one of them is not a matching edge, so it must be an outgoing one.

This little argument provides a simplified example of the type of considerations that we need in order to prove Theorem 11.2. To get a little more structural understanding we introduce a certain generalization of collapsing orders.

Definition 11.8. Given a poset P, a *linear extension* L of P is a total order $<_L$ on the elements of P, such that $x < y$, for $x, y \in P$, implies $x <_L y$.

Linear extensions are easy to define, but can turn out to be surprisingly complicated. Even for the Boolean algebra the set of all linear extensions is an interesting object, and the cardinality of this set is a subject of research.

Theorem 11.9 (Acyclic matchings via linear extensions). *A partial matching on a poset P is acyclic if and only if there exists a linear extension L of P, such that the elements a and $\mu(a)$ follow consequently in L.*

Proof. Assume first that we have a linear extension L satisfying this property, and, at the same time we have a cycle as in (10.1). Set $a_i = \mu_-(b_i)$ for $i = 1, \dots, n$. Then

$$b_{i+1} \succ a_i \Rightarrow a_i <_L b_{i+1} \Rightarrow a_i <_L a_{i+1}$$

(since a_{i+1}, b_{i+1} follow consequently in L). Thus $a_n >_L a_{n-1} >_L \cdots >_L a_1 >_L a_0 = a_n$, yielding a contradiction.

In order to show the reverse direction, assume that we are given an acyclic matching, and let us define L inductively. Let Q denote the set of elements which are already ordered in L. We start with $Q = \emptyset$. Let W denote the set of the minimal elements in $P \setminus Q$. At each step we have one of the following cases.

Case 1. *One of the elements* c *in* W *is critical.*

In this case, we simply add c to the order L as the largest element, and proceed with $Q \cup \{c\}$.

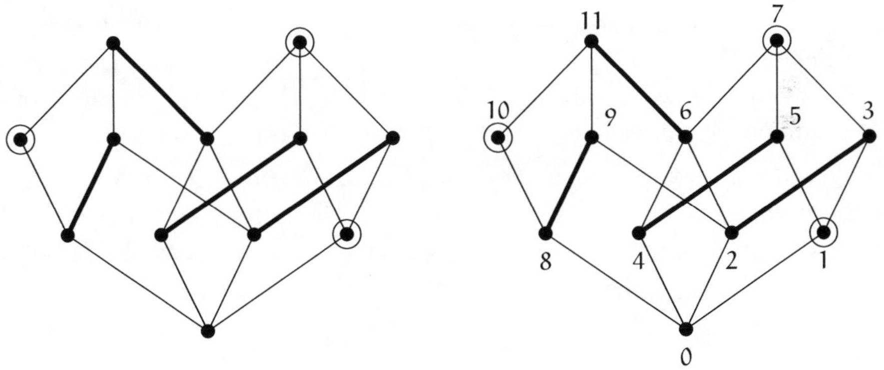

Figure 11.5. Acyclic matching and the corresponding linear extension.

Case 2. *All elements in* W *are matched.*

Consider the subgraph of the underlying graph of the Hasse diagram of $P \setminus Q$ induced by $W \cup \mu(W)$. Orient its edges as described above, i.e., they should point from the larger element to the smaller one in all cases, except when these two elements are matched, in which case the edge should point from the smaller element to the larger one. Call this directed graph G.

If there exists an element $a \in W$, such that the only element in $W \cup \mu(W)$, which is smaller than $\mu(a)$, is a itself, then we can add elements a and $\mu(a)$ on top of L and proceed with $Q \cup \{a, \mu(a)\}$. Otherwise, we see that the outdegree of $\mu(a)$ in G is positive, for each $a \in W$. On the other hand, the outdegrees in G of all $a \in W$ are equal to 1. Since, therefore, outdegrees of all vertices in the directed graph G are positive, we conclude that G must have a cycle, which clearly contradicts the assumption that the considered matching is acyclic. □

An example of a linear extension derived from an acyclic matching by this procedure is shown on Figure 11.5.

We now proceed with the proof of Theorem 11.2.

Proof of Theorem 11.2. Theorem 11.9 tells us that $\mathcal{K}$ can be obtained constructively by starting with a vertex and then at each step either adding a critical simplex, or performing the inverse of a collapse, which, as we recall, is called *expansion*.

So take a linear extension L satisfying the conditions of Theorem 11.9. We perform induction on the cardinality of $\mathsf{F}(\mathcal{K})$. If $|\mathsf{F}(\mathcal{K})| = 1$, the statement is clear. For the induction step, let σ be the last cell in L.

Case 1. *The cell σ is critical.*

Let $\widetilde{\mathcal{K}} = \mathcal{K} \setminus \sigma$, so $|\widetilde{\mathcal{K}}| = |\mathcal{K}| \setminus \operatorname{Int}\sigma$. Let $\varphi : \partial\sigma \to \widetilde{\mathcal{K}}$ be the attaching map of σ in $\mathcal{K}$. The matching μ restricted to $\widetilde{\mathcal{K}}$ is again acyclic, and the critical simplices are the same, with σ missing. Hence, by induction, there exists a CW complex $\widetilde{\mathcal{X}}$, with cells of $\widetilde{\mathcal{X}}$ enumerated by the critical simplices of $\widetilde{\mathcal{K}}$, and a homotopy equivalence $\mathsf{h} : |\widetilde{\mathcal{K}}| \to \widetilde{\mathcal{X}}$.

Consider the composition attaching map $\mathsf{h} \circ \varphi : \partial\sigma \to \widetilde{\mathcal{X}}$; see Figure 11.6. By Theorem 11.7, we conclude that we have a homotopy equivalence $|\widetilde{\mathcal{K}}| \cup_\varphi \sigma \simeq \widetilde{\mathcal{X}} \cup_{\mathsf{h}\circ\varphi} \sigma$. Note that $|\mathcal{K}| = |\widetilde{\mathcal{K}}| \cup_\varphi \sigma$. The theorem follows by induction if we set $\mathcal{X} := \widetilde{\mathcal{X}} \cup_{\mathsf{h}\circ\varphi} \sigma$.

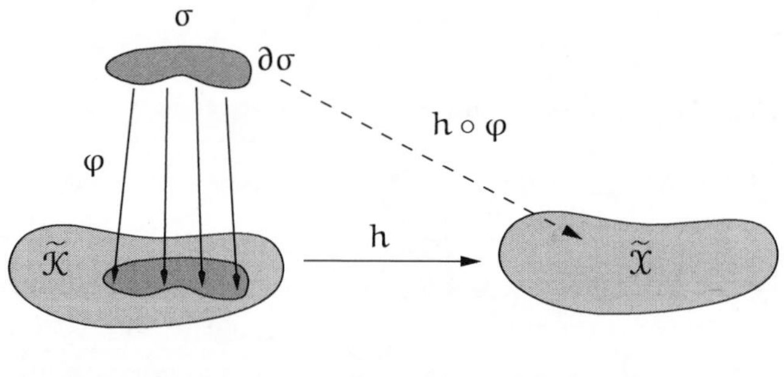

Figure 11.6. Attaching a critical cell.

Case 2. *The cell σ is not critical.*

In this case we must have $\sigma, \mu_-(\sigma) \in \mathsf{M}$. Note that $\mu_-(\sigma)$ is maximal in $\mathsf{F}(\mathcal{K}) \setminus \sigma$, and let $\widetilde{\mathcal{K}} = \mathcal{K} \setminus (\sigma, \mu_-(\sigma))$, so $|\widetilde{\mathcal{K}}| = |\mathcal{K}| \setminus (\operatorname{Int}\sigma \cup \operatorname{Int}\mu_-(\sigma))$.

Clearly, removing the pair $(\sigma, \mu_-(\sigma))$ is a simplicial collapse, in particular, there exists a homotopy equivalence $\mathsf{f} : |\mathcal{K}| \to |\widetilde{\mathcal{K}}|$. On the other hand, by the induction assumption, there exists a CW complex $\widetilde{\mathcal{X}}$, whose cells are indexed by the critical simplices of $\widetilde{\mathcal{X}}$, and a homotopy equivalence $\widetilde{\mathsf{f}} : |\widetilde{\mathcal{K}}| \to \widetilde{\mathcal{X}}$. Hence, setting $\mathcal{X} := \widetilde{\mathcal{X}}$, we obtain the desired homotopy equivalence $\widetilde{\mathsf{f}} \circ \mathsf{f} : |\mathcal{K}| \to \mathcal{X}$. □

11.5. Examples of computation

11.5.1. Complexes of disconnected graphs. As our first example we return to considering the simplicial complex of disconnected graphs on n vertices.

Definition 11.10. Let n be a positive integer. A *recursive tree* on n vertices is a labeled rooted tree whose vertices are distinctly labeled by integers $1, 2, \dots, n$, such that the labels are strictly increasing along each path starting at the root.

Note that as a consequence of the condition in Definition 11.10, in a recursive tree the root itself must always be labeled 1, and, if $n \geqslant 2$, one of its adjacent vertices must have label 2.

For the purposes of this subsection, let R_n denote the set of all recursive trees on n vertices. Recursive trees are also known as *increasing Cayley trees.* They can alternatively be defined as the trees on vertices labeled 1 through n, satisfying the following property:

> for each $2 \leqslant k \leqslant n$, the vertex labeled k is adjacent to exactly one of the vertices labeled $1, \dots, k-1$.

From this, one can easily construct all the recursive trees by scanning the vertices 2 through n, and choosing for each vertex k to which of the vertices $1, \dots, k-1$ it must be connected. In particular, the number of recursive trees on n vertices is $(n-1)!$.

From now on, let us assume that $n \geqslant 2$, and let us label the edges with the pair of labels associated to its vertices. As mentioned above, each recursive tree must have the edge labeled $(1, 2)$. Let Q_n denote the set of graphs obtained from the recursive trees in R_n by deleting this edge. Of course, we have the equality $|Q_n| = |R_n| = (n-1)!$, and all the graphs in Q_n are disconnected, with precisely two connected components, where vertices 1 and 2 belong to different components.

Proposition 11.11. *For each integer n, $n \geqslant 3$, there exists an acyclic matching μ on the simplicial complex* Disc_n*, such that the set of critical simplices of μ is Q_n. In particular,* Disc_n *is homotopy equivalent to the wedge of $(n-1)!$ copies of $(n-3)$-dimensional spheres.*

Proof. To construct an acyclic matching we start by taking a disconnected graph G and matching it with $G \operatorname{XOR}(1, 2)$, when possible. Consider the graphs left unmatched: these are

- the graph consisting of a single edge $(1, 2)$; this will be the critical 0-simplex in our matching;

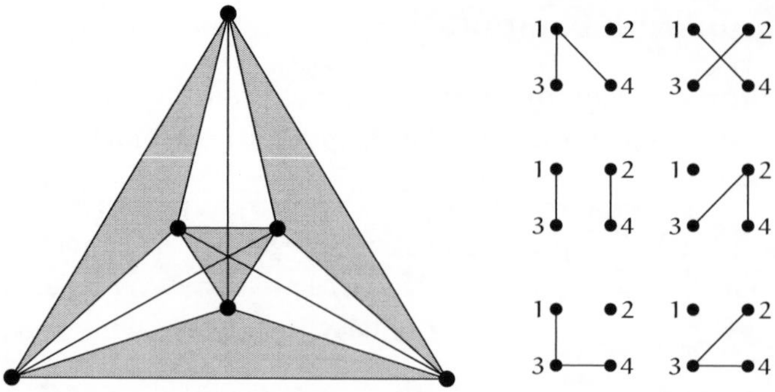

Figure 11.7. The acyclic matching on the complex of disconnected graphs on 4 vertices defined in the proof of Proposition 11.11, and the graphs labeling the critical simplices.

- the disconnected graphs G which do not contain the edge $(1, 2)$, and which will become connected if the edge $(1, 2)$ is added.

Now let H be a disconnected graph, such that $H \cup (1, 2)$ is connected. It must have precisely two connected components, one of them containing the vertex 1 and the other one containing the vertex 2. Accordingly, we label these components H_1 and H_2. Assume the vertex 3 belongs to H_k, where $k \in \{1, 2\}$. Now, if possible, match H with $H\,\mathrm{XOR}(i, 3)$.

Let us see which graphs will be left unmatched. Clearly, since 3 is already in the connected component H_k, adding the edge $(k, 3)$ will not make the graph connected. So the only way something may go wrong is that H_k contains the edge $(k, 3)$, and removing it would increase the number of connected components. This is because the graph $H_k \setminus (i, 3)$ has already been matched with $H_k \cup (1, 2) \setminus (i, 3)$. So the only graphs which are left unmatched are precisely those which have two connected components, containing 1 and 2 respectively, and furthermore containing an edge $(k, 3)$ for some $k \in 1, 2$, such that this edge is a bridge.[1]

We now proceed performing a similar matching for vertices 4 through n. At each step, for $4 \leqslant k \leqslant n$, we have unmatched simplices G which have the following structure:

- the subgraph H of G induced by the vertices $1, \ldots, k$ lies in Q_k;
- the edges of H (it has $k-2$ edges) are all bridges in G, and removing these edges from G produces a graph with k connected components T_i, each one containing one of the vertices $1, \ldots, k$.

[1]Recall that a *bridge* in the graph is an edge whose removal increases the number of connected components.

Let C_k denote the set of graphs satisfying these conditions. Figure 11.8 shows schematically what such an unmatched graph looks like. We note that C_{n+1} coincides with Q_n.

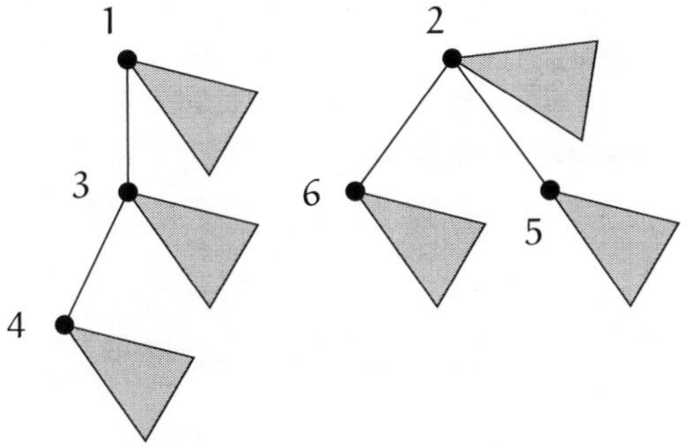

Figure 11.8. Tree decomposition used in the proof of Proposition 11.11.

When performing step k, choose $1 \leqslant m \leqslant k-1$, such that k belongs to T_m. We would now like to match the graph G with $G\,\mathrm{XOR}(m,k)$, if possible. The argument now repeats the one above, where $k = 3$. Adding the edge (m,k) is always possible, but removing may not be. Specifically, removing (m,k) will not work if it is a bridge. In this case the number of connected components would increase, resulting in the graph $G \setminus (m,k)$, which in turn has already been matched with $G \cup (1,2) \setminus (m,k)$. We conclude that the set of graphs indexing the simplices which are left unmatched after the step k is precisely C_k.

Let us show that the matching which we produced is acyclic. Assume the contrary and take a cycle

$$b_1 \prec \mu(b_1) \succ b_2 \prec \mu(b_2) \succ \cdots \succ b_t \prec \mu(b_t) \succ b_1,$$

where $t \geqslant 2$. Assume $\mu(b_i) = b_i \cup (m_i, k_i)$, with $m_i < k_i$, for all $i = 1, \dots, t$. Without loss of generality, we can assume that k_2 is the minimal element of the set $\{k_1, \dots, k_t\}$.

If $k_2 = 2$, then $(m_2, k_2) = (1,2)$. This implies that $(1,2) \in \mu(b_1)$, which is a contradiction, since when the edge $(1,2)$ belongs to the graph, the matching μ will always delete it.

We can thus assume $k_2 \geqslant 3$. Since adding the edge (m_2, k_2) to b_2 is allowed, we know m_2 and k_2 are in the same connected component of b_2. But then, clearly, they are also in the same connected component of $\mu(b_1)$. By our assumption, $k_2 < k_1$, so applying μ to $\mu(b_1)$ should add the edge (m_2, k_2), rather than to delete the edge (m_1, k_1). This yields the contradiction to the existence of the cycle above.

Finally, the set of critical simplices is $C_{n+1} = Q_n$, so the conclusion follows from Corollary 11.5. Figure 11.7 illustrates our argument. □

11.5.2. The order complex of the partition lattice. Let us now return to the partition lattice Π_n. For convenience, we shall skip the singletons in our partition notation. We shall call partitions which have a unique nonsingleton part *blocks*. Finally, for the purposes of this subsection, the *special blocks* are the blocks containing n in that unique nonsingleton part.

Let A_n be the set of all *saturated chains*[2] in $\Pi_n \setminus \{\hat{0}, \hat{1}\}$ consisting entirely of special blocks, i.e.,

$$A_n := \{(\alpha_1 n) < \cdots < (\alpha_1 \ldots \alpha_{n-2} n) \,|\, \alpha_1, \ldots, \alpha_{n-2} \in \{1, \ldots, n-1\}\}. \tag{11.2}$$

Note that $|A_n| = (n-1)!$.

Proposition 11.12. *Let $\mathcal{K}_n$ be the reduced order complex of the partition lattice, i.e., $\mathcal{K}_n := \widetilde{\Delta}(\Pi_n)$, $n \geqslant 3$. Then there exists an acyclic matching μ on $\mathcal{K}_n$, such that the set of critical simplices of μ is A_n. In particular, $\mathcal{K}_n$ is homotopy equivalent to the wedge of $(n-1)!$ copies of $(n-3)$-dimensional spheres.*

Of course, we already know the validity of the last statement of Proposition 11.12, as it follows from Propositions 10.38 and 11.11. What we are interested in here is the actual collapsing sequence.

Proof of Proposition 11.12. By definition of the order complex, the maximal simplices of $\mathcal{K}_n$ are indexed by saturated chains of $\Pi_n \setminus \{\hat{0}, \hat{1}\}$. We describe a matching μ such that the set of critical simplices $R(\mu)$ is precisely A_n.

Let a chain of the type

$$(\alpha_1 n) < (\alpha_1 \alpha_2 n) < \cdots < (\alpha_1 \ldots \alpha_k n), \text{ where } \alpha_1, \ldots, \alpha_k \in \{1, \ldots, n-1\},$$

be called a *special* k-*prefix*. For an arbitrary simplex σ, we let $h(\sigma)$ denote the maximal k, such that σ contains a special k-prefix. We call $h(\sigma)$ the *prefix height* of σ. In particular, we have $h(\sigma) = n-2$ if and only if $\sigma \in A_n$; cf. (11.2). We set $h(\sigma) := 0$ if σ does not contain any special k-prefix at all.

Let us now pick a simplex σ in $\mathcal{K}_n \setminus A_n$, say $\sigma = (\pi_1 < \cdots < \pi_t)$, and set $h := h(\sigma)$, $h \leqslant n-3$. We can write

$$\sigma = (\alpha_1 n) < (\alpha_1 \alpha_2 n) < \cdots < (\alpha_1 \ldots \alpha_h n) < \pi_{h+1} < \ldots,$$

where π_{h+1} may not exist, but if it does, then we have $\pi_{h+1} \neq (\alpha_1 \ldots \alpha_{h+1} n)$, for any α_{h+1}. Set $B_\sigma := \{\alpha_1 \ldots \alpha_h n\}$, and consider a specific coatom[3] γ_σ

[2] Recall that a poset chain is called *saturated* if it is properly contained in any other chain.
[3] Recall that in a poset P with maximal element $\hat{1}$, a *coatom* is an element covered only by $\hat{1}$.

of Π_n, which consists of two parts: B_σ and its complement, i.e., set

$$\gamma_\sigma := (B_\sigma)(\{1,\dots,n\} \setminus B_\sigma).$$

Recall that $\wedge$ denotes the meet operation in the lattice, where the meet of two elements x and y is the maximal element which is less than or equal to than both x and y. Let π be a partition, such that B_σ is contained in one of the parts of π. Then, the meet $\pi \wedge \gamma_\sigma$ is obtained from π by splitting off B_σ from the part that contains it.

Next, let m denote the maximal index in the range $h \leqslant m \leqslant t-1$, such that π_m contains B_σ as a part, whereas π_{m+1} does not. If all partitions $\pi_h, \dots, \pi_t$ contain the set B_σ as a part, we set $m := t$, and furthermore $\pi_{m+1} := (1\dots n) = \hat{1}$.

We are now ready to define the partition $\mu(\sigma)$. In the short notation, we could simply write

$$\mu(\sigma) := \sigma \,\mathrm{XOR}(\pi_{m+1} \wedge \gamma_\sigma).$$

When expanded, this formula would read

$$\mu(\sigma) := \begin{cases} \sigma \setminus \pi_m, & \text{if } \pi_m = \pi_{m+1} \wedge \gamma_\sigma, \\ \sigma \cup (\pi_{m+1} \wedge \gamma_\sigma), & \text{if } \pi_m \neq \pi_{m+1} \wedge \gamma_\sigma, \end{cases}$$

where $\sigma \setminus \pi_m$ means that we delete the partition π_m from the chain σ, whereas $\sigma \cup (\pi_{m+1} \wedge \gamma_\sigma)$ means that we insert the partition $\pi_{m+1} \wedge \gamma_\sigma$ into the chain σ. The latter is well-defined since obviously $\pi_{m+1} > \pi_{m+1} \wedge \gamma_\sigma$, and furthermore, by our choice of m, we have $\pi_{m+1} \wedge \gamma_\sigma \geqslant \pi_m$. An example of matching μ for $n = 4$ is shown in Figure 11.9.

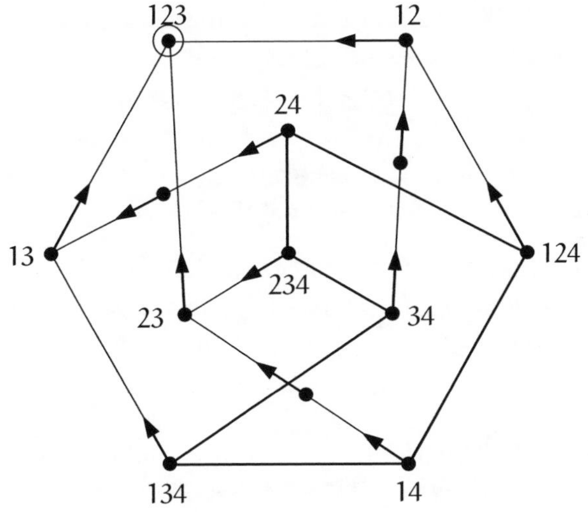

Figure 11.9. The matching μ for Π_4.

To see that μ is well-defined and that $R(\mu) = A_n$ is a straightforward verification.

To see that the matching μ is acyclic, pick a presumptive cycle. For any two simplices σ and τ, $\sigma \succ \tau$ implies $h(\sigma) \geqslant h(\tau)$. Since we also have the equality along the matching edges, this means that the prefix height is preserved in a cycle. Furthermore, let the *capacity* of σ be the number of partitions outside of the special prefix which do not contain B_σ as a part. Matched partitions have equal capacity. We leave it as an exercise to show that following the non-matching edges down along a cycle will always decrease capacity by 1. This yields a contradiction. □

11.6. An acyclic matching associated to a sequence of vertices

In this section we describe a standard way to obtain an acyclic matching associated to an ordered subset of the set of vertices of an arbitrary simplicial complex.

Let $\mathcal{K}$ be a simplicial complex, and let $S = \{v_1, \dots, v_n\}$ be a subset of the set of vertices of $\mathcal{K}$. Fix the order on the set S given by the indices. We now construct a matching, which we call μ_S, using the following procedure.

Step 1. For each simplex σ, such that $\sigma \,\mathrm{XOR}\, v_1$ belongs to $\mathcal{K}$, we match σ with $\sigma \,\mathrm{XOR}\, v_1$. Let M_1 denote the set of all matched simplices.

For all $k = 2, \dots, n$, starting with $k = 2$, and increasing k by 1 at each step, repeat the following.

Step k. For each simplex σ in $\mathcal{K} \setminus (M_1 \cup \dots \cup M_{k-1})$, such that $\sigma \,\mathrm{XOR}\, v_k$ also belongs to $\mathcal{K} \setminus (M_1 \cup \dots \cup M_{k-1})$, we match σ with $\sigma \,\mathrm{XOR}\, v_k$. Let M_k denote the set of all simplices newly matched at this step.

In the end, we call the obtained matching μ_S, denote the set of matched simplices by $M_S := M_1 \cup \dots \cup M_n$, and, finally, denote the set of critical simplices by $C_S := \mathcal{K} \setminus M_S$. It is useful to know that the obtained matching is always acyclic as the next theorem states.

Theorem 11.13. *Assume $\mathcal{K}$ is an arbitrary simplicial complex, $S = \{v_1, \dots, v_n\}$ is a subset of the set of vertices of $\mathcal{K}$, and μ_S is the corresponding matching as defined above. Then, for any choice of S, the matching μ_S is acyclic.*

Proof. Assume, on the contrary, that the matching μ_S is not acyclic. This means that there exists an integer $t \geqslant 2$, and simplices $\sigma_1, \dots, \sigma_t$ in $\mathcal{K}$, such that

$$\sigma_1 \prec \mu_S(\sigma_1) \succ \sigma_2 \prec \mu_S(\sigma_2) \succ \dots \succ \sigma_t \prec \mu_S(\sigma_t) \succ \sigma_1. \tag{11.3}$$

Choose the minimal index k, for which there exists $1 \leqslant m \leqslant t$, such that $\sigma_m \in M_k$. Without loss of generality, we can shift the indices of $\sigma_1, \dots, \sigma_t$, so that $m = 1$. So $\sigma_1 \in M_k$, and, in particular, we have $v_k \notin \sigma_1$, and $\mu_S(\sigma_1) = \sigma_1 \cup v_k$.

Furthermore, since σ_2 is obtained from $\mu_S(\sigma_1)$ by deleting one vertex, and $\sigma_1 \neq \sigma_2$ (as we have assumed that $t \geqslant 2$), we must have $v_k \in \sigma_2$. On the other hand, by our construction, we have $\mu_S(\sigma_t) \succ \sigma_1$, $v_k \notin \sigma_1$, and $\mu_S(\sigma_t) \neq \mu_S(\sigma_1) = \sigma_1 \cup v_k$. Therefore, we must have $v_k \notin \mu_S(\sigma_t)$, and so, of course, also $v_k \notin \sigma_t$.

Now let l be the minimal index, such that $l \neq 1$, and $v_k \notin \sigma_l$. By what is said above, we must have $3 \leqslant l \leqslant t$. Assume first that $v_k \notin \mu_S(\sigma_{l-1})$. Then also $v_k \notin \sigma_{l-1}$. This contradicts the minimality of l, since $l > 2$. So we conclude that $v_k \in \mu_S(\sigma_{l-1})$, which means that $\mu_S(\sigma_{l-1}) = \sigma_l \cup v_k$.

Since σ_l and $\mu_S(\sigma_{l-1})$ are not matched to each other, there exist indices p and q, such that $\sigma_l \in M_p$, $\mu_S(\sigma_{l-1}) \in M_q$, and $p, q \neq k$. We have chosen k to be minimal, so $p, q > k$. We clearly have $\sigma_l, \mu_S(\sigma_{l-1}) \in \mathcal{K} \setminus (M_1 \cup \dots \cup M_{k-1})$. But then nothing is stopping us from matching σ_l with $\mu_S(\sigma_{l-1}) = \sigma_l \,\mathrm{XOR}\, v_k$ at step k above. This clearly contradicts the fact that $\sigma_l \in M_p$, $\mu_S(\sigma_{l-1}) \in M_q$.

Hence the situation given by (11.3) cannot happen, and the matching μ_S must be acyclic. □

Exercises

(1) Describe the set of all collapsing sequences of a given tree using the language of increasing Cayley trees.

(2) Show that a d-skeleton of an n-cube is homotopy equivalent to a wedge of d-dimensional spheres, by using the same technique as in our proof of Proposition 11.6. What about general polytopes?

(3) Use Theorem 11.2 to find the homotopy type of the independence complex of the graph G, where
  (1) G is a path graph;
  (2) G is an arbitrary tree;
  (3) G is a cycle.

(4) Find the homotopy type of the simplicial complex of independent sets of a matroid.

(5) A *flag* in a vector space V is a sequence of vector subspaces strictly containing each other. The simplicial complex of flags is defined by taking all vector subspaces of V as vertices, and taking flags as simplices.

Let $\mathrm{Flag}_{\mathbf{k}}^{\mathrm{d}}$ denote the simplicial complex of flags in the d-dimensional vector space over a finite field $\mathbf{k}$. Find the homotopy type of $\mathrm{Flag}_{\mathbf{k}}^{\mathrm{d}}$.

(6) Complete the proof of Theorem 11.7.

(7) Complete the proof of Proposition 11.12.

Chapter 12

Explicit Homology Classes Associated to Critical Cells

12.1. The graph $G_d(\mu)$ and its use

Let us now describe how in some cases discrete Morse theory allows us to find explicit homology classes.

Definition 12.1. Assume we are given an abstract simplicial complex $\mathcal{K}$ and an acyclic matching μ. For every d, between 0 and $\dim \mathcal{K}$, the directed graph $G_d(\mu)$ is defined as follows:

- the vertices of $G_d(\mu)$ are indexed by the d-dimensional simplices of $\mathcal{K}$;
- the edges of $G_d(\mu)$ are given by the rule: (α, β) is an edge of $G_d(\mu)$ if and only if $\mu(\beta)$ is defined, and $\alpha \succ \mu(\beta)$; see Figure 12.1.

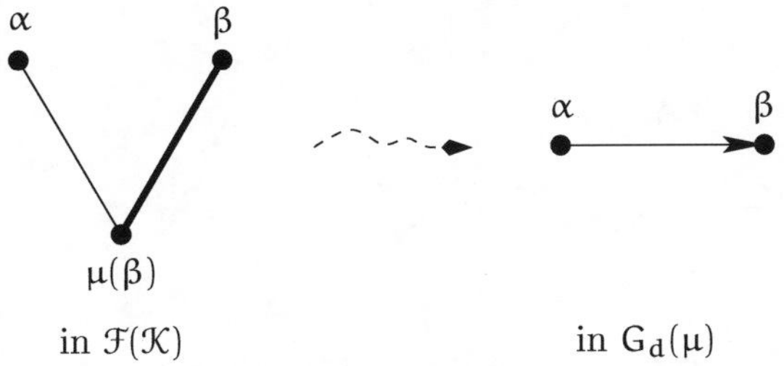

Figure 12.1. The rule defining the edges of the directed graph $G_d(\mu)$.

Obviously, the acyclicity of the matching μ is equivalent to the acyclicity of the directed graph $G_d(\mu)$.

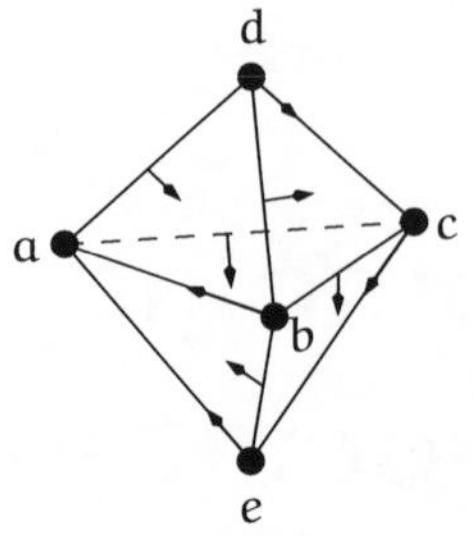

Figure 12.2. A simplicial complex with an acyclic matching.

It is a well-known fact in graph theory that the vertex set of a finite acyclic directed graph $G_d(\mu)$ can be decomposed into layers, that is, represented as a disjoint union $V_0 \cup \cdots \cup V_t$, such that

(1) for any $\alpha \in V_i$, there exists $\beta \in V_{i-1}$, such that (α, β) is an edge of $G_d(\mu)$,

(2) for any $\alpha \in V_i$, $\beta \in V_j$, such that (α, β) is an edge of $G_d(\mu)$, we have $i > j$.

In other words, V_0 consists of all the *sinks*, the vertices with outdegree equal to 0; V_1 consists of all the vertices with edges pointing to sinks only, and, in general, for each i, the set V_i consists of vertices α such that the longest path from α to a sink has length i. Another way to say this is that the sets $V_1, \dots, V_t$ are precisely the sets which would be produced by the breadth-first search algorithm, starting from the set of all sinks V_0, and tracing the edges in the opposite direction.

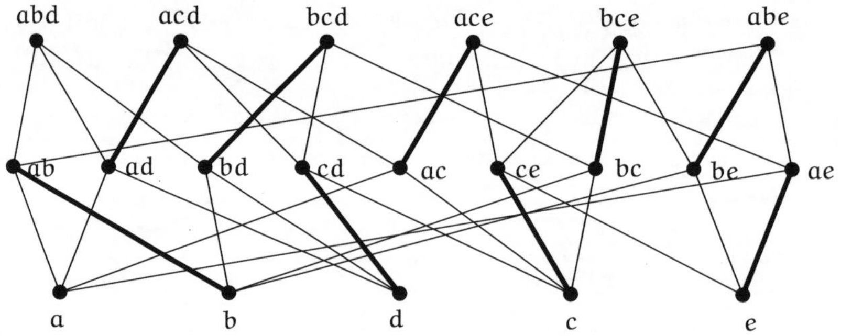

Figure 12.3. The acyclic matching on the face poset (with $\emptyset$ omitted) of the simplicial complex from Figure 12.2.

An instance of how this construction works is shown in Figures 12.2 to 12.4. Note that, in general, edges are allowed to skip levels, by which we mean that we may have edges (α, β), such that $\alpha \in V_i$, $\beta \in V_j$, and $i \geqslant j+2$. For example, in the graph in Figure 12.4 the edge between abd and acd skips a level.

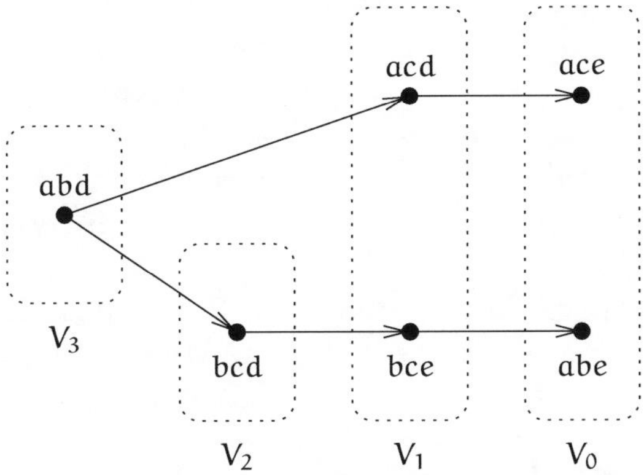

Figure 12.4. The directed graph $G_2(\mu)$, for the acyclic matching μ from Figures 12.2 and 12.3, and its decomposition into layers $V_0, \dots, V_3$.

Let μ be the acyclic matching, and, as previously defined, let R, $M^{\uparrow}$, and $M^{\downarrow}$ be the corresponding decomposition. Let us now consider consequences for the d-chains of $\mathcal{K}$.

Proposition 12.2. *Assume* $\sigma \in C_d(\mathcal{K})$ *and* $\operatorname{supp} \sigma \subseteq M^{\uparrow}$.

(1) *If* σ *is a cycle, then* $\sigma = 0$.

(2) *More generally, if* $\sigma \neq 0$, *then*

$$\operatorname{supp} \partial\sigma \cap \mu(\operatorname{supp} \sigma) \neq \emptyset. \tag{12.1}$$

In other words, there exists an element $\nu \in \operatorname{supp} \sigma$, *such that* $\mu(\nu)$ *belongs to* $\operatorname{supp} \partial\sigma$.

Proof. We start by proving (1). Set $A := \operatorname{supp} \sigma$, and assume $\sigma \neq 0$, or, equivalently, $A \neq \emptyset$. Let $\mathcal{L}$ be the subcomplex of the simplicial complex $\mathcal{K}$ obtained by taking the union of the closures of all the simplices in A. In other words, the simplicial complex $\mathcal{L}$ consists of all the simplices contained in one of the simplices in A. This a pure simplicial complex of dimension d, and its maximal simplices are indexed by the set A.

By our construction, for each $\beta \in A$, the simplex $\mu(\beta)$ is defined and has dimension $d-1$. Consider a matching λ on $\mathcal{L}$ which matches each d-simplex $\beta \in A$ with the $(d-1)$-simplex $\mu(\beta)$. Since this is a restriction of the acyclic matching μ, the matching λ is itself a well-defined acyclic matching. The unmatched part of $\mathcal{L}$ forms a subcomplex $\widetilde{\mathcal{L}}$, whose dimension is strictly less than d. We now use Theorem 10.9 to conclude that the simplicial complex $\mathcal{L}$ can be collapsed to its subcomplex $\widetilde{\mathcal{L}}$. In particular, $H_d(\mathcal{L}) = 0$, which, since d is the top dimension of $\mathcal{L}$, means that every d-dimensional cycle of $\mathcal{L}$ must in fact be 0. Since $\partial_d \sigma = 0$ in $\mathcal{L}$ as well, we conclude that $\sigma = 0$.

Let us now show (2). As before, set $A := \operatorname{supp} \sigma$, and now let H be the subgraph of $G_d(\mu)$ induced by the vertex set A. This graph is acyclic, since the original graph $G_d(\mu)$ is acyclic. Let v be any of the sources of H, and set $w := \mu(v)$. By construction, $w \in \mu(\operatorname{supp} \sigma)$. On the other hand, there can be no $u \in A \setminus v$, such that $w \in \operatorname{supp} \partial u$, as otherwise the edge (u, v) would belong to H, contradicting the fact that v is a source. However, if there is no such u, then we must have $v \in \operatorname{supp} \partial \sigma$, and we are done. □

Clearly, (2) implies (1) in Proposition 12.2, as $\partial \sigma = 0$ and $\sigma \neq 0$ being valid at the same time would contradict Equation (12.1).

12.2. The closure map φ

Let us now define a function φ which maps each vertex of $G_d(\mu)$ to a set of vertices of $G_d(\mu)$. Algebraically, we will let φ map each d-simplex of $\mathcal{K}$ to a d-chain of $\mathcal{K}$ with coefficients in $\mathbb{Z}_2$.

Definition 12.3. We define φ recursively on the sets V_i of $G_d(\mu)$, in the order of growing indices. As the base, we set $\varphi(\alpha) := \alpha$, for all $\alpha \in V_0$, that is, when α is a sink.

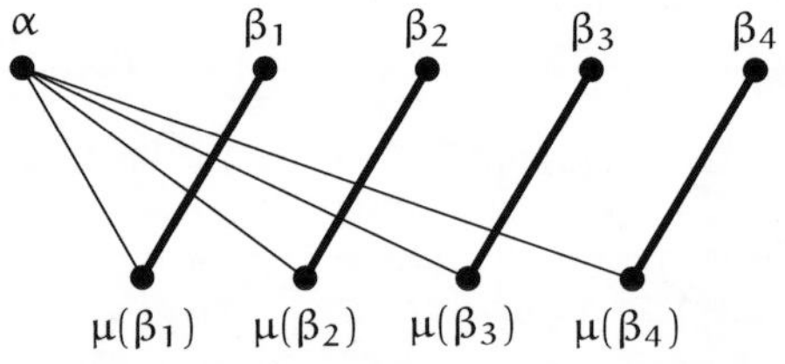

Figure 12.5. The setting defining the function φ in Definition 12.3.

Next, assume that the function φ has already been defined for all vertices in the set $V_0 \cup \cdots \cup V_{i-1}$, for some $1 \leqslant i \leqslant t$, and pick a vertex α in V_i. Let $(\alpha, \beta_1), \ldots, (\alpha, \beta_m)$ be the complete list of edges emanating from α. The sets $V_0, \ldots, V_t$ were constructed so that all edges point from higher-indexed levels to the lower-indexed ones, so we know that $\beta_1, \ldots, \beta_m \in V_0 \cup \cdots \cup V_{i-1}$. We then set

$$\varphi(\alpha) := \alpha + \sum_{i=1}^{m} \varphi(\beta_i), \tag{12.2}$$

which is well-defined by what we just said; see also Figure 12.5.

For the running example from Figures 12.2 to 12.4 we obtain the values

$$\begin{aligned}
\varphi(abe) &= abe,\\
\varphi(ace) &= ace,\\
\varphi(acd) &= acd + ace,\\
\varphi(bce) &= bce + abe,\\
\varphi(bcd) &= bcd + bce + abe,\\
\varphi(abd) &= abd + bcd + bce + abe + acd + ace.
\end{aligned}$$

Let us make a couple of remarks.

Remark 12.4. A criticial simplex σ must be a *source* in graph $G_d(\mu)$. This is because, whenever $G_d(\mu)$ has an edge (α, β), the simplex β must be matched by μ, so it cannot be a critical one.

The converse of Remark 12.4 is false. The graph $G_d(\mu)$ may have sources which are not critical.

Remark 12.5. If σ is not critical, then the support of $\varphi(\sigma)$ does not contain any critical simplices. Otherwise, if σ is critical, the support of $\varphi(\sigma)$ must contain a unique critical simplex, namely, σ itself.

Of course, Remark 12.5 follows at once from Remark 12.4.

Once we have defined φ for the d-simplices, we can take the linear extension and obtain a linear map between the chain groups

$$\varphi : C_d(\mathcal{K}; \mathbb{Z}_2) \to C_d(\mathcal{K}; \mathbb{Z}_2).$$

Next, let us look at an alternative way to compute the function φ.

Definition 12.6. Assume $\mathcal{K}$ is an abstract simplicial complex, and μ is an arbitrary matching on the set of simplices of $\mathcal{K}$. Let α and β be arbitrary simplices of $\mathcal{K}$ such that $\dim \alpha = \dim \beta$. A *reaching path* p from α to β is any sequence

$$\alpha \succ \mu(\beta_1) \prec \beta_1 \succ \mu(\beta_2) \prec \beta_2 \succ \cdots \succ \mu(\beta_m) \prec \beta_m = \beta, \tag{12.3}$$

where $m \geqslant 0$, $\beta_1 \neq \beta_2, \ldots, \beta_{m-1} \neq \beta_m$; see Figure 12.6.

Given a reaching path p from α to β, we set $p_\bullet := \alpha$ and $p^\bullet := \beta$.

Proposition 12.7. *Assume we are given a simplicial complex $\mathcal{K}$ and an acyclic matching μ. Let the function φ be given by Definition* 12.3. *Then the following formula is valid:*

$$\varphi(\alpha) = \sum_{p : p_\bullet = \alpha} p^\bullet, \tag{12.4}$$

where the notation means that the sum is taken over all reaching paths p*, such that* $p_\bullet = \alpha$.

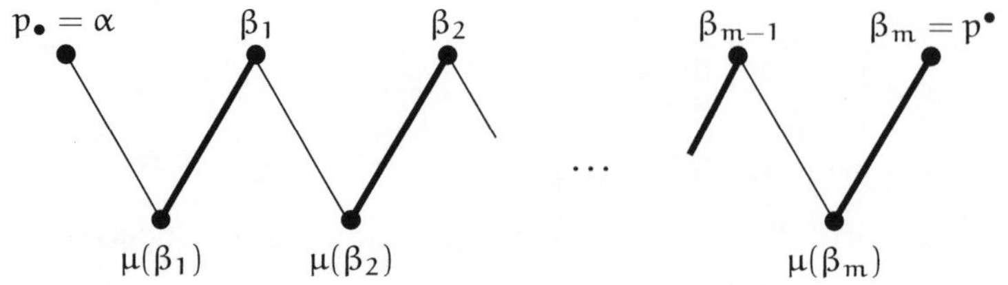

Figure 12.6. An example of a reaching path p.

Proof. Equation (12.4) is obviously valid when α is a sink, i.e., $\alpha \in V_0$, because the only reaching path which starts and terminates in α is the path consisting only of α. We call this path id_α.

We can verify that Equation (12.4) holds for all $\alpha \in V_k$, using induction on k. We already know it is true for $k = 0$, and by the induction hypothesis it is true for V_i, for all $i \leqslant k-1$. By Equation (12.2) we now have

$$\varphi(\alpha) = \alpha + \sum_{i=1}^{m} \varphi(\beta_i) = (\mathrm{id}_\alpha)^\bullet + \sum_{i=1}^{m} \sum_{p:p_\bullet=\beta_i} p^\bullet = \sum_{p:p_\bullet=\alpha} p^\bullet,$$

where the last equality follows from the fact that any non-identity reaching path which starts at the simplex α will first pass through one of the simplices $\beta_1, \dots, \beta_m$. □

Proposition 12.8. *For any* $\sigma \in C_d$ *we have* $\operatorname{supp} \partial(\varphi(\sigma)) \subseteq R_{d-1} \cup M_{d-1}^{\uparrow}$.

Proof. Assume that on the contrary, $\operatorname{supp} \partial(\varphi(\sigma)) \cap M_{d-1}^{\downarrow} \neq \emptyset$, and pick an element β from that intersection. Applying the boundary operator ∂_d to the equation in Proposition 12.7, we have

$$\partial_d \varphi(\sigma) = \sum_{p} \partial_d p^\bullet, \tag{12.5}$$

where the sum is taken over all reaching paths p such that $p_\bullet = \sigma$. This means that the coefficient with which β appears on the right-hand side of Equation (12.5) is equal to the parity of the number of reaching paths p, such that

(1) $p_\bullet = \sigma$,

(2) the d-simplex $p^\bullet$ contains the $(d-1)$-simplex β.

Since we have assumed that $\beta \in \operatorname{supp} \partial(\varphi(\sigma))$, we must have an odd number of such paths.

Let A denote the set of all such paths. We now describe a complete matching ν on the set A; see Figure 12.7. For each path $p \in A$ we match

$$p \overset{\nu}{\longleftrightarrow} p\,\mathrm{XOR}\{\beta, \mu(\beta)\}.$$

In other words, if $\beta \in p$, then since p is a reaching path, and β is a $(d-1)$-simplex, we must have $\mu(\beta) \in p$. Furthermore, we must then also have $p^\bullet = \mu(\beta)$, so we can match p with the path obtained from p by deleting both β and $\mu(\beta)$.

On the other hand, assume $\beta \notin p$ and set $\gamma := p^\bullet$. We know that γ contains β. Furthermore, $\mu(\beta) \neq \gamma$, as otherwise, we would have β in p. This means that neither β nor $\mu(\beta) \in p$, and adding β and $\mu(\beta)$ to p is again a reaching path originating at σ.

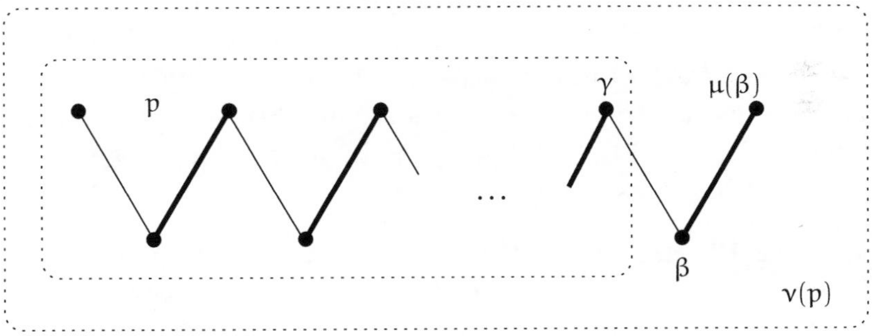

Figure 12.7. Matching ν on the set A.

Thus we have shown that ν is a complete matching on the set A. In particular, the cardinality of the set A is even, contradicting the previous assumption that it was odd. We conclude that $\operatorname{supp} \partial(\varphi(\sigma)) \cap M^{\downarrow}_{d-1}$ is an empty set. □

Also, the converse of Proposition 12.8 is true, in the sense made precise in the next statement.

Proposition 12.9. *Assume* $\operatorname{supp} \sigma \subseteq R_d$ *and* $\operatorname{supp} \alpha \subseteq M^{\uparrow}_d$. *Assume furthermore that* $\operatorname{supp} \partial(\sigma + \alpha) \subseteq R_{d-1} \cup M^{\uparrow}_{d-1}$. *Then* $\varphi(\sigma) = \sigma + \alpha$.

Proof. First, note that by definition of φ, there exists β, such that $\operatorname{supp} \beta \subseteq M^{\uparrow}_d$ and $\varphi(\sigma) = \sigma + \beta$. Let us now consider $\gamma := \varphi(\sigma) + \sigma + \alpha = \beta + \alpha$.[1] Assume $\varphi(\sigma) \neq \sigma + \alpha$, in other words, $\gamma \neq 0$. Obviously, $\operatorname{supp} \gamma \subseteq M^{\uparrow}_d$. On the other hand, by Proposition 12.8 we have $\operatorname{supp} \partial(\varphi(\sigma)) \subseteq R_{d-1} \cup M^{\uparrow}_{d-1}$, and by our assumptions, we have $\operatorname{supp} \partial(\sigma + \alpha) \subseteq R_{d-1} \cup M^{\uparrow}_{d-1}$. It follows that $\operatorname{supp} \partial\gamma \subseteq R_{d-1} \cup M^{\uparrow}_{d-1}$. However, Proposition 12.2(2) tells us that

[1]Remember that the calculations are done mod $\mathbb{Z}_2$.

there must exist $\rho \in \operatorname{supp}\gamma$, such that $\mu(\rho) \in \operatorname{supp}\partial\gamma$. This, of course, is impossible, since $\mu(\rho) \in M^{\downarrow}_{d-1}$, and we have just shown that $\operatorname{supp}\partial\gamma \subseteq R_{d-1} \cup M^{\uparrow}_{d-1}$. We conclude that $\gamma = 0$, and subsequently $\varphi(\sigma) = \sigma + \alpha$. □

Verbally, Propositions 12.8 and 12.9 can be summarized as follows: φ is the closure operator which expands a chain from R with a chain from $M^{\uparrow}$, so that the $M^{\downarrow}$-component of the boundary is annihilated. The operator φ is well-defined since there is a unique way to perform such an extension.

12.3. Homology generators associated to critical cells in an isolated dimension

Assume we are given an abstract simplicial complex $\mathcal{K}$ and an acyclic matching μ. The case we would like to investigate in detail in this subsection is when we only have critical simplices in some chosen dimension d, and no critical simplices in neighboring dimensions. In other words, all the simplices of dimension $d+1$ and $d-1$ are matched by μ. The following statement is the main result of this section.

Theorem 12.10. *Assume, as above, that we are given a simplicial complex $\mathcal{K}$ and an acyclic matching μ, such that, for a certain positive integer d, all the simplices of $\mathcal{K}$ in dimensions $d-1$ and $d+1$ are matched, i.e., $R_{d-1} = R_{d+1} = \emptyset$.*

Assume furthermore that we are given a critical simplex σ of dimension d. Then, with the function φ being defined as above, the value $\varphi(\sigma)$ is a homology class, such that σ is a unique critical d-simplex contained in the support of $\varphi(\sigma)$.

Proof. According to Remark 12.5, we already know that σ is a unique critical d-simplex contained in the support of $\varphi(\sigma)$. Let us now show that $\varphi(\sigma)$ is actually a cycle.

Assume $\partial_d\varphi(\sigma) \neq 0$, and let S denote the support set of $\partial_d\varphi(\sigma) \neq 0$. Set $S_I := S \cap M^{\downarrow}$ and $S_{II} := S \cap M^{\uparrow}$. Since we have assumed that all $(d-1)$-simplices of $\mathcal{K}$ are matched, $\mu(\tau)$ is well-defined for all $\tau \in S$, so the set S is a disjoint union of the sets S_I and S_{II}. This means that we can write

$$\partial_d\varphi(\sigma) = \tau_I + \tau_{II}, \text{ where } \tau_I = \sum_{\tau \in S_I} \tau \text{ and } \tau_{II} = \sum_{\tau \in S_{II}} \tau.$$

The situation is illustrated in Figure 12.8.

All we need to do is to show that $\tau_I = \tau_{II} = 0$. First, $\tau_I = 0$ by Proposition 12.8. Second, the chain τ_{II} must be a cycle. Indeed, since $\tau_I = 0$, we get $\partial_d\varphi(\sigma) = \tau_I + \tau_{II} = \tau_{II}$. Taking boundary once more, we

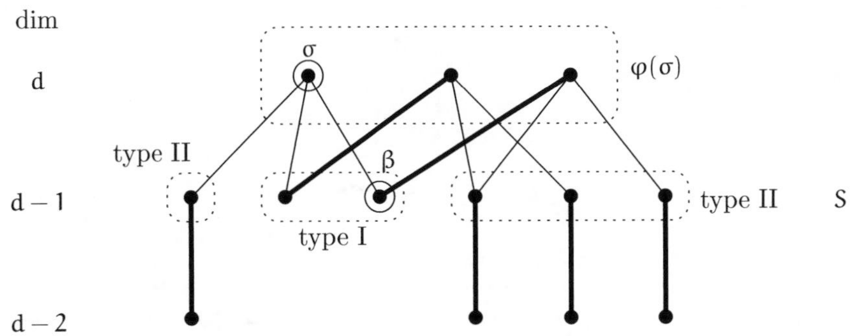

Figure 12.8. Taking the boundary of $\varphi(\alpha)$.

obtain

$$0 = \partial_{d-1}\partial_d\varphi(\sigma) = \partial_{d-1}\tau_{II}.$$

Since $\operatorname{supp}\tau_{II} \subseteq M^{\uparrow}$, we can now use Proposition 12.2(1) to conclude that $\tau_{II} = 0$.

We have shown that $\varphi(\alpha)$ is a cycle. As the last part of the proof, let us see that $\varphi(\alpha)$ represents a non-trivial homology generator. Our main characters are the following disjoint sets:

$$\begin{aligned} M^{\downarrow}_{d+1} &= \{\sigma \in \mathcal{K} \mid \dim\sigma = d+1 \text{ and } \dim\mu(\sigma) = d+2\}, \\ M^{\uparrow}_{d+1} &= \{\sigma \in \mathcal{K} \mid \dim\sigma = d+1 \text{ and } \dim\mu(\sigma) = d\}, \\ M^{\uparrow}_{d+2} &= \{\sigma \in \mathcal{K} \mid \dim\sigma = d+2 \text{ and } \dim\mu(\sigma) = d+1\}, \\ M^{\downarrow}_{d} &= \{\sigma \in \mathcal{K} \mid \dim\sigma = d \text{ and } \dim\mu(\sigma) = d+1\}. \end{aligned}$$

We know that μ matches $M^{\uparrow}_{d+2}$ with $M^{\downarrow}_{d+1}$, it matches $M^{\downarrow}_{d}$ with $M^{\uparrow}_{d+1}$, and the set of $(d+1)$-simplices of $\mathcal{K}$ is a disjoint union of the sets $M^{\downarrow}_{d+1}$ and $M^{\uparrow}_{d+1}$. Let $\mathcal{E}$ denote the subcomplex of the simplicial complex $\mathcal{K}$, defined by

$$\mathcal{E} := \{\sigma \in \mathcal{K} \mid \dim\sigma \leqslant d+1\} \cup M^{\uparrow}_{d+2},$$

and let $\mathcal{F}$ be the subcomplex defined by

$$\mathcal{F} := \mathcal{E} \setminus (M^{\downarrow}_{d} \cup M^{\downarrow}_{d+1} \cup M^{\uparrow}_{d+1} \cup M^{\uparrow}_{d+2}).$$

See Figure 12.9. Since μ is also acyclic on $\mathcal{E}$, Theorem 10.9 implies that there exists a sequence of simplicial collapses from $\mathcal{E}$ to $\mathcal{F}$. In particular, the inclusion map $\iota : \mathcal{F} \hookrightarrow \mathcal{E}$ induces isomorphisms of homology groups.

By our construction, the support of the homology class $\varphi(\sigma)$ is disjoint from the set $M^{\downarrow}_{d}$, hence $\varphi(\sigma)$ is a homology class in the simplicial complex $\mathcal{F}$. Now $\dim\mathcal{F} = d$, so $\varphi(\sigma)$ is in the top dimension. It is also not equal to 0, since it contains σ, so it must be a non-trivial homology class in $\mathcal{F}$. Since the inclusion map $\iota : \mathcal{F} \hookrightarrow \mathcal{E}$ induces isomorphisms of homology groups,

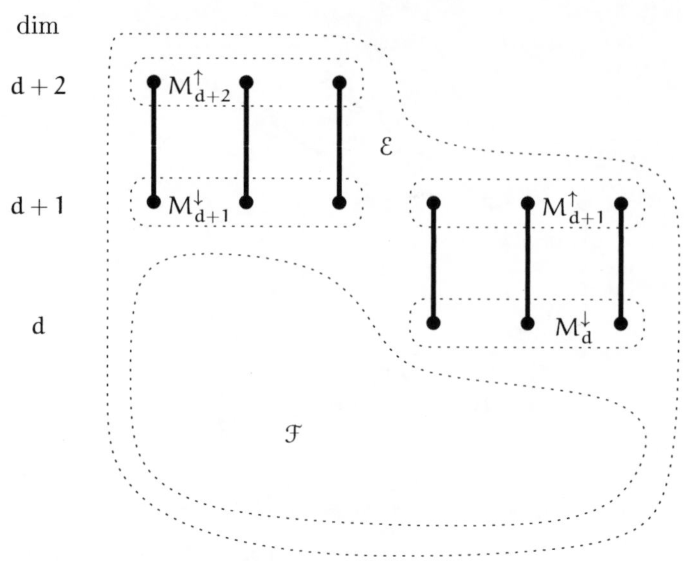

Figure 12.9. The construction of $\mathcal{E}$ and $\mathcal{F}$.

$\varphi(\sigma)$ is also non-trivial in $\mathcal{E}$. It must then also be non-trivial on $\mathcal{K}$, since $\mathcal{E}$ contains the entire $(d+1)$-skeleton of $\mathcal{K}$. Finally, Remark 12.5 tells us that σ is a unique critical d-simplex contained in the support of $\varphi(\sigma)$. □

Remark 12.11. Note that Theorem 12.10 provides a canonical procedure to associate a non-trivial homology generator to an acyclic matching μ and a critical d-simplex, assuming there are no critical simplices in dimensions $d-1$ and $d+1$.

Theorem 12.10 has the following useful corollary.

Corollary 12.12. *Under the same conditions as in Theorem* 12.10, *the homology classes* $[\varphi(\sigma)]$, $\sigma \in R_d$ *form a basis for* $H_d(K)$.

Proof. We already know that the number of the homology classes $[\varphi(\sigma)]$ is equal to the d-th Betti number, so it is enough to see that they are linearly independent. This can be done by using essentially the same argument as the one in the last part of proof of Theorem 12.10. If a linear combination of $\varphi(\sigma)$'s would represent a trivial homology class, then it would already do so in the subcomplex $\mathcal{F}$. This, however, is impossible, as every non-zero cycle in the top dimension always represents a non-trivial homology class. □

12.4. Sample applications

Let us now see how this knowledge can be applied in practice.

12.4.1. The d-skeleton of an n-simplex. In this example, we return to the situation dealt with in Proposition 11.6. We have seen there that using discrete Morse theory it is easy to show that the d-skeleton of an n-simplex is homotopy equivalent to $\binom{n}{d+1}$ copies of d-dimensional spheres. We can now use Theorem 12.10 to describe explicit homology generators.

Pick a critical d-simplex σ indexed by $0 \leqslant x_0 < \cdots < x_d \leqslant n-1$. The boundary $(d-1)$-simplices of σ are all given by

$$\tau_i := \{x_0, \dots, \widehat{x}_i, \dots, x_d\}, \quad \text{for} \quad 0 \leqslant i \leqslant d.$$

Using the matching μ used in the proof of Proposition 11.6, we obtain

$$\mu(\tau_i) = \{x_0, \dots, \widehat{x}_i, \dots, x_d\} \cup \{n\}.$$

Switching to the graph $G_d(\mu)$, we see that all the vertices $\mu(\tau_0), \dots, \mu(\tau_d)$ are sinks, hence $\varphi(\mu(\tau_i)) = \mu(\tau_i)$, for all $0 \leqslant i \leqslant d$. By Theorem 12.10 we then conclude that the canonical homology class associated to the d-simplex σ under the acyclic matching μ is given by

$$\varphi(\sigma) = \sigma + \mu(\tau_0) + \cdots + \mu(\tau_d).$$

A handy way to write this cycle is to say $\varphi(\sigma) = \partial_{d+1}(\sigma \cup \{n\})$, where the boundary is taken in the full ambient n-simplex.

12.4.2. The complex of disconnected graphs. Consider the simplicial complex Disc_n of disconnected graphs on n vertices, $n \geqslant 3$. In this case each critical $(n-3)$-simplex σ is obtained from a recursive tree T_σ by deleting the edge $(1,2)$. One can see that

$$\varphi(\sigma) = \partial_{n-2} T_\sigma. \tag{12.6}$$

Indeed, for each edge $e \in \sigma$, the graph $\tau_e := \sigma \backslash e$ has 3 connected components, so $\mu(\tau_e)$ is well-defined, and

$$\mu(\tau_e) = (\sigma \setminus e) \cup (1,2).$$

Then, for each $(n-4)$-simplex ν, which is contained in $\mu(\tau_e)$, such that $\nu \neq \tau_e$, we have $(1,2) \in \nu$, hence $\mu(\nu)$ is well-defined, and $\mu(\nu) = \nu \setminus (1,2)$. So, each $\mu(\tau_e)$ is a sink of the directed graph $G_{n-3}(\mu)$, and Equation (12.6) follows.

12.4.3. Order complex of the partition lattice Π_n. Let us now return to considering the order complex of the lattice of all partitions of the set $[n]$, $n \geqslant 3$. Our notation for this simplicial complex was $\widetilde{\Delta}(\Pi_n)$. This complex has dimension $n-3$.

Let μ be the acyclic matching which we have described in Subsection 11.5.2. For this matching, the critical simplices of μ all have dimension $n-3$, so our framework applies and we may attempt to calculate the canonical homology classes associated to the critical simplices.

Recall that each critical simplex is obtained as follows. Choose a permutation π of $[n]$ of the form $1x_2\dots x_n$. The $(n-3)$-simplex σ_π is a chain of partitions $\alpha_2 < \dots < \alpha_{n-1}$, such that

$$\alpha_i = 1x_2\dots x_i|x_{i+1}|\dots|x_n.$$

We would like to describe the canonical homology class $\varphi(\sigma_\pi)$. The standard action of the permutation group S_{n-1}, on the set of elements $x_2\dots x_n$, induces an action on the chains in Π_n. This action is transitive on the set of critical simplices. Hence, if we want to calculate $\varphi(\sigma_\pi)$ in general, it is enough to do that for the ordered tuple $(x_2,\dots,x_n) = (2,\dots,n)$.

So let π be fixed to be the identity permutation. Consider the subposet Q of Π_n consisting of all permutations λ of the form

$$\lambda = 1\dots i_1\,|\,i_1+1\dots i_2\,|\,\dots\,|\,i_t+1\dots n,$$

for some $1 \leqslant i_1 < \dots < i_t < n$. It is easy to see that Q is a Boolean algebra on $n-1$ elements. Indeed, each element in Q is simply determined by where the separators $|$ are inserted in the ordered sequence $1,\dots,n$. There are $n-1$ potential positions where the separator can be inserted and any choice of positions is allowed. The order relation is given by inclusion of the sets of positions, and it corresponds precisely to the refinement order in the partition lattice.

Now, the order complex of a Boolean algebra is homeomorphic to a sphere, in fact, it is a barycentric subdivision of the boundary of a simplex. Taking the sum of all the top-dimensional simplices in the order complex of Q yields the fundamental homology class γ_π of the corresponding sphere. It can be shown, see Exercise (5), that γ_π is precisely the canonical homology class associated to the acyclic matching μ and the critical simplex σ_π. When π varies across the set of all $(n-1)!$ permutations of the type above, we get the canonical homology classes associated to all the critical simplices.

Exercises

(1) Use Corollary 12.12 to describe an explicit homology basis for the independence complexes of the graph G, where
   (1) G is a path graph;
   (2) G is an arbitrary tree;
   (3) G is a cycle.

(2) Describe an explicit homology basis for the complex of independent sets of a matroid.

(3) Describe an explicit homology basis for $\mathrm{Flag}_{\mathbf{k}}^{\mathrm{d}}$. The latter complex was defined in Exercise (5) of Chapter 11.

(4) Investigate the computational complexity of finding the homology basis using Corollary 12.12.

(5) Complete the argument in Subsection 12.4.3.

Chapter 13

The Critical Morse Complex

13.1. A basis for the chain groups associated to the acyclic matching

For our purposes it is useful to modify the basis $R_d \cup M_d^{\uparrow} \cup M_d^{\downarrow}$ in a way which will make the effect of the boundary operator more transparent. Specifically, let us set

$$\mathcal{B}_d^R := \{\varphi(\gamma) \mid \gamma \in R_d\},$$
$$\mathcal{B}_d^{\uparrow} := M_d^{\uparrow},$$
$$\mathcal{B}_d^{\downarrow} := \left\{\partial\beta \mid \beta \in M_{d+1}^{\uparrow}\right\}.$$

We would like to show that the union of these three sets is a basis for $C_d(\mathcal{K})$. Before proceeding with the proof, it is useful to define a directed graph, which we call $H_d(\mu)$, and which is quite analogous to the directed graph $G_d(\mu)$. The definition, see Figure 13.1, is as follows:

- the set $M_d^{\uparrow}$ is taken as the set of vertices of $H_d(\mu)$;
- there is a directed edge from α to β, for some $\alpha, \beta \in M_d^{\uparrow}$ if and only if $\mu(\alpha) \succ \beta$.

When the matching μ is acyclic, then, in the same way as we have seen in the case of the graph $G_d(\mu)$, the graph $H_d(\mu)$ is acyclic. This again means that the vertices of $H_d(\mu)$ can be ordered so that the edges are always pointing down in the chosen order.

Proposition 13.1. *The set* $\mathcal{B}_d^R \cup \mathcal{B}_d^{\uparrow} \cup \mathcal{B}_d^{\downarrow}$ *is a basis for* $\mathcal{C}_d(\mathcal{K})$.

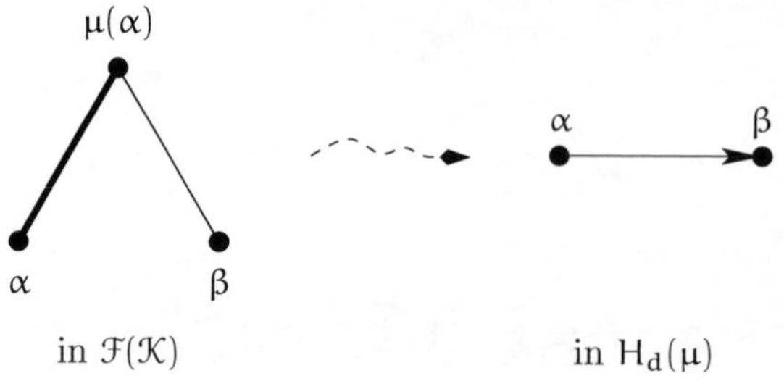

Figure 13.1. The rule defining the edges of the directed graph $H_d(\mu)$.

Proof. For brevity, set $\mathcal{B}_d := \mathcal{B}_d^R \cup \mathcal{B}_d^\uparrow \cup \mathcal{B}_d^\downarrow$ and $\mathcal{S}_d := R_d \cup M_d^\uparrow \cup M_d^\downarrow$. Let us first show that each element from $\mathcal{S}_d$ can be obtained as a linear combination of the elements from $\mathcal{B}_d$. For $\gamma \in M_d^\uparrow$ this is trivial, since $M_d^\uparrow = \mathcal{B}_d^\uparrow$.

Next, take $\gamma \in R_d$. By Remark 12.5 we know that $\varphi(\gamma) = \gamma + \beta$, where $\beta \in \mathcal{B}_d^\uparrow$, so each element of R_d is a linear combination of the elements of $\mathcal{B}_d$.

Finally, take $\gamma \in M_d^\downarrow$. Set $\beta := \mu(\gamma)$. By construction $\beta \in M_{d+1}^\uparrow$. Consider an arbitrary $\alpha \in \operatorname{supp} \partial\beta$, such that $\alpha \neq \gamma$. If $\alpha \in R_d$ or $\alpha \in M_d^\uparrow$, then we have already seen that α is a linear combination of the elements of $\mathcal{B}_d$. If, instead, $\alpha \in M_d^\downarrow$, we have an edge in $H_d(\mu)$ directed from β to α. Now using induction on the distance from the sink of β seen as a vertex of $H_d(\mu)$, we can conclude that α is a linear combination of the elements of $\mathcal{B}_d$ as well. All in all, we see that all the elements of $\operatorname{supp} \partial\beta$, which are different from γ, are in the space generated by $\mathcal{B}_d$. Since $\partial\beta$ itself is an element of $\mathcal{B}_d$, we see that also γ is a linear combination of the elements of $\mathcal{B}_d$.

We have shown that $\mathcal{B}_d$ generates the vector space $\mathcal{C}_d(\mathcal{K})$. It is easy, using a similar argument, to show that the set $\mathcal{B}_d$ is also linearly independent. However, this is not necessary as we can reach our conclusion using dimensional reasoning. Indeed, since the number of vectors in $\mathcal{B}_d$ is the same as in $\mathcal{S}_d$, we conclude that $\mathcal{B}_d$ is actually a basis. □

An illuminating way to rephrase our proof of Proposition 13.1 is to look at the transformation matrix between $\mathcal{B}_d$ and $\mathcal{S}_d$. For this we need to choose an order on $\mathcal{S}_d$, which we do as follows. First in that order are all the elements of $M_d^\downarrow$, then come all the elements of R_d, and finally all the elements of $M_d^\uparrow$. The internal order on R_d and the internal order on $M_d^\uparrow$ can be chosen arbitrarily. The internal order on $M_d^\downarrow$ is chosen so that the edges of $H_d(\mu)$ point from a lower-indexed vertex to a higher-indexed one. Such a choice is possible, since the graph $H_d(\mu)$ is acyclic. Finally, the order on $\mathcal{B}_d$ is chosen accordingly, using the obvious bijection: $\gamma \leftrightarrow \varphi(\gamma)$, for $\gamma \in R_d$, and $\alpha \leftrightarrow \partial(\mu(\alpha))$, for $\alpha \in M_d^\downarrow$.

It is then easy to see that our proof of Proposition 13.1 is essentially saying that the corresponding transformation matrix is upper-triangular. The fact that $\mathcal{S}_d$ is a basis clearly implies that $\mathcal{B}_d$ is also a basis.

13.2. Decomposition of the chain complex

The basis $\mathcal{B}_d$ provides the best framework to describe a direct sum decomposition of a chain complex of a simplicial complex, associated to an acyclic matching on its simplices. The key fact is provided by the following proposition.

Proposition 13.2. *For any* $\alpha \in R_d$, *there is a set* $S(\alpha) \subseteq R_{d-1}$, *such that*

$$\partial(\varphi(\alpha)) = \sum_{\beta \in S(\alpha)} \varphi(\beta).$$

Proof. We already know, by Proposition 12.8, that

$$\operatorname{supp} \partial(\varphi(\alpha)) \subseteq R_{d-1} \cup M_{d-1}^{\uparrow}.$$

So let us say $\partial(\varphi(\alpha)) = \beta + \gamma$, where $\operatorname{supp} \beta \subseteq R_{d-1}$ and $\operatorname{supp} \gamma \subseteq M_{d-1}^{\uparrow}$. We have $\partial(\beta+\gamma) = \partial(\partial(\varphi(\alpha))) = 0$. In particular, the condition $\operatorname{supp} \partial(\beta+\gamma) \subseteq R_{d-2} \cup M_{d-2}^{\uparrow}$ is satisfied, so we can use Proposition 12.9 to conclude that $\beta + \gamma = \varphi(\beta)$. This is exactly what we want, with $S(\alpha) := \operatorname{supp} \beta$. □

It is not difficult to give a precise definition of the set $S(\alpha)$. However, it is best done using some further terminology, so we delay doing this for a short while. Instead, we proceed to formulate our main decomposition theorem.

Theorem 13.3. *Given a simplicial complex* $\mathcal{K}$ *and an acyclic matching* μ, *we define chain subcomplexes of* $\mathcal{C}(\mathcal{K})$, *which we call* $\mathcal{C}\mathtt{rit}(\mathcal{K}, \mu)$ *and* $\mathcal{M}\mathtt{atch}(\mathcal{K}, \mu)$, *as follows: for each* $d \geqslant 0$, *we take*

- *the group* $\mathcal{C}\mathtt{rit}_d(\mathcal{K}, \mu)$ *to be generated by the set* $\mathcal{B}_d^R$,
- *the group* $\mathcal{M}\mathtt{atch}_d(\mathcal{K}, \mu)$ *to be generated by the set* $\mathcal{B}_d^{\uparrow} \cup \mathcal{B}_d^{\downarrow}$.

In particular, the boundary operators of $\mathcal{C}\mathtt{rit}(\mathcal{K}, \mu)$ *and* $\mathcal{M}\mathtt{atch}(\mathcal{K}, \mu)$ *are induced by the boundary operator of* $\mathcal{C}(\mathcal{K})$. *Then, the chain complex* $\mathcal{C}(\mathcal{K})$ *decomposes as a direct sum*

$$\mathcal{C}(\mathcal{K}) = \mathcal{C}\mathtt{rit}(\mathcal{K}, \mu) \oplus \mathcal{M}\mathtt{atch}(\mathcal{K}, \mu). \tag{13.1}$$

Proof. Let us first see that $\mathcal{C}\mathtt{rit}(\mathcal{K}, \mu)$ and $\mathcal{M}\mathtt{atch}(\mathcal{K}, \mu)$ are well-defined as chain subcomplexes of $\mathcal{C}(\mathcal{K})$. This means that we have to check that they are closed with respect to applying the boundary operator. For the subcomplex $\mathcal{C}\mathtt{rit}(\mathcal{K}, \mu)$ this is an immediate consequence of Proposition 13.2. For the subcomplex $\mathcal{M}atch(\mathcal{K},\mu)$ this can be checked directly: $\partial\beta = 0$, for each $\beta \in \mathcal{B}_d^{\downarrow}$, and $\partial\beta \in \mathcal{B}_{d-1}^{\downarrow}$, for each $\beta \in \mathcal{B}_d^{\uparrow}$.

On the other hand, we already know by Proposition 13.1 that $\mathcal{C}_d(\mathcal{K}) = \mathcal{C}rit_d(\mathcal{K},\mu) \oplus \mathcal{M}atch_d(\mathcal{K},\mu)$, for all d. This immediately implies that the decomposition described in Equation (13.1) holds. □

As a matter of fact, the chain complex $\mathcal{M}atch(\mathcal{K},\mu)$ can further be decomposed into the so-called *atomic chain complexes*. We do not need this fact for now.

13.3. The language of alternating paths

Our next task is to describe the set $S(\alpha)$ which has appeared in Proposition 13.2. To do that, we need some new terminology. Recall that when σ and τ are simplices of an abstract simplicial complex $\mathcal{K}$, we write $\sigma \succ \tau$ if $\sigma \supset \tau$ and $\dim\sigma = \dim\tau + 1$.

Definition 13.4. Assume $\mathcal{K}$ is an abstract simplicial complex, and μ is an arbitrary matching on the set of simplices of $\mathcal{K}$. Let σ and τ be arbitrary simplices of $\mathcal{K}$ such that $\dim\sigma = \dim\tau + 1$. An *alternating path* from σ to τ is any sequence

$$\sigma \succ \gamma_1 \prec \mu(\gamma_1) \succ \gamma_2 \prec \mu(\gamma_2) \succ \cdots \succ \gamma_t \prec \mu(\gamma_t) \succ \tau, \tag{13.2}$$

where $t \geqslant 0$, $\gamma_1 \neq \gamma_2, \ldots, \gamma_{t-1} \neq \gamma_t$, $\gamma_t \neq \tau$, and $\sigma \neq \mu(\gamma_1)$.

Clearly, an alternating path is obtained from a reaching path by adding a non-matching edge at the end of that path.

Let $P_\sigma(\gamma_1,\ldots,\gamma_t,\tau)$ denote the alternating path given by Equation 13.2; see Figure 13.2. Note that the case $t = 0$ corresponds to the alternating path $\sigma \succ \tau$, which is the shortest possible alternating path. That path is denoted by $P_\sigma(\tau)$.

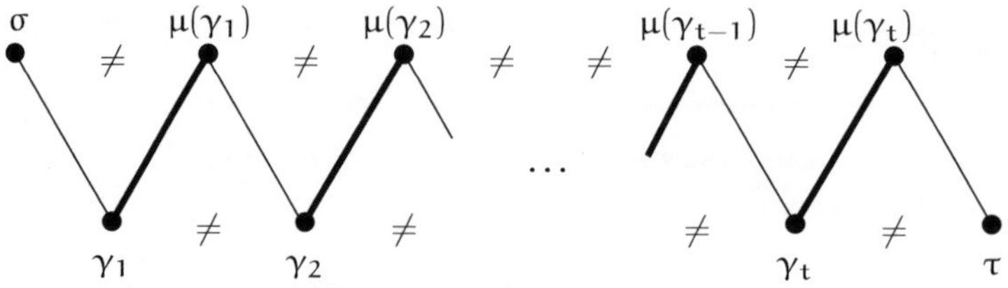

Figure 13.2. An example of an alternating path $P_\sigma(\gamma_1,\ldots,\gamma_t,\tau)$.

When $\sigma = \mu(\tau)$ and $t \geqslant 1$, adding the edge (σ,τ) to $P_\sigma(\gamma_1,\ldots,\gamma_t,\tau)$ produces the alternating cycle, which we denote $AC(\gamma_1,\ldots,\gamma_t,\tau)$.

Note also that for $1 \leqslant i \leqslant t-1$, the inequality $\gamma_i \neq \gamma_{i+1}$ implies $\mu(\gamma_i) \neq \mu(\gamma_{i+1})$. For acyclic matchings a stronger conclusion can be made.

Proposition 13.5. *Let μ be an acyclic matching on a set of simplices of an abtract simplicial complex $\mathcal{K}$. Then, for an arbitrary alternating path $P_\sigma(\gamma_1, \dots, \gamma_t, \tau)$, all the simplices $\gamma_1, \dots, \gamma_t, \tau$ are distinct.*

Proof. Assume that the conclusion of the proposition does not hold, and assume first that there exists $1 \leqslant k \leqslant t-1$, such that $\gamma_k = \gamma_{k+l}$, for some $l \geqslant 1$. By construction we must have $l \geqslant 2$, and without loss of generality we can assume that all the simplices $\gamma_k, \dots, \gamma_{k+l-1}$ are distinct. Then we have an alternating cycle $AC(\gamma_k, \dots, \gamma_{k+l-1})$, which is a contradiction to the acyclicity of μ.

Similarly, if $\tau = \gamma_k$, for some $1 \leqslant k \leqslant t-1$, then we have an alternating cycle $AC(\gamma_k, \dots, \gamma_t)$. □

Corollary 13.6. *For fixed $\mathcal{K}$ and μ, the length of an alternating path is bounded from above.*

Proof. Since $\mathcal{K}$ is assumed to be finite, the statement follows immediately from Proposition 13.5. □

Let $\Lambda_\mu(\sigma, \tau)$ denote the set of all alternating paths from σ to τ.

Proposition 13.7. *The set $S(\alpha)$ consists of all $\beta \in R_{d-1}$, for which the set $\Lambda_\mu(\alpha, \beta)$ has an odd number of elements.*

Proof. Take $\gamma \in \operatorname{supp} \varphi(\alpha)$, and assume p is a reaching path from α to γ. Assume, furthermore, that $\beta \in \operatorname{supp} \partial\gamma$ and $\beta \in R_{d-1}$. Then, adding β to p will yield an alternating path from α to β. Also reversely, every alternating path from α to β arises in this way. This means that the number of alternating paths from α to β is equal to the number of reaching paths from γ to some simplex which contains β in its boundary. Our proposition now follows from Proposition 12.7. □

13.4. Morse complex for $\mathbb{Z}_2$-coefficients

We can now describe a combinatorially defined chain complex whose homology will compute the homology of the simplicial complex $\mathcal{K}$, but which potentially can be much smaller in size.

Definition 13.8. For σ and τ as above, we set

$$\operatorname{cap}^{\mu}_{\mathbb{Z}_2}(\sigma, \tau) := \begin{cases} 1, & \text{if } |\Lambda_\mu(\sigma, \tau)| \text{ is odd;} \\ 0, & \text{otherwise.} \end{cases}$$

We call the number $\mathrm{cap}^{\mu}_{\mathbb{Z}_2}(\sigma,\tau)$ the *channel capacity over* $\mathbb{Z}_2$ between σ and τ.

Definition 13.9. Assume $\mathcal{K}$ is an abstract simplicial complex and μ is an acyclic matching on the set of simplices of $\mathcal{K}$. We define a chain complex $\mathcal{C}^{\mu}(\mathcal{K};\mathbb{Z}_2)$ as follows:

- for each d, $C^{\mu}_{d}(\mathcal{K};\mathbb{Z}_2)$ is the vector space over $\mathbb{Z}_2$ with basis $\{\gamma^{\mu}\,|\,\gamma \in R_d(\mu)\}$;
- for each d and each $\sigma \in R_d(\mu)$, the boundary operator is given by

$$\partial^{\mu}_{d}\sigma^{\mu} = \sum_{\tau\in R_{d-1}(\mu)} \mathrm{cap}^{\mu}_{\mathbb{Z}_2}(\sigma,\tau)\tau^{\mu}. \tag{13.3}$$

The chain complex $\mathcal{C}^{\mu}(\mathcal{K};\mathbb{Z}_2)$ is called the *Morse complex with* $\mathbb{Z}_2$*-coefficients associated to* μ.

The reader who has been following the developments in the previous subsections will immediately recognize that, in particular, Proposition 13.7 implies that $\mathcal{C}^{\mu}(\mathcal{K};\mathbb{Z}_2)$ is isomorphic as a chain complex to the chain subcomplex $\mathcal{C}rit(\mathcal{K},\mu)$.

Theorem 13.10 (Theorem C for $\mathbb{Z}_2$-coefficients). *The Morse complex* $\mathcal{C}^{\mu}(\mathcal{K};\mathbb{Z}_2)$ *computes the* $\mathbb{Z}_2$*-homology of* $\mathcal{K}$*. In other words, for any* t *we have an isomorphism* $H_t(\mathcal{C}^{\mu}(\mathcal{K};\mathbb{Z}_2)) \approx H_t(\mathcal{K};\mathbb{Z}_2)$.

Proof. The decomposition from Theorem 13.3 implies that

$$H_*(\mathcal{C}(\mathcal{K})) = H_*(\mathcal{C}rit(\mathcal{K},\mu)) \oplus H_*(\mathcal{M}atch(\mathcal{K},\mu)).$$

Now, the chain complex $\mathcal{M}atch(\mathcal{K},\mu)$ is acyclic, i.e., $H_*(\mathcal{M}atch(\mathcal{K},\mu)) = 0$, while, as mentioned above, the chain complex $\mathcal{C}rit(\mathcal{K},\mu)$ is isomorphic to $\mathcal{C}^{\mu}(\mathcal{K};\mathbb{Z}_2)$, so the homology of $\mathcal{C}^{\mu}(\mathcal{K};\mathbb{Z}_2)$ must be the same as that of $\mathcal{K}$. □

13.5. Morse complex for $\mathbb{Z}$-coefficients and Theorem C

Now let $\mathcal{K}$ be an abstract simplicial complex with a total order chosen on the set of its vertices.

Definition 13.11. For any two simplices σ and τ such that $\sigma = (v_1,\dots,v_t)$, for $v_1 < \dots < v_t$, and $\tau = (v_1,\dots,\hat{v}_k,\dots,v_t)$, we set $\mathrm{sgn}(\sigma,\tau) := (-1)^k$. Furthermore, for an arbitrary alternating path $p = P_{\sigma}(\gamma_1,\dots,\gamma_t,\tau)$ between σ and τ, we set

$$\begin{aligned}\mathrm{sgn}(p) := {} & \mathrm{sgn}(\sigma,\gamma_1)\,\mathrm{sgn}(\mu(\gamma_t),\tau) \\ & \times \prod_{i=1}^{t} \mathrm{sgn}(\gamma_i,\mu(\gamma_i)) \prod_{i=1}^{t-1} \mathrm{sgn}(\mu(\gamma_i,\gamma_{i+1})).\end{aligned} \tag{13.4}$$

Note that for $t = 0$, Equation (13.4) is to be interpreted as $\mathrm{sgn}(p) = \mathrm{sgn}(\sigma, \tau)$.

Definition 13.12. For critical simplices σ and τ, we set

$$\mathrm{cap}^{\mu}_{\mathbb{Z}}(\sigma, \tau) := \sum_{p \in \Lambda(\sigma, \tau)} \mathrm{sgn}(p),$$

and call this number the *channel capacity over* $\mathbb{Z}$ between σ and τ.

Definition 13.13. Assume $\mathcal{K}$ is an abstract simplicial complex, and μ is an acyclic matching on the set of simplices of $\mathcal{K}$. We define a chain complex $\mathcal{C}^{\mu}(\mathcal{K}; \mathbb{Z})$ as follows:

- for each d, $C^{\mu}_{d}(\mathcal{K}; \mathbb{Z})$ is the free abelian group generated by $\{\gamma^{\mu} \mid \gamma \in R_d(\mu)\}$;
- for each d and each $\sigma \in R_d(\mu)$, the boundary operator is given by

$$\partial^{\mu}_{d} \sigma^{\mu} = \sum_{\tau \in R_{d-1}(\mu)} \mathrm{cap}^{\mu}_{\mathbb{Z}}(\sigma, \tau) \tau^{\mu}. \tag{13.5}$$

The chain complex $\mathcal{C}^{\mu}(\mathcal{K}; \mathbb{Z})$ is called the *Morse complex with $\mathbb{Z}$-coefficients associated to* μ.

Theorem 13.14. (Theorem C for $\mathbb{Z}$-coefficients). *The Morse complex $\mathcal{C}^{\mu}(\mathcal{K}; \mathbb{Z})$ computes the $\mathbb{Z}$-homology of $\mathcal{K}$. In other words, for any t we have an isomorphism $H_t(\mathcal{C}^{\mu}(\mathcal{K}; \mathbb{Z})) \approx H_t(\mathcal{K}; \mathbb{Z})$.*

Proof. Analogous to proof of Theorem 13.10. □

Exercises

(1) Describe the chain complex decomposition from Theorem 13.3 for our standard acyclic matching for the d-skeleton of an n-simplex.

(2) Use the machinery described in this chapter to compute the homology groups of the simplicial complex, which was introduced as a sample application in the preface.

Chapter 14

Implications and Variations

14.1. Relaxing the simplicial structure

14.1.1. Generalized simplicial complexes. The most natural first step which we can take to get away from the rather rigid definition of simplicial complexes is to allow more than one simplex to be supported by the same set of vertices. In dimension 1 this corresponds to allowing multiple edges, while in higher dimensions we need to be careful when saying precisely what we want to allow.

Definition 14.1. A finite *generalized abstract simplicial complex* $\mathcal{K}$ is given by the following data:

- a finite vertex set V;
- a possibly empty set Σ_S, for every non-empty subset $S \subseteq V$;
- a map $\delta_{ST} : \Sigma_S \to \Sigma_T$ for every pair of non-empty subsets $T \subset S \subseteq V$.

This data is subject to the following conditions:

- for each $v \in V$, we have $\Sigma_{\{v\}} = \{v\}$;
- we have $\delta_{TR} \circ \delta_{ST} = \delta_{SR}$ whenever $R \subset T \subset S$.

Each set Σ_S contains all the simplices whose set of vertices is S. These sets are certainly allowed to be empty.

Given a generalized abstract simplicial complex $\mathcal{K}$, we can associate to it a semisimplicial set $\Delta = ((S_k)_{k \geqslant 0}, \{B_f\}_f)$ as follows. Assume for technical simplicity that the set V is equal to $[t]$, for some nonnegative integer t. The set of k-simplices of Δ is then simply taken to be $S_k := \bigcup_A \Sigma_A$, where the union is taken over all subsets $A \subseteq [t]$, such that $|A| = k+1$. Assume $f : [m] \hookrightarrow [n]$ is an order-preserving injection. We can then define a map $B_f : S_n \to S_m$. Take $\sigma \in S_n$. By definition there exists a subset $A \subseteq [t]$, such that $|A| = n+1$, and $\sigma \in \Sigma_A$. Let $\varphi : [n] \to A$ be the order-preserving bijection, and set $X := \mathrm{Im}(\varphi \circ f)$. We then define $B_f(\sigma) := \delta_{AX}(\sigma)$. We leave checking the semisimplicial set axioms as an exercise.

When we say that a simplex $\tau \in \Sigma_T$ *is contained* in a simplex $\sigma \in \Sigma_S$, we mean that

(1) $T \subset S$;

(2) $\delta_{ST}(\sigma) = \tau$.

Alternatively, we say that τ is a boundary simplex of σ. The simplices in Σ_S have dimension $|S|-1$, and when $\tau \in \Sigma_T$ is contained in a simplex $\sigma \in \Sigma_S$ the *codimension* of τ in σ is equal to $|S| - |T|$.

Using that terminology, Definition 9.1 of the elementary simplicial collapse can be adapted verbatim to the context of generalized simplicial complexes. Moreover, Proposition 9.9 remains true, and the simplicial complex still corresponds to a strong deformation retraction for the geometric realization.

The concept of the face poset of a generalized simplicial complex is defined without changes. The only difference to the abstract simplicial complexes is that we end up with a more general class of posets; for example, they do not have to be semilattices anymore.

Theorem A of discrete Morse theory then holds precisely as stated if the following is taken as a definition of a subcomplex.

Definition 14.2. Assume $\mathcal{K} = (V, \Sigma_*, \delta_*)$ is a generalized simplicial complex. A *subcomplex* of $\mathcal{K}$ is $\widetilde{\mathcal{K}} = (V, \widetilde{\Sigma}_*, \tilde{\delta}_*)$, such that $\widetilde{\Sigma}_S \subseteq \Sigma_S$, for all $S \subseteq V$, $\tilde{\delta}_{ST}$ is the restriction of δ_{ST} to $\widetilde{\Sigma}_S$, and $\mathrm{Im}\,\tilde{\delta}_{ST} \subseteq \widetilde{\Sigma}_T$.

Theorem B also holds precisely as stated for the generalized simplicial complexes, and proofs of both theorems go through without any change.

14.1.2. Polyhedral complexes. In Section 3.1 we have looked at the situation, where instead of allowing more than one simplex with the same set of vertices, one can go in a slightly different direction and replace simplices by polyhedras. This includes frequently used families, such as cubical complexes. We shall sketch this in a rather brief way, since the details are straightforward, and, furthermore, a lot of these considerations are subsumed and made precise by switching to chain complexes altogether.

Recall that a *convex polytope* P in $\mathbb{R}^n$ is a convex hull of a finite set of points. This includes the empty set. Any hyperplane H divides $\mathbb{R}^n$ into two closed half-spaces, whose intersection is H. A hyperplane H is called a *bounding hyperplane* for P, if P is contained entirely in one of these closed half-spaces. A *face* of a convex polytope P is an intersection of P with an arbitrary bounding hyperplane H. Note that this includes the case when $P \cap H = \emptyset$, corresponding to the empty face of P. If P is not full-dimensional, then P itself is also considered one of its faces.

Definition 14.3. A *polyhedral complex* in a Euclidean space $\mathbb{R}^n$ is a set Σ of convex polytopes satisfying the following two conditions:

(1) every face of a polytope in Σ also belongs to Σ;

(2) the intersection of any two polytopes in Σ is either empty or is a face of both of them.

Definition 14.4. A *polyhedral collapse* is defined in precisely the same way as in the simplicial case: it is a deletion of two polytopes σ and τ from Σ, such that

- σ is maximal, i.e., it is not a face of any other polytope in Σ;
- τ is a face of σ, and it is not a face of any $\gamma \in \Sigma$, $\gamma \neq \sigma, \tau$.

We formulate the following result without proof.

Theorem 14.5 (Main theorem of discrete Morse theory for polyhedral complexes)**.** *Let Δ be a polyhedral complex, and let M be an acyclic matching on $F(\Delta) \setminus \{\hat{0}\}$. Let c_i denote the number of critical i-dimensional cells of Δ.*

(a) *If the critical cells form a subcomplex Δ_c of Δ, then there exists a sequence of polyhedral collapses leading from Δ to Δ_c.*

(b) *In general, the space Δ is homotopy equivalent to Δ_c, where Δ_c is a CW complex with c_i cells in dimension i.*

(c) *There is a natural indexing of cells of Δ_c with the critical cells of Δ, such that, for any two cells σ and τ of Δ_c, satisfying* $\dim\sigma = \dim\tau + 1$, *the incidence number $[\tau : \sigma]$ is given by*

$$[\tau : \sigma] = \sum_{c} w(c). \tag{14.1}$$

Here the sum is taken over all alternating paths c connecting σ with τ, i.e., over all sequences $c = (\sigma, a_1, u(a_1), \dots, a_t, u(a_t), \tau)$, such that $\sigma \succ a_1$, $u(a_t) \succ \tau$, and $u(a_i) \succ a_{i+1}$, for $i = 1, \dots, t-1$. For such an alternating path, the quantity $w(c)$ is defined by

$$w(c) := (-1)^t [a_1 : \sigma][\tau : u(a_t)] \prod_{i=1}^{t} [a_i : u(a_i)] \prod_{i=1}^{t-1} [a_{i+1} : u(a_i)], \tag{14.2}$$

where the incidence numbers on the right-hand side are taken in the complex Δ.

Remark 14.6. The converse of Theorem 14.5(a) is clearly true in the following sense: if Δ_c is a subcomplex of Δ, and if there exists a sequence of collapses from Δ to Δ_c, then the matching on the cells of $\Delta \setminus \Delta_c$ induced by this sequence of collapses is acyclic. In particular, a polyhedral complex Δ is collapsible if and only if the poset $F(\Delta) \setminus \{\hat{0}\}$ allows a complete acyclic matching.

14.1.3. A toy application to Hom-complexes.

Assume we are given two graphs T and G.

Definition 14.7. A *graph homomorphism* between T and G is an arbitrary map between their sets of vertices $\varphi : V(T) \to V(G)$, such that for every edge (x, y) in T the pair $(\varphi(x), \varphi(y))$ is an edge in G.

Definition 14.8. A *multihomomorphism* from a graph T to a graph G is an assignment $\lambda : V(T) \to 2^{V(G)}$, such that

- each set $\lambda(v)$ is non-empty,
- if the vertices v and w of T are connected by an edge, then any two vertices $x \in \lambda(v)$ and $y \in \lambda(w)$ are also connected by an edge.

The complex $\mathrm{Hom}(T, G)$ is the complex of all multihomomorphisms from T to G. The boundary relation is given by deleting vertices from the sets $\lambda(v)$.

In particular, a cell in $\mathrm{Hom}(T, K_n)$ is an assignment of subsets of $[n]$ to vertices of T, such that an arbitrary choice of one color per list yields an admissible coloring of T.

In general, the complexes $\mathrm{Hom}(T, G)$ are not simplicial. They are polyhedral, with each cell being a direct product of simplices. This type of complex is called a *prodsimplicial complex.*

The complex $\mathrm{Hom}(K_2, K_n)$ has the following combinatorial description:

- the cells are indexed by ordered pairs (A, B), where A and B are non-empty disjoint subsets of $[n]$,
- the boundary relation is indexed by deleting elements from the subsets A and B.

Let us describe a matching on the set of cells of $\mathrm{Hom}(K_2, K_n)$, for $n \geqslant 3$. To start with, for a cell $\sigma = (A, B)$, we set

$$\rho(\sigma) := \min([n] \setminus B).$$

The matching μ is then defined by the formula

$$\mu(\sigma) = \mu(A, B) := \begin{cases} (A \operatorname{XOR} \rho, B), & \text{if } A \neq \{\rho\}, \\ (\rho, B \operatorname{XOR} \{\rho + 1\}), & \text{otherwise}, \end{cases} \tag{14.3}$$

where $\rho = \rho(A, B)$. Verbally, the rule given by Equation (14.3) can be formulated as follows. Take the pivot element $\rho = \rho(\sigma)$ and add it to the first set A, if it is not there already. If it is, then try deleting it. The only reason deleting may not work is that A would become empty, that is, $A = \{\rho\}$. In that case, add the element $\rho + 1$ to the second set B, if, of course, it is not there already. If it is, then delete $\rho + 1$ from B instead. The only case where this is not possible is when $B = \{\rho + 1\}$.

Proposition 14.9. *The described matching μ is acyclic. It has one critical 0-cell indexed by $(1, 2)$, and one critical $(n-2)$-cell indexed by $(n, [n-1])$.*

Proof. Let us first see for which cells $\sigma = (A, B)$ the function μ is *not* defined. First, if $\rho \notin A$, then adding ρ will always work. Furthermore, $\rho \in A$ and $|A| \geqslant 2$; then deleting ρ also results in a well-defined cell of $\operatorname{Hom}(K_2, K_n)$. So, in order for μ not to be defined, we must have $A = \{\rho\}$.

So, assume $\sigma = (\rho, B)$, with $[\rho - 1] \subseteq B$. If $\rho = n$, then $\sigma = (n, [n-1])$ and we find the first cell for which μ is not defined. Otherwise, we have $\rho \leqslant n - 1$, so $\rho + 1 \in [n]$. Again, if $\rho + 1 \notin B$, we can add $\rho + 1$ to B, and μ is defined. If $\rho + 1 \in B$ and $|B| \geqslant 2$, then $\rho + 1$ can be deleted and μ is defined again. The final case is that $B = \{\rho + 1\}$. Since $[\rho - 1] \subseteq B$, we must have $\rho = 1$. We then conclude that $\sigma = (1, 2)$, finding the second and the final cell for which μ is not defined.

A case-by-case analysis of Equation (14.3) shows that $\rho(\sigma) = \rho(\mu(\sigma))$. This, in turn, implies that $\mu \circ \mu = \text{id}$, so μ really defines a matching.

Let us now show that μ is acyclic. We shall assign labels to the matched pairs in μ as follows. The matched pair $(A, B) \leftrightarrow (A \operatorname{XOR} \rho, B)$ gets the label (I, ρ), and we call it the matched pair of the *first kind*. The matched pair $(A, B) \leftrightarrow (\rho, B \operatorname{XOR} \{\rho + 1\})$ gets the label (II, ρ), and we call it the matched pair of the *second kind*. In both cases ρ is called the *weight* of the matched pair.

Assume now that μ is not acyclic and consider a cycle

$$a_1 < \mu(a_1) > a_2 < \mu(a_2) > \cdots > a_t < \mu(a_t) > a_1,$$

where all a_i's are different and $t \geqslant 2$. Without loss of generality we can assume that the matching pair $a_1 \leftrightarrow \mu(a_1)$ has the lowest weight w among all the matching pairs in this cycle. Furthermore, if there are matching pairs of weight w both of the first and the second kind, we can reindex to ensure that the matching pair $a_1 \leftrightarrow \mu(a_1)$ is of the second kind.

Assume first that the latter is the case and that $a_1 \leftrightarrow \mu(a_1)$ is of the second kind. This means that $a_1 = (w, [w-1] \cup B)$, where B might be empty, $w+1 \notin B$, and $\mu(a_1) = (w, [w-1] \cup B \cup \{w+1\})$. The cell a_2 is obtained from $\mu(a_1)$ by either deleting an element of $[w-1]$ or deleting an element of B.

Consider the first subcase that it is obtained by deleting $x \in [w-1]$. We have

$$a_2 = (w, [x-1] \cup \{x+1, \dots, w-1\} \cup \{w+1\} \cup B).$$

In that case $\mu(a_2) = (\{w, x\}, [x-1] \cup \{x+1, \dots, w-1\} \cup \{w+1\} \cup B)$, and the matching pair $a_2 \leftrightarrow \mu(a_2)$ has weight $x \leqslant w-1$, which contradicts our assumption that w is the minimal weight in the cycle.

Now consider the second subcase in which an element of B is deleted instead. We have

$$a_2 = (w, [w-1] \cup \{w+1\} \cup (B \setminus x)),$$

for some $x \in B$. In that case, $\mu(a_2)$ should be obtained by deleting $w+1$, so $\mu(a_2) = (w, [w-1] \cup (B \setminus x))$, and $a_2 > \mu(a_2)$, clearly a contradiction. The only exceptional case is when the set $[w-1] \cup (B \setminus x)$ is empty. This will happen if $w = 1$ and $|B| = 1$. However, then $a_2 = (1, 2)$, which is a critical cell, and we again arrive at a contradiction.

Assume now that the matching pair $a_1 \leftrightarrow \mu(a_1)$ is of the first kind. We then have

$$a_1 = (A, [w-1] \cup B), \quad \mu(a_1) = (\{w\} \cup A, [w-1] \cup B),$$

where A and B are disjoint non-empty subsets of $[n] \setminus [w]$. There are three cases to consider: a_2 is obtained from $\mu(a_1)$ by deleting an element from either $[w-1]$, B, or A.

Case 1. We delete $x \in [w-1]$. We then have

$$a_2 = (\{w\} \cup A, [x-1] \cup \{x+1, \dots, w-1\} \cup B).$$

The rule in Equation (14.3) then tells us that

$$\mu(a_2) = (\{x, w\} \cup A, [x-1] \cup \{x+1, \dots, w-1\} \cup B).$$

The matching pair $a_2 \leftrightarrow \mu(a_2)$ is then of the first kind and has the weight $x \leqslant w-1$. This is a contradiction to the minimality of w.

Case 2. We delete $x \in B$ and have

$$a_2 = (\{w\} \cup A, [w-1] \cup (B \setminus x)).$$

Since A is non-empty, we have $\mu(a_2) = (A, [w-1] \cup (B \setminus x))$. In particular, $a_2 > \mu(a_2)$, which is a contradiction.

Case 3. Assume we delete $x \in A$, so

$$a_2 = (\{w\} \cup (A \setminus x), [w-1] \cup B).$$

If $|A| \geqslant 2$, i.e., $A \setminus x$ is non-empty, Equation (14.3) tells us that $\mu(a_2) = (A \setminus x, [w-1] \cup B)$, so $\mu(a_2) < a_2$, which is a contradiction. Finally, if $|A| = 1$, i.e., $A = \{x\}$, we have $a_2 = (w, [w-1] \cup B)$. If $w = n$, the cell $a_2 = (n, [n-1])$ is critical. Otherwise $\mu(a_2) = (w, ([w-1] \cup B)\,\mathrm{XOR}\{w+1\})$, so the matching pair $a_2 \leftrightarrow \mu(a_2)$ is of the second kind and has the same weight w. In both subcases we obtain a contradiction to our previous assumptions.

All in all, we have shown that the matching μ is acyclic and that it has two critical cells: one in dimension 0 and one in dimension $n-2$. □

Clearly, Proposition 14.9 implies that $\mathrm{Hom}(K_2, K_n)$ is homotopy equivalent to an $(n-2)$-sphere. In fact, with a little more work one can show that it is in fact homeomorphic to $\mathcal{S}^{n-2}$.

14.2. Discrete Morse functions and gradient vector fields

Historically, discrete Morse theory was introduced by Forman, see [**Fo98**], using the concepts of *discrete Morse functions*, *combinatorial vector fields*, and *discrete gradient vector fields*. The modern treatment presented here deals exclusively with combinatorial matchings, jetissoning the unnecessary topological information. Still, a certain amount of literature uses that previous terminology, so here we include a brief description of the connection between the two.

Let us recall the definition of a discrete Morse function. For simplicity we restrict ourselves to the simplicial setting. Let $\mathcal{K}$ be a simplicial complex, and let $\mathcal{F}(\mathcal{K})$, as before, be its face poset.

Definition 14.10. A function $\varphi : \mathcal{F}(\mathcal{K}) \to \mathbb{R}$ is called a *discrete Morse function* if it satisfies the following two properties:

- For any simplex $\sigma \in \mathcal{F}(\mathcal{K})$, the number of simplices $\tau \in \mathcal{F}(\mathcal{K})$ in the boundary of σ, which satisfy $\varphi(\sigma) \leqslant \varphi(\tau)$ and $\dim\tau = \dim\sigma - 1$, is at most one.
- For any simplex $\sigma \in \mathcal{F}(\mathcal{K})$, the number of simplices $\tau \in \mathcal{F}(\mathcal{K})$ containing σ in their boundary, which satisfy $\varphi(\sigma) \geqslant \varphi(\tau)$ and $\dim\sigma = \dim\tau - 1$, is at most one.

Given a discrete Morse function φ we can construct a matching $\mu(\varphi)$ as follows: for $\sigma, \tau \in \mathcal{F}(\mathcal{K})$, we match σ with τ if the following two conditions are satisfied:

- τ is a boundary simplex of σ with $\dim\tau = \dim\sigma - 1$,
- $\varphi(\tau) \geqslant \varphi(\sigma)$.

The following proposition describes the relation between acyclic matchings and discrete Morse functions.

Proposition 14.11. *Assume $\mathcal{K}$ is a simplicial complex. Given a discrete Morse function φ, the associated matching $\mu(\varphi)$ must be acyclic.*

Reversely, given an acyclic matching γ, there exist discrete Morse functions φ realizing this specific matching, that is, such that $\gamma = \mu(\varphi)$.

Proof. The first claim is obvious. Simply trace the value of φ following the cycle, if one exists. This value will not increase when we follow the matching edges upwards, and it will decrease when we follow the non-matching edges downwards. As a result, the function value will decrease after following the entire cycle, which is of course a contradiction.

For the opposite direction, recall that Theorem 11.9 tells us that there is a linear extension l of $\mathcal{F}(\mathcal{K})$ such that $\mu(x)$ follows directly after x whenever x is matched and $\dim \mu(x) > \dim x$. By recording for each $x \in \mathcal{F}(\mathcal{K})$ its position in the linear extension, we can identify l with the corresponding function $\mathcal{F}(\mathcal{K}) \to [d]$, where d is the number of the elements in $\mathcal{F}(\mathcal{K})$. We can now define the function $\varphi : \mathcal{F}(\mathcal{K}) \to \mathbb{R}$ by setting

$$\varphi(x) := \begin{cases} l(x) + 1, & \text{if } x \text{ is matched and } \dim \mu(x) > \dim x; \\ l(x), & \text{otherwise.} \end{cases}$$

Whenever x is matched and $\dim \mu(x) > \dim x$, we have $\varphi(x) = \varphi(\mu(x))$. This, together with the fact that l is a linear extension, implies that φ is a discrete Morse function. □

Proposition 14.11 is well known in the literature using discrete Morse function terminology, where what we call acyclic matchings appear under the name *discrete gradient vector fields*. Here we prefer the acyclic matchings as it is a well-established terminology in graph theory.

As Proposition 14.11 shows, any discrete Morse function yields a unique acyclic matching, whereas each acyclic matching is generated by many different discrete Morse functions. As the entire topological information is derived from the matching itself, we feel it is unnecessary to deal with the discrete Morse functions at all.

14.3. Subsuming shellability

Recall that a simplex σ of an abstract simplicial complex $\mathcal{K}$ is called *maximal* if there is no simplex of $\mathcal{K}$ which properly contains σ. Using maximal simplices we can think about an abstract simplicial complex in a *constructive* way.

Indeed, assume we are given some ordering $(\sigma_1, \dots, \sigma_t)$ on the set of maximal simplices of $\mathcal{K}$. Let us say that we build up $\mathcal{K}$ successively as follows. We start with taking the simplex σ_1, and of course all of its subsimplices. Next, we add the simplex σ_2, and all its subsimplices, and so forth, until the simplex σ_t. In the end we will get $\mathcal{K}$. Notationally, the simplex σ and all its subsimplices is the set family 2^σ, so our building workflow is

$$\emptyset \rightsquigarrow 2^{\sigma_1} \rightsquigarrow 2^{\sigma_1} \cup 2^{\sigma_2} \rightsquigarrow \ldots \rightsquigarrow 2^{\sigma_1} \cup \cdots \cup 2^{\sigma_t} = \mathcal{K}.$$

At step k we are adding the set of simplices 2^{σ_k}. The set of those simplices which are already there is denoted by $2^{\sigma_k} \cap (2^{\sigma_1} \cup \cdots \cup 2^{\sigma_{k-1}})$. One can define various classes of abstract simplicial complexes by imposing different conditions on these intersections. Shellable simplicial complexes is one of these concepts.

Definition 14.12. Let $\mathcal{K}$ be an abstract simplicial complex. It is called *shellable* if there exists an ordering $(\sigma_1, \ldots, \sigma_t)$ on the set of maximal simplices of $\mathcal{K}$, such that for each $2 \leqslant k \leqslant t$ the intersection

$$2^{\sigma_k} \cap (2^{\sigma_1} \cup \cdots \cup 2^{\sigma_{k-1}})$$

is a pure abstract simplicial complex of dimension $\dim \sigma_k - 1$.

An ordering on the maximal simplices of an abstract simplicial complex $\mathcal{K}$ satisfying conditions of Definition 14.12 is called a *shelling order*. Figure 14.1 shows different shelling orders, as well as a sequence which is not a shelling order.

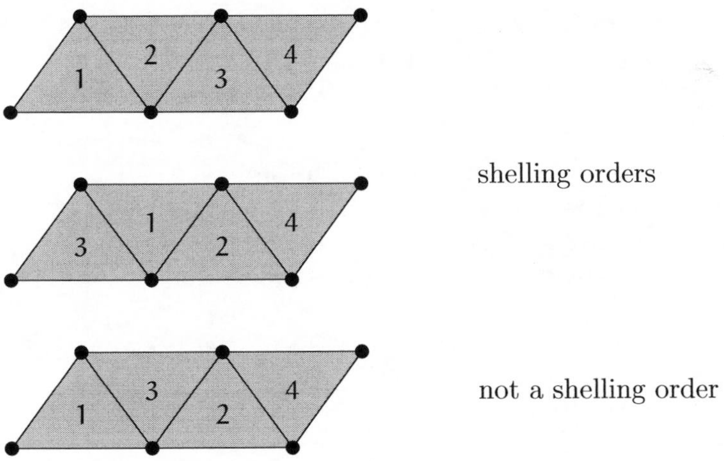

Figure 14.1. Different shelling and non-shelling orders.

Given a shelling order $(\sigma_1, \ldots, \sigma_t)$, we call the simplex σ_k *filling* with respect to that shelling order if the intersection of σ_k with previous simplices is the entire boundary of σ_k; in other words,

$$2^{\sigma_k} \cap (2^{\sigma_1} \cup \cdots \cup 2^{\sigma_{k-1}}) = \{\tau \mid \tau \subset \sigma_k\}.$$

Each time our construction process arrives at a filling simplex σ_k, we actually only add the simplex σ_k itself, as its boundary is already completely in. Since the filling simplices cannot contain each other, this means that, given any shelling order, we can form a new well-defined shelling order by pulling out all the filling simplices and then adding them in arbitrary order at the end of the sequence.

Traditionally, shellability is used to show that the abstract simplicial complex is homotopy equivalent to a wedge of spheres, and also to provide examples of explicit homology generators. It turns out that this tool can be subsumed by discrete Morse theory in the following precise sense.

Theorem 14.13. *Assume $\mathcal{K}$ is a shellable abstract simplicial complex, and assume $(\sigma_1, \dots, \sigma_t)$ is a shelling order on the set of maximal simplices of $\mathcal{K}$. Assume $\{\tau_1, \dots, \tau_m\}$ are the filling simplices. Then $\mathcal{K} \setminus \{\tau_1, \dots, \tau_m\}$ is collapsible.*

Equivalently, there exists an acyclic matching μ, such that the set of criticial simplices with respect to μ coincides with the set of filling simplices with respect to the selected shelling order.

Proof. By Theorem 10.9 the second statement follows from the first one, so it is enough to show that $\mathcal{K}\setminus\{\tau_1, \dots, \tau_m\}$ is collapsible. The easiest way to do that is to consider a shelling order in which the filling simplices $\{\tau_1, \dots, \tau_m\}$ all come in the end, after all other simplices. By our previous remarks, this can always be assumed without loss of generality. Let d be the number of maximal simplices of $\mathcal{K}$ which are not filling.

Now, let us simply verify that $2^{\sigma_1} \cup \cdots \cup 2^{\sigma_k}$ is collapsible for all $k \leqslant d$. This can be done by induction on k with the base $k = 1$ being trivial. For the induction step we are going to show that adding 2^{σ_k} to $2^{\sigma_1} \cup \cdots \cup 2^{\sigma_{k-1}}$ is a compound collapse. Indeed, we know that $2^{\sigma_k} \cap (2^{\sigma_1} \cup \cdots \cup 2^{\sigma_{k-1}})$ is pure, so there exists a set $\{x_1, \dots, x_s\} \subseteq \sigma_k$, such that

$$2^{\sigma_k} \cap (2^{\sigma_1} \cup \cdots \cup 2^{\sigma_{k-1}}) = \{\gamma \subseteq \sigma_k \,|\, \gamma \subseteq (\sigma_k \setminus x_i), \text{ for some } 1 \leqslant i \leqslant s\}.$$

But then we also have

$$(14.4) \quad 2^{\sigma_k} \setminus (2^{\sigma_k} \cap (2^{\sigma_1} \cup \cdots \cup 2^{\sigma_{k-1}})) = \{\gamma \subseteq \sigma_k \,|\, \gamma \supseteq (\sigma_k \setminus \{x_1, \dots, x_s\})\}.$$

Since σ_k is not filling, we must have $s \leqslant \dim \sigma_k$. Equation (14.4) then implies that adding 2^{σ_k} to $2^{\sigma_1} \cup \cdots \cup 2^{\sigma_{k-1}}$ is the compound collapse

$$(\sigma_k, \sigma_k \setminus \{x_1, \dots, x_s\}).$$

This finishes the proof. □

14.4. Infinite simplicial complexes

Until now we have always assumed that our complexes are finite. A natural question arises: *can some of the results be generalized to the infinite case?*

The short answer to this is yes, as long as the set of matched pairs remains finite. To start with Theorem 10.9 (Theorem A) holds with the simple requirement that $\mathcal{K} \setminus \mathcal{K}'$ is finite. Theorem 11.2 (Theorem B) holds under the assumption that M is finite. Both proofs go through virtually without changes.

Furthermore, when M is finite, all the alternating paths are finite. So the closure map φ can be defined in the same way as in Chapter 12 and the explicit homology classes can also be computed using the same recursive formula.

Finally, the definition of the critical Morse complex is identical, and the basis change in Theorem 13.3 still works, since it proceeds in the number of steps equal to the cardinality of M, which we assume to be finite.

In all these cases the details are mundane, and we relegate their check to the interested reader.

Exercises

(1) Check that the semisimplicial set which we associated to the generalized abstract simplicial complex in Subsection 14.1.1 is well-defined.

(2) Give an example of a collapsible simplicial complex which is not shellable.

(3) Prove that the geometric realization of a shellable simplicial complex is homotopy equivalent to a wedge of spheres.

(4) Find a triangulation of a 3-dimensional sphere, which is not shellable.

Suggested further reading for Part 3

The idea of defining a combinatorial homotopy theory based on the notions of collapse and anti-collapse (also known as *expansion*) was developed by Whitehead, who coined the term simple homotopy theory. The original articles are still instructive and worth consulting; see [**Wh50**] and the references therein.

In 1973 Marshall Cohen has written a concise text, [**Co73**], which remains the standard textbook reference on the subject to this day, and which we highly recommend as an entry point. The basics of the theory and the notion of Whitehead torsion are developed there in the CW category.

For the readers interested in the broader subject of algebraic torsion, such as Reidemeister torsion, etc., we recommend the book by Turaev, [**Tu01**].

Discrete Morse theory was introduced by Robin Forman, whose original paper [**Fo98**] is still very much worth checking up. The idea of viewing the resulting complex deformation as a sequence of internal collapses can be traced back to [**Ko08**, Section 11.2].

The reader will appreciate switching to the purely combinatorial notion of matchings, whose theory is richly developed; see [**Lo86**] for an introduction. The general combinatorial background can be found in textbooks [**Har69**, **MSTY**].

We have used the rich plethora of combinatorially defined simplicial complexes to illustrate managing collapsing sequences. If these examples appeared appealing, the reader may want to consult the author's previous textbook [**Ko08**], devoted entirely to the topic. Further useful background references on topological combinatorics are [**Bj96, Ko02, Zi97**].

A large class of combinatorially defined cell complexes is provided by the so-called Hom-complexes; the references here are [**BK03a, BK03b, BK04, CK04a, CK04b, Ko04, Ko05a, Lo78**]. Some applications in topological combinatorics, including details of the structures used here, can be found [**Ko99, Ko00, LPV13, SW12, Sh01, Zh18**].

Further afield, discrete Morse theory has been used for questions in geometry in topology; see, e.g., [**CGN16, FS05, GMS11, Ga10, MS11, NTT18, Oz17, RW10, ZhP17**]. The specific notion of compound collapse has found its applications in [**BE17**].

Despite of our focus on acyclic matchings, rather than discrete Morse functions, the latter were and remain to be a subject of intense scrutiny; see, e.g., [**AGORS, CM17, Ch00, CJ05**].

One of the considered subdivisions of the simplex, the standard chromatic one, is a central object in the field of applications of combinatorial topology to theoretical distributed computing. If this is of interest, the textbook [**HKR14**], as well as research articles [**BR18, Ko12**], are warmly recommended.

Part 4

Extensions of Discrete Morse Theory

Chapter 15

Algebraic Morse Theory

15.1. Replacing simplicial complexes with general chain complexes

In Chapter 11 we have learned how to think intuitively about discrete Morse theory for simplicial complexes as a procedure which starts with a collection of the so-called *internal collapses* and then progresses by performing these collapses, in a certain order, while tracing the gluing maps of the simplices. While being beautifully geometrically intuitive, this procedure is not as impeccably formal as one might prefer. Furthermore, any real-life algorithmic realizations will have their share of difficulty implementing "continuous deformations of gluing maps." It turns out that switching to a purely algebraic setting allows us to kill two birds with one stone: gaining both the formal, algorithmically implementable framework for our procedures, as well as gaining broader generality.

As a general plan, we would like to replace simplicial complexes, or any cell complexes for that matter, with their corresponding chain complexes. In order to model the "set of simplices" algebraically, we choose a basis in each chain group. So the algebraic object which is to serve as a main subject of study in the theory, which was appropriately dubbed *algebraic Morse theory*, is a chain complex, where each chain group has a chosen basis, and there is a certain partial matching on these bases.

As the next step in the algebraic direction, we replace the geometrically intuitive internal collapses from the topological context by simultaneous *changes of bases.* Specifically, each internal collapse is replaced by the simultaneous changes of bases in *two* chain groups, and the indices of these chain groups are the dimensions of the two simplices which are being matched. As a result, the entire topological collapsing procedure is then replaced by a sequence of such basis changes, which can easily be implemented algorithmically using row and column operations for the corresponding adjacency matrices.

In Chapter 12 we have developed a certain tracing procedure which allowed us to write down explicitly the homology classes in the final Morse complex. The concept of alternating paths can be carried over to the chain complexes. So, in the algebraic context, this procedure can be repeated in better clarity and in broader generality.

Before moving on to dealing with the general context, let us illustrate what we mean to accomplish in this chapter by means of a small toy example. Consider a 3-simplex as an abstract simplicial complex, which we denote by $\mathcal{K}$. Let the vertices be indexed $1, 2, 3, 4$, and for every set $S \subseteq \{1, 2, 3, 4\}$, let σ_S denote the simplex whose set of vertices is indexed by the set S. For brevity of notations, we shall skip some commas and curly brackets, and, for instance, write σ_{123} instead of $\sigma_{\{1,2,3\}}$.

We shall work with coefficients in $\mathbb{Z}_2$. The initial chain complex is

$$0 \to \langle \sigma_{1234} \rangle \to \langle \sigma_{123}, \sigma_{124}, \sigma_{134}, \sigma_{234} \rangle \\ \to \langle \sigma_{12}, \sigma_{13}, \sigma_{14}, \sigma_{23}, \sigma_{24}, \sigma_{34} \rangle \to \langle \sigma_1, \sigma_2, \sigma_3, \sigma_4 \rangle \to 0,$$

where each chain group is actually a vector space over $\mathbb{Z}_2$.

For the sake of our example, let us consider a very simple matching consisting of a single pair $\sigma_{23} \leftrightarrow \sigma_{234}$. In the topological picture, we would remove the simplices σ_{23} and σ_{234}, changing the rest of the gluing maps and thinking of this as an internal collapse. The new gluing maps can be described, but this would require some technical work, as well as making some choices; something which we would always rather avoid.

In the algebraic context, we start with the vectors spaces

$$C_1 = \langle \sigma_{12}, \sigma_{13}, \sigma_{14}, \sigma_{23}, \sigma_{24}, \sigma_{34} \rangle \text{ and } C_2 = \langle \sigma_{123}, \sigma_{124}, \sigma_{134}, \sigma_{234} \rangle .$$

We now pick some specific new bases for C_1 and C_2. The new basis for the vector space C_1 is

$$\{\sigma_{12}, \sigma_{13}, \sigma_{14}, \partial\sigma_{234}, \sigma_{24}, \sigma_{34}\},$$

where of course $\partial\sigma_{234} = \sigma_{23} + \sigma_{24} + \sigma_{34}$. The new basis for the vector space C_2 is

$$\{\sigma_{123} + \sigma_{234}, \sigma_{124}, \sigma_{134}, \sigma_{234}\}.$$

The incidence matrices will change as follows:

	σ_{123}	σ_{124}	σ_{134}	σ_{234}
σ_{12}	1	1	0	0
σ_{13}	1	0	1	0
σ_{14}	0	1	1	0
σ_{23}	1	0	0	①
σ_{24}	0	1	0	1
σ_{34}	0	0	1	1

$\longrightarrow$

	$\sigma_{123}+$ σ_{234}	σ_{124}	σ_{134}	σ_{234}
σ_{12}	1	1	0	0
σ_{13}	1	0	1	0
σ_{14}	0	1	1	0
$\partial\sigma_{234}$	0	0	0	①
σ_{24}	1	1	0	0
σ_{34}	1	0	1	0

	σ_{1234}
σ_{123}	1
σ_{124}	1
σ_{134}	1
σ_{234}	1

$\longrightarrow$

	σ_{1234}
$\sigma_{123}+\sigma_{234}$	1
σ_{124}	1
σ_{134}	1
σ_{234}	0

and

	σ_{12}	σ_{13}	σ_{14}	σ_{23}	σ_{24}	σ_{34}
σ_1	1	1	1	0	0	0
σ_2	1	0	0	1	1	0
σ_3	0	1	0	1	0	1
σ_4	0	0	1	0	1	1

$\downarrow$

	σ_{12}	σ_{13}	σ_{14}	$\partial\sigma_{234}$	σ_{24}	σ_{34}
σ_1	1	1	1	0	0	0
σ_2	1	0	0	0	1	0
σ_3	0	1	0	0	0	1
σ_4	0	0	1	0	1	1

The summary of these matrix operations is as follows. In the first case, the encircled entry must be 1 (otherwise the matching would not be allowed). We then use the column operations to eliminate all other 1's in that row. After this one uses the row operations to eliminate all other 1's in that column, which of course simply amounts to replacing all 1's in that column by 0's. In the last matrix transformation, we simply take the column corresponding to the matched element and replace all the entries there by 0's.

15.2. Eliminating the matched part

Let us now put the matrix transformation procedure from the previous section on the industrial footing. For now, we shall stay with the chain complexes of vector spaces over $\mathbb{Z}_2$, with only finitely many of these vector spaces being non-trivial. We call such a chain complex a *finite* $\mathbb{Z}_2$*-chain complex*. The next definition describes the main characters of this and the next section.

Definition 15.1. A *finite based* $\mathbb{Z}_2$*-chain complex* is a finite $\mathbb{Z}_2$-chain complex $\mathcal{C} = (C_*, \partial_*)$, together with the choice of a basis Ω_n, in the $\mathbb{Z}_2$-vector space C_n, for all indices n.

Given a finite based $\mathbb{Z}_2$-chain complex $\mathcal{C} = (C_*, \partial_*)$, we set $\Omega := \bigcup_n \Omega_n$, and then also write the pair $(\mathcal{C}, \Omega)$ to emphasize that choice of the basis.

Definition 15.2. Assume V is a vector space over $\mathbb{Z}_2$, and $\mathcal{A}$ is some fixed basis of V. Then, there is unique scalar product on V in which the basis $\mathcal{A}$ is orthonormal. We use $\langle \mid \rangle_{\mathcal{A}}$ as the notation for this scalar product.

As we are working with $\mathbb{Z}_2$-coefficients, when v is any vector and a is a basis vector in $\mathcal{A}$, the value of the scalar product $\langle v \mid a\rangle_{\mathcal{A}}$ simply tells us whether or not a is present in the $\mathcal{A}$-decomposition of v. When dealing with chain complexes, the standard piece of information we need is to know whether a certain basis vector is present in the *boundary* of another vector. Accordingly, we need appropriate shorthand notation, which are provided by the next definition.

Definition 15.3. Assume we are given a finite based $\mathbb{Z}_2$-chain complex $(\mathcal{C}, \Omega)$, and assume that for some d we have chosen elements $b \in C_d$ and $a \in C_{d-1}$. Then, we set

$$w_\Omega(b \succ a) := \langle \partial_d b \mid a\rangle_{\Omega_{d-1}}. \tag{15.1}$$

When the choice of the basis Ω is clear from the context, we may skip it from the notation, and simply write $w(b \succ a)$.

Note that Equation (15.1) means

$$w_\Omega(b \succ a) = \begin{cases} 1, & \text{if } a \text{ is contained in the linear combination} \\ & \text{representing } \partial_d b \text{ in basis } \Omega_{d-1}, \\ 0, & \text{otherwise.} \end{cases}$$

We now note that a finite based $\mathbb{Z}_2$-chain complex $(\mathcal{C}, \Omega)$ can be represented by a certain poset.

Definition 15.4. Assume $(\mathcal{C}, \Omega)$ is a finite based $\mathbb{Z}_2$-chain complex. Its *basis poset*, which we denote $P(\mathcal{C}, \Omega)$, is defined as follows:

- the elements of $P(\mathcal{C}, \Omega)$ are the elements of Ω;
- the partial order is given by saying that for $b \in \Omega_d$, $a \in \Omega_{d-1}$, b covers a if and only if $w_\Omega(b \succ a) = 1$.

For future reference, we note that a direct sum of finite based $\mathbb{Z}_2$-chain complexes $(\mathcal{C}^1, \Omega^1)$ and $(\mathcal{C}^2, \Omega^2)$ is again a finite based $\mathbb{Z}_2$-chain complex, denoted $(\mathcal{C}^1 \oplus \mathcal{C}^2, \Omega^1 \cup \Omega^2)$. Furthermore, the associated poset of the basis elements $P(\mathcal{C}^1 \oplus \mathcal{C}^2, \Omega^1 \cup \Omega^2)$ is a disjoint union of the posets $P(\mathcal{C}^1, \Omega^1)$ and $P(\mathcal{C}^2, \Omega^2)$.

Definition 15.5. Let $(\mathcal{C}, \Omega)$ be a finite based $\mathbb{Z}_2$-chain complex. A subset $M \subseteq \Omega \times \Omega$ is called a *partial matching* on $(\mathcal{C}, \Omega)$, if $(a, b) \in M$ implies that b covers a in the poset $P(\mathcal{C}, \Omega)$, and no two tuples from M have an element in common.

We say that the (partial) matching M is *acyclic* if and only if it is acyclic as a partial matching in the poset $P(\mathcal{C}, \Omega)$; see Definition 10.7.

In the simplicial version of the discrete Morse theory, the pairs of matched simplices simply vanished after each collapse, with the rest of the simplices being re-glued in a convoluted way. In the algebraic version, where we perform a basis change rather than a collapse, the matched pairs of basis elements leave a residue in the form of the following, essentially simplest possible, chain complex.

Definition 15.6. The chain complex

$$\dots \longrightarrow 0 \longrightarrow \mathbb{Z}_2 \xrightarrow{\text{id}} \mathbb{Z}_2 \longrightarrow 0 \longrightarrow \dots,$$

where the only non-trivial modules are in the dimensions d and $d-1$, is called an *atomic chain complex*, and is denoted by $\text{Atom}(d)$.

Clearly, there is a unique way to pick a basis in the atomic chain complex, and the associated basis poset will consist of two comparable elements.

The next definition shall provide us with the main operation which we perform on the bases of chain complexes. Beforehand, we need a little piece of notation. Assume we are given a finite based $\mathbb{Z}_2$-chain complex $(\mathcal{C}, \Omega)$, and assume that, for some d, we have chosen $b \in \Omega_d$ and $a \in \Omega_{d-1}$, so that $w_\Omega(b \succ a) = 1$. Let $\eta_\Omega(a, b)$ denote the set of elements from Ω_d, other than b, which cover a; in other words, we set

$$\eta_\Omega(a, b) := \{c \in \Omega_d \,|\, w_\Omega(c \succ a) = 1,\ c \neq b\}.$$

Whenever the choice of Ω is clear, we shall skip the index and simply write $\eta(a, b)$.

Definition 15.7. In the situation above, we define a new basis $\widetilde{\Omega} = \cup_n \widetilde{\Omega}_n$, where for each n, the set $\widetilde{\Omega}_n$ is a basis for C_n, as follows:

$$\begin{aligned} \widetilde{\Omega}_{d-1} &:= (\Omega_{d-1} \setminus a) \cup \{\partial_d b\}, \\ \widetilde{\Omega}_d &:= (\Omega_d \setminus \eta(a,b)) \cup \{x+b \,|\, x \in \eta(a,b)\}, \\ \widetilde{\Omega}_n &:= \Omega_n, \text{ if } n \neq d, d-1. \end{aligned}$$

We say that $\widetilde{\Omega}$ is obtained from Ω by *bonding* b with a, and denote it by $\text{bond}_{a,b}\,\Omega$; see Figure 15.1.

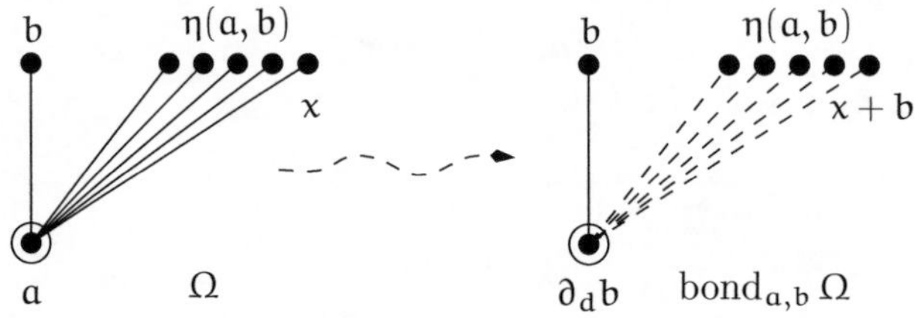

Figure 15.1. The effects of bonding on the basis poset.

Let us formalize a natural bijection between the sets Ω and $\widetilde{\Omega}$. For each $x \in \Omega$, we let $\widetilde{x}$ denote the corresponding element of $\widetilde{\Omega}$. Specifically, we set

$$\begin{aligned} \widetilde{a} &:= \partial_d b, \\ \widetilde{c} &:= c + b, \text{ for all } c \in \eta(a,b), \qquad (15.2) \\ \widetilde{x} &:= x, \text{ for all other } x \in \Omega. \end{aligned}$$

For future reference, we let $\rho(a,b)$ denote this bijection between Ω and $\widetilde{\Omega}$.

Proposition 15.8. *Assume we are given a finite based $\mathbb{Z}_2$-chain complex $(\mathcal{C}, \Omega)$, and assume that, for some d, we have chosen $b \in \Omega_d$ and $a \in \Omega_{d-1}$, such that $w_\Omega(b \succ a) = 1$. Set $\widetilde{\Omega} := \text{bond}_{a,b}\,\Omega$. Then $\widetilde{\Omega}$ is again a basis in which the elements b and a have bonded with each other in the following precise sense:*

$$w_{\widetilde{\Omega}}(\widetilde{b} \succ \widetilde{a}) = 1, \qquad (15.3)$$

$$w_{\widetilde{\Omega}}(\widetilde{c} \succ \widetilde{a}) = 0, \textit{ for all } c \in \Omega_d,\ c \neq b, \qquad (15.4)$$

$$w_{\widetilde{\Omega}}(\widetilde{a} \succ \widetilde{c}) = 0, \textit{ for all } c \in \Omega_{d-2}, \qquad (15.5)$$

$$w_{\widetilde{\Omega}}(\widetilde{b} \succ \widetilde{c}) = 0, \textit{ for all } c \in \Omega_{d-1},\ c \neq a, \qquad (15.6)$$

$$w_{\widetilde{\Omega}}(\widetilde{c} \succ \widetilde{b}) = 0, \textit{ for all } c \in \Omega_{d+1}. \qquad (15.7)$$

Proof. Let us first verify that $\widetilde{\Omega}$ is a basis or, to be more explicit, that $\widetilde{\Omega}_n$ is a basis for C_n, for all n. Here is a case-by-case argument.

- For $n \neq d, d-1$, we simply have $\widetilde{\Omega}_n = \Omega_n$, so $\widetilde{\Omega}_n$ is still a basis for C_n.
- For $n = d-1$, the set $\widetilde{\Omega}_{d-1}$ is obtained from Ω_{d-1} by replacing a fixed basis element a with another element that contains a in its linear expansion. Clearly, this again gives a basis for C_{d-1}.
- In the last case, when $n = d$, the set $\widetilde{\Omega}_d$ is obtained from Ω_d by adding a fixed basis element b to some other basis elements. Again, this must result in a basis for C_d.

We now show that Equations (15.3) to (15.7) are valid.

Verification of Equation (15.3). We have

$$w_{\widetilde{\Omega}}(\tilde{b} \succ \tilde{a}) = \langle \partial_d b \mid \tilde{a} \rangle_{\widetilde{\Omega}_{d-1}} = \langle \tilde{a} \mid \tilde{a} \rangle_{\widetilde{\Omega}_{d-1}} = 1,$$

where the last equality follows from the fact $\tilde{a} \in \widetilde{\Omega}_{d-1}$, and hence $\tilde{a}$ has norm 1 in the corresponding scalar product.

Verification of Equation (15.4). Pick a basis element $c \in \Omega_d$, $c \neq b$. Assume first that $c \notin \eta(a, b)$. Then, we have $\partial_d c \in \operatorname{span}(\Omega_{d-1} \setminus \{a\})$. On the other hand, we have $\tilde{c} = c$, and $\tilde{x} = x$ for all $x \in \Omega_{d-1} \setminus \{a\}$, so also $\partial_d \tilde{c} \in \operatorname{span}(\widetilde{\Omega}_{d-1} \setminus \{\tilde{a}\})$. This in turn implies $\langle \partial_d \tilde{c} \mid \tilde{a} \rangle_{\widetilde{\Omega}_{d-1}} = 0$, so $w_{\widetilde{\Omega}}(\tilde{c} \succ \tilde{a}) = 0$, as required.

Assume now that instead $c \in \eta(a, b)$. In that case, $\tilde{c} = c + b$, hence

$$w_{\Omega}(\tilde{c} \succ a) = w_{\Omega}(c \succ a) + w_{\Omega}(b \succ a) = 1 + 1 = 0,$$

and so $\partial_d \tilde{c} \in \operatorname{span}(\Omega_{d-1} \setminus \{a\})$. Just as in the first case, we now use the fact that $\tilde{x} = x$, for all $x \in \Omega_{d-1} \setminus \{a\}$, to conclude that $\partial_d \tilde{c} \in \operatorname{span}(\widetilde{\Omega}_{d-1} \setminus \{\tilde{a}\})$, and therefore $\langle \partial_d \tilde{c} \mid \tilde{a} \rangle_{\widetilde{\Omega}_{d-1}} = 0$, again implying $w_{\widetilde{\Omega}}(\tilde{c} \succ \tilde{a}) = 0$.

Verification of Equation (15.5). The relevant calculation here is

$$\partial_{d-1}(\tilde{a}) = \partial_{d-1}(\partial_d b) = 0,$$

which implies

$$w_{\widetilde{\Omega}}(\tilde{a} \succ \tilde{c}) = \langle \partial_{d-1} \tilde{a} \mid \tilde{c} \rangle_{\widetilde{\Omega}} = \langle 0 \mid \tilde{c} \rangle_{\widetilde{\Omega}} = 0.$$

Verification of Equation (15.6). This is immediate, since $\partial_d \tilde{b} \in \widetilde{\Omega}_{d-1}$, so $\partial_d \tilde{b}$ is orthogonal to all other basis vectors from $\widetilde{\Omega}_{d-1}$.

Verification of Equation (15.7). This final argument requires a bit of computation. Let $c \in \Omega_{d+1}$, and assume that $w_{\widetilde{\Omega}}(\tilde{c} \succ \tilde{b}) = 1$. This means that we have sets $I \subseteq \eta(a, b)$ and $J \subseteq \Omega_d \setminus (\eta(a, b) \cup \{b\})$, such that

$$\partial_{d+1}(\tilde{c}) = \tilde{b} + \sum_{x \in I} \tilde{x} + \sum_{y \in J} \tilde{y}. \tag{15.8}$$

Now, substituting $\tilde{c} = c$, $\tilde{b} = b$, $\tilde{x} = b + x$, for all $x \in I$, and $\tilde{y} = y$, for all $y \in J$, into Equation (15.8), we obtain

$$\partial_{d+1} c = b + \sum_{x \in I} (b + x) + \sum_{y \in J} y. \tag{15.9}$$

Applying ∂_d to Equation (15.9) we then get

$$0 = \partial_d(\partial_{d+1} c) = \partial_d b + \sum_{x \in I} (\partial_d b + \partial_d x) + \sum_{y \in J} \partial_d y.$$

Now take the scalar product $\langle \mid \rangle_\Omega$ associated with the basis Ω. By our hitherto assumptions, the following identities hold:

- $\langle \partial_d b \mid a \rangle_\Omega = 1$,
- $\langle x \mid a \rangle_\Omega = 1$, for all $x \in \eta(a, b)$,
- $\langle y \mid a \rangle_\Omega = 0$, for all $y \notin \eta(a, b)$.

As the last step, we evaluate the scalar product $\langle \mid \rangle_\Omega$ between a and both sides of Equation (15.9):

$$\begin{aligned} 0 &= \langle \partial_d(\partial_{d+1} c) \mid a \rangle_\Omega \\ &= \langle \partial_d b \mid a \rangle_\Omega + \sum_{x \in I} (\langle \partial_d b \mid a \rangle_\Omega + \langle \partial_d x \mid a \rangle_\Omega) + \sum_{y \in J} \langle \partial_d y \mid a \rangle_\Omega \\ &= 1 + \sum_{x \in I} (1 + 1) + \sum_{y \in J} 0 = 1. \end{aligned}$$

This is a contradiction, so our initial assumption saying that $w_{\widetilde{\Omega}}(\tilde{c} \succ \tilde{b}) = 1$ was wrong. □

We have shown that the bonding transformation isolates the matched pair in the poset associated to the new basis. The next proposition describes what happens to the rest of the basis poset.

Proposition 15.9. *Assume again we are given a finite based $\mathbb{Z}_2$-chain complex $(\mathcal{C}, \Omega)$, and that, for some d, we have $b \in \Omega_d$ and $a \in \Omega_{d-1}$, such that $w_\Omega(b \succ a) = 1$. Assume that furthermore, we have chosen $x \in \Omega_n$ and $y \in \Omega_{n-1}$, for some n, such that $x, y \notin \{a, b\}$. We then have*

$$w_{\widetilde{\Omega}}(\tilde{x} \succ \tilde{y}) = \begin{cases} w_\Omega(x \succ y) + w_\Omega(b \succ y), & \textit{if } x \in \eta(a, b), \\ w_\Omega(x \succ y), & \textit{otherwise}, \end{cases} \tag{15.10}$$

where as above we have $\widetilde{\Omega} = \operatorname{bond}_{a,b} \Omega$.

Proof. Set

$$B_\Omega(x) := \{z \in \Omega_{n-1} \mid w_\Omega(x \succ z) = 1\}.$$

If $\tilde{x} = x$ and $\tilde{z} = z$, for all $z \in B_\Omega(x)$, then

$$\partial_n \tilde{x} = \partial_n x = \sum_{z \in B_\Omega(x)} z = \sum_{z \in B_\Omega(x)} \tilde{z},$$

and hence Equation (15.10) holds.

So assume from now on that either $\tilde{x} \neq x$ or that there exists $z \in B_\Omega(x)$, such that $\tilde{z} \neq z$. In general of course, the definition of the bonding transformation tells us that if $\tilde{t} \neq t$, then $t \in \{a\} \cup \eta(a, b)$.

Assume first that $\tilde{x} \neq x$. By our choice of x and y, we know that $x \neq a$, so $x \in \eta(a, b)$. At the same time, we know that $y \neq a$, so $\tilde{y} = y$. We compute the $\widetilde{\Omega}_{d-1}$-decomposition of $\partial_d \tilde{x}$ as follows:

$$\begin{aligned}
\partial_d \tilde{x} = \partial_d(x + b) &= \partial_d x + \partial_d b \\
&= \sum_{z \in \Omega_{d-1}} w_\Omega(x \succ z)z + \sum_{z \in \Omega_{d-1}} w_\Omega(b \succ z)z \\
&= \sum_{z \in \Omega_{d-1} \setminus \{a\}} (w_\Omega(x \succ z) + w_\Omega(b \succ z))z \\
&= \sum_{z : \tilde{z} \in \widetilde{\Omega}_{d-1} \setminus \{\tilde{a}\}} (w_\Omega(x \succ z) + w_\Omega(b \succ z))\tilde{z},
\end{aligned}$$

where the penultimate equality follows from the fact that $w_\Omega(x \succ a) + w_\Omega(b \succ a) = 0$. Since $\tilde{y} \in \widetilde{\Omega}_{d-1} \setminus \{\tilde{a}\}$, we conclude that Equation (15.10) holds.

Assume next that there exists $z \in B_\Omega(x)$, such that $\tilde{z} \neq z$. If $z = a$, then $x \in \eta(a, b)$, and that case has just been considered. So we must have $z \in \eta(a, b)$, and in particular, $n = d + 1$.

Set $I := \Omega_d \setminus (\{b\} \cup \eta(a, b))$. In the following calculation it is handy to use the shorthand notation $\alpha_t := w_\Omega(x \succ t)$, for all $t \in \Omega_d$. We then have

$$\begin{aligned}
(15.11) \quad \partial_{d+1}(\tilde{x}) = \partial_{d+1}(x) &= \sum_{t \in \Omega_d} \alpha_t t = \sum_{t \in I} \alpha_t t + \sum_{t \in \eta(a,b)} \alpha_t t + \alpha_b b \\
&= \sum_{t \in I} \alpha_t t + \sum_{t \in \eta(a,b)} \alpha_t (t + b) + (\alpha_b + \sum_{t \in \eta(a,b)} \alpha_t) b \\
&= \sum_{t \in I} \alpha_t \tilde{t} + \sum_{t \in \eta(a,b)} \alpha_t \tilde{t} + (\alpha_b + \sum_{t \in \eta(a,b)} \alpha_t) \tilde{b}.
\end{aligned}$$

Since $y \neq b$, we see that the coefficient of $\tilde{y}$ in the $\widetilde{\Omega}_d$-expansion of $\partial_{d+1}(\tilde{x})$ is the same as the coefficient of y in the Ω_d-expansion of $\partial_{d+1}(x)$, which is precisely what Equation (15.10) says. □

Corollary 15.10. *If the pair* (c, d) *is isolated in* Ω*, then* $(\tilde{c}, \tilde{d})$ *is isolated in* $\widetilde{\Omega} = \text{bond}_{a,b}(\Omega)$.

Proof. Clearly, since the pair (c, d) is isolated, we have $c, d \notin \eta(a, b)$. By Proposition 15.9 it follows that

$$w_{\widetilde{\Omega}}(\tilde{c} \succ \tilde{z}) = w_{\Omega}(c \succ z) = 0 \text{ and } w_{\widetilde{\Omega}}(\tilde{d} \succ \tilde{z}) = w_{\Omega}(d \succ z) = 0,$$

for all $z \neq d$ in the appropriate dimension.

If $z \notin \eta(a, b)$, $z \notin \{c, d\}$, then in the same way we get

$$w_{\widetilde{\Omega}}(\tilde{z} \succ \tilde{c}) = w_{\Omega}(z \succ c) = 0 \text{ and } w_{\widetilde{\Omega}}(\tilde{z} \succ \tilde{d}) = w_{\Omega}(z \succ d) = 0.$$

Finally, assume $z \in \eta(a, b)$. Of course, we then have $z \notin \{c, d\}$. By Proposition 15.9 we have the following computations:

$$w_{\widetilde{\Omega}}(\tilde{z} \succ \tilde{c}) = w_{\Omega}(z \succ c) + w_{\Omega}(b \succ c) = 0 + 0 = 0,$$

and the same way

$$w_{\widetilde{\Omega}}(\tilde{z} \succ \tilde{d}) = w_{\Omega}(z \succ d) + w_{\Omega}(b \succ d) = 0 + 0 = 0.$$

This finishes the proof. □

It is now time to proceed to formulate the first theorem of algebraic Morse theory. It will bring to light a certain structure in the chain complex $\mathcal{C}$. Namely, in a different basis, we shall represent $\mathcal{C}$ as a direct sum of two chain complexes, of which one is a direct sum of atomic chain complexes, and the other one is isomorphic to a certain chain complex, which we denote $\mathcal{C}^{\mu}$, and which will be described later. For convenience, the choice of a basis can be performed in several steps, one step for each matched pair of the basis elements.

Before formulating our main theorem, we need one last piece of notation. Set $R(\Omega) := \Omega \setminus \{a_1, b_1, \dots, a_t, b_t\}$ and $R_n(\Omega) := R(\Omega) \cap \Omega_n$.

Theorem 15.11. *Assume that we have a finite based $\mathbb{Z}_2$-chain complex $(\mathcal{C}, \Omega)$, together with an acyclic matching M on that complex. Then $\mathcal{C}$ decomposes as a direct sum of chain complexes*

$$\mathcal{C} \simeq \mathcal{D} \oplus \mathcal{T}, \tag{15.12}$$

where $\mathcal{T} \simeq \bigoplus_{(a,b)\in M} \mathrm{Atom}(\dim b)$ and $\mathcal{D}$ is some chain complex, such that each vector space D_n has a basis indexed by the set $R_n(\Omega)$.[1]

Proof. The rough plan of our proof is as follows. Starting with the given basis Ω, we produce a sequence of bases, such that just looking at the final basis will make it obvious the fact that Equation (15.12) holds. Each next basis will be produced from a previous one by the bonding transformation defined above.

[1]The maps in the chain complex $\mathcal{D}$ will be investigated in detail in Theorem 15.14.

To begin with, we recall that by Theorem 11.9 we can order the pairs in the acyclic matching M, let us say the order is $(a_1, b_1), \dots, (a_t, b_t)$, so that, for each $1 \leqslant k \leqslant t$, the element a_k is *not* covered by any of the elements $a_{k+1}, \dots, a_t, b_{k+1}, \dots, b_t$.

The sequence of the chain complex bases, which we aim to produce, is denoted by $\Omega[0]$, $\Omega[1]$, ..., $\Omega[t]$. We start with setting $\Omega[0] := \Omega$, and $a_i[0] := a_i$, $b_i[0] := b_i$, for all $1 \leqslant i \leqslant t$. The further bases are defined recursively, by setting

$$\Omega[k] := \mathrm{bond}_{a_k[k-1], b_k[k-1]} \Omega[k-1], \tag{15.13}$$

where

$$x[k] := \rho(a_k[k-1], b_k[k-1])(x[k-1]),$$

for all $x \in \Omega$ and all $1 \leqslant k \leqslant t$.

The next fact traces what is happening with the poset associated to the basis as the latter is being transformed.

Fact. For all $0 \leqslant k \leqslant t$ the following two statements hold:

(1) The pairs $(a_1[k], b_1[k]), \dots, (a_k[k], b_k[k])$ are isolated in $P(\mathcal{C}, \Omega[k])$.

(2) Whenever $m \geqslant k+1$, we have

$$\eta_{\Omega[k]}(a_m[k], b_m[k]) \cap \{a_i[k], b_i[k] \mid i \in I_{k,m}\} = \emptyset, \tag{15.14}$$

where $I_{k,m} = \{1, \dots, k\} \cup \{m+1, \dots, t\}$.

Proof. We shall prove this fact by induction on k. To express the dependence on the parameter k, let us refer to the statements above as Fact (1)[k] and Fact (2)[k].

For the base of the induction take $k = 0$. The Fact (1)[0] is tautologically true, since the considered set of pairs is empty. The Fact (2)[0] is the condition which we made sure was fulfilled when choosing the ordering on the matched pairs.

Let us now proceed with proving the induction step. Assume $k \geqslant 1$, and for all smaller values of k the statements have already been proved. By the Fact (1)[k-1] we know that the pairs $(a_1[k-1], b_1[k-1])$, ..., $(a_{k-1}[k-1], b_{k-1}[k-1])$ are isolated in $P(\mathcal{C}, \Omega[k-1])$. By Corollary 15.10 we then conclude that the pairs $(a_1[k], b_1[k])$, ..., $(a_{k-1}[k], b_{k-1}[k])$ are isolated in $P(\mathcal{C}, \Omega[k])$. Finally, the last pair $(a_k[k], b_k[k])$ is isolated by Proposition 15.8, so Fact (1)[k] is proved.

We now show Fact (2)[k]. Take $m \geqslant k+1$. First, we have

$$\eta_{\Omega[k]}(a_m[k], b_m[k]) \cap \{a_i[k], b_i[k] \mid 1 \leqslant i \leqslant k\} = \emptyset,$$

because these pairs are isolated. Furthermore, we have

$$\eta_{\Omega[k]}(a_m[k], b_m[k]) \cap \{a_i[k], b_i[k] \mid m+1 \leqslant i \leqslant t\} = \emptyset.$$

Indeed, if $w_{\Omega[k]}(a_i[k] \succ a_m[k]) = 1$, for some $m+1 \leqslant i \leqslant t$, then by Proposition 15.9 we would have $w_{\Omega[k-1]}(a_i[k-1] \succ a_m[k-1]) = 1$ as well, yielding a contradiction. In the same way, we cannot have $w_{\Omega[k]}(b_i[k] \succ a_m[k]) = 1$, so the statement is proved. □

After performing all the transformations, we end up with the basis $\Omega[t]$. We have shown that the pairs $(a_1[t], b_1[t]), \dots, (a_t[t], b_t[t])$ are isolated in $P(\mathcal{C}, \Omega[t])$, and thus, the fact that the direct sum decomposition is valid follows from the construction of Atom(d). Obviously, $\mathcal{D}$ has the basis $R(\Omega) := \Omega \setminus \{a_1, b_1, \dots, a_t, b_t\}$. Now, set $R_n(\Omega) := R(\Omega) \cap \Omega_n$, and the proof is finished. □

15.3. Algebraic Morse complex

Assume $(\mathcal{C}, \Omega)$ is a finite based $\mathbb{Z}_2$-chain complex. Let M be an acyclic matching, say the set of matched pairs is (a_1, b_1), $\dots$, (a_t, b_t). In this section we want to expand on the statement of Theorem 15.11 and to give a precise combinatorial description of the chain complex $\mathcal{D}$.

As before, by Theorem 11.9, we can assume that the order of the pairs is chosen so that, for each $1 \leqslant k \leqslant t$, the element a_k is not covered by any of the elements $a_{k+1}, \dots, a_t, b_{k+1}, \dots, b_t$.

We now adapt Definition 13.4 to the setting of finite based $\mathbb{Z}_2$-chain complexes.

Definition 15.12. An *alternating path* in the basis Ω of the chain complex $\mathcal{C}$ is a sequence

$$p = (x, a_{i_1}, b_{i_1}, \dots, a_{i_p}, b_{i_p}, y),$$

such that

$$\begin{aligned} w_\Omega(x \succ a_{i_1}) &= w_\Omega(b_{i_1} \succ a_{i_1}) = w_\Omega(b_{i_1} \succ a_{i_2}) \\ &= \cdots = w_\Omega(b_{i_{p-1}} \succ a_{i_p}) = w_\Omega(b_{i_p} \succ a_{i_p}) = w_\Omega(b_{i_p} \succ y) = 1. \end{aligned}$$

We set $p^\bullet := x$ and $p_\bullet := y$.

Given such an alternating path, we remark that the choice of order of the matched pairs guarantees that $i_1 < \cdots < i_p$.

Recall the sets $R(\Omega)$ and $R_n(\Omega)$ from the proof of Theorem 15.11. For brevity, we shall write R_n and R, whenever the choice of Ω is clear from the context.

Definition 15.13. In the situation above, the *algebraic Morse complex* $\mathcal{C}^\mu$,

$$\cdots \xrightarrow{\partial^\mu_{n+2}} C^\mu_{n+1} \xrightarrow{\partial^\mu_{n+1}} C^\mu_n \xrightarrow{\partial^\mu_n} C^\mu_{n-1} \xrightarrow{\partial^\mu_{n-1}} \cdots,$$

is defined as follows.

- The $\mathbb{Z}_2$-vector space C_n^μ has a basis indexed by R_n. We shall use the notation $\{x^\mu \mid x \in R_n\}$.
- The boundary operator is defined by

$$\partial_n^\mu x^\mu = \sum_p (p_\bullet)^\mu, \tag{15.15}$$

for all $x \in R_n$, where the sum is taken over all alternating paths p satisfying $p^\bullet = x$, and $p_\bullet \in R_{n-1}$.

When the degree is clear, we shall simply write ∂^μ instead of ∂_n^μ.

Before proceeding with the statement of the main theorem of this section, let us introduce another piece of notation. For $k = 0, \dots, t$, we set

$$R[k] := R \cup \{a_{k+1}, \dots, a_t, b_{k+1}, \dots, b_t\} = \Omega \setminus \{a_1, \dots, a_k, b_1, \dots, b_k\}$$

and $R_n[k] := R[k] \cap \Omega_n$. Furthermore, we say that the alternating path $p = (x, a_{i_1}, b_{i_1}, \dots, a_{i_p}, b_{i_p}, y)$ has *depth* k if $i_p \leqslant k$.

Theorem 15.14. *The chain complex $\mathcal{D}$ in Theorem 15.11 is isomorphic to $\mathcal{C}^\mu$, with a specific isomorphism given by $x[t] \mapsto x^\mu$, for all $x \in R$.*

Proof. Let us go back to the proof of Theorem 15.11 and let $\mathcal{D}[k]$ be the chain subcomplex of $\mathcal{C}$ generated by $\{x[k] \mid x \in R[k]\}$. In particular, $\mathcal{D}[0] = \mathcal{C}$ and $\mathcal{D}[t] = \mathcal{D}$. As a counterpart to the family $\mathcal{D}[0], \dots, \mathcal{D}[t]$, define a family of chain complexes $\mathcal{C}^\mu[0], \dots, \mathcal{C}^\mu[t]$ as follows:

- The $\mathbb{Z}_2$-vector space $C_n^\mu[k]$ has a basis indexed by $R_n[k]$; this time we denote it by $\{x^\mu[k] \mid x \in R_n\}$.
- The boundary operator is defined by

$$\partial_n^\mu(x^\mu[k]) = \sum_p (p_\bullet)^\mu[k],$$

for all $x \in R_n[k]$, where the sum is taken over all alternating paths p of depth k, satisfying $p^\bullet = x$, and $p_\bullet \in R_{n-1}[k]$.

Clearly, $\mathcal{C}^\mu[0] = \mathcal{C}$ and $\mathcal{C}^\mu[t] = \mathcal{C}^\mu$.

Let us show that the chain complex $\mathcal{C}^\mu[k]$ is isomorphic to $\mathcal{D}[k]$, for all $0 \leqslant k \leqslant t$. For $k = 0$ we already know this, since both chain complexes are isomorphic to $\mathcal{C}$. We now proceed by induction on k. We want to show that an isomorphism is given by

$$\begin{aligned} \varphi_k : \mathcal{C}^\mu[k] &\longrightarrow \mathcal{D}[k], \\ x^\mu[k] &\longmapsto x[k]. \end{aligned}$$

Obviously, this is a bijection between the sets of generators, so we just need to check that the map is compatible with the boundary operators. The latter are given by the formulae

$$(15.16) \qquad \partial_n(x[k]) = \sum_{y \in \Omega_{n-1}[k]} w_{\Omega[k]}(x \succ y) y$$

and

$$(15.17) \qquad \partial_n^\mu(x^\mu[k]) = \sum_p (p_\bullet)^\mu[k],$$

where the last sum is taken over all alternating paths p of depth k, satisfying $p^\bullet = x$, and $p_\bullet \in R_{n-1}[k]$.

By induction assumption we know that φ_{k-1} is an isomorphism, so we need to see how Equations (15.16) and (15.17) change when passing from $k-1$ to k. The transformation of Equation (15.16) is governed by Equation (15.10), which in a nutshell says that nothing changes except for one case: when $x \in \eta(a_k[k], b_k[k])$ and $w_{\Omega[k-1]}(b_k[k-1] \succ y[k-1]) = 1$, in which case 1 is added to $w_{\Omega[k-1]}(x[k-1] \succ y[k-1])$.

On the other hand, the transformation of Equation (15.16) is described by the fact that we now additionally consider alternating paths p of depth k, which do not have depth $k-1$, which were previously unaccounted for. Such a path must necessarily contain the elements a_k, b_k, so it can be written as

$$(15.18) \qquad p = (x, a_{i_1}, b_{i_1}, \dots, a_{i_m}, b_{i_m}, a_k, b_k, y),$$

for some $m \geqslant 0$ and $i_1 < \dots < i_m < k$. For such a path to exist at all, we must have $w_\Omega(b_k \succ y) = 1$, so assume that this is the case. Since we also know that $w_\Omega(b_k \succ a_k) = 1$, we conclude that the number of alternating paths of the type given by Equation (15.18) is equal to the the number of alternating paths of depth $k-1$ from x to a_k. This number is given by the coefficient $w_{\Omega[k-1]}(x[k-1] \succ a_k[k-1])$. Note furthermore, that there are no non-trivial alternating paths of depth $k-1$ between b_k and y, so $w_\Omega(b_k \succ y) = w_{\Omega[k-1]}(b_k[k-1] \succ y[k-1])$.

We can now return to the interpretation of Equation (15.10). The term $w_{\Omega[k-1]}(x[k-1] \succ y[k-1])$ counts all the alternating paths of depth $k-1$ from x to y. The interesting case above happens when $x \in \eta(a_k[k], b_k[k])$ and $w_{\Omega[k-1]}(b_k[k-1] \succ y[k-1]) = 1$. First, $x \in \eta(a_k[k], b_k[k])$ is equivalent to $w_{\Omega[k-1]}(x[k-1] \succ a_k[k-1]) = 1$, and second $w_{\Omega[k-1]}(b_k[k-1] \succ y[k-1]) = 1$ is equivalent to $w_\Omega(b_k \succ y) = 1$. We conclude that adding a new alternating path of depth k (but not of depth $k-1$) transforms Equation (15.17) in the same way as Equation (15.10) transforms Equation (15.16). This proves the induction step.

Since $\mathcal{C}^\mu[t] = \mathcal{C}^\mu$, $\mathcal{D}[t] = \mathcal{D}$, and we have shown that $\mathcal{C}^\mu[k]$ is isomorphic to $\mathcal{D}[k]$, for all $0 \leqslant k \leqslant t$, the theorem is now proved. □

15.4. An example

Let us now illustrate the usage of Theorems 15.11 and 15.14. Our main source of examples is the following family of combinatorial chain complexes.

Definition 15.15. Given any set S, we define a *word* w in the alphabet S to be any finite ordered tuple $(a_1, \dots, a_n)$ of elements of S; we allow repetitions in that tuple. For brevity, we also write $a_1, \dots, a_n$ or even $a_1 \dots a_n$.

The elements a_1, ..., a_n are referred to as *letters* of w. The number n is called the *length* of w, which we denote by $l(w)$. We set $\mathrm{supp}(w) := \{a_1, \dots . a_n\}$, and call it the *support set* of w.

Here we simply take S to be the regular latin alphabet, so strings like aba and $abaaa$ are valid words. For brevity we can use the power notation and write aba^3 instead of $abaaa$.

Definition 15.16. Assume we are given a word $w = a_1, \dots, a_n$, and a subset $I \subseteq [n]$, say $I = \{i_1, \dots, i_k\}$, where $i_1 < \dots < i_k$. We set $w_I := a_{i_1} \dots a_{i_k}$, and call it the I-subword of w.

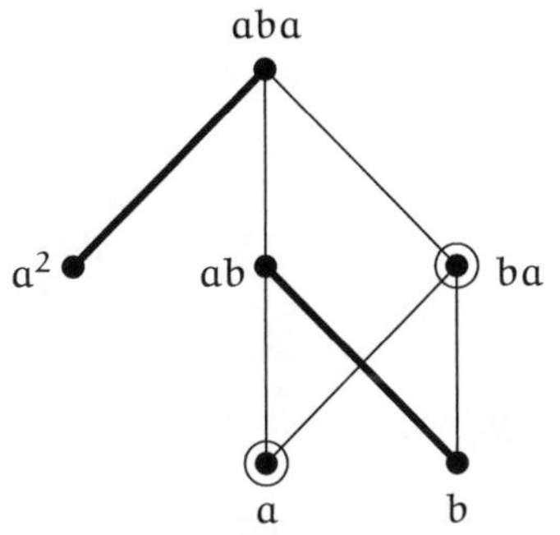

Figure 15.2. The poset associated to the standard basis of the chain complex $\mathcal{W}(aba)$.

Definition 15.17. Given a word $w = a_1, \dots, a_n$, we define a chain complex $\mathcal{W}(w)$ as follows:

- the $\mathbb{Z}_2$-vector space $W_t(w)$ is generated by all the subwords w_I, for $|I| = t + 1$;
- the boundary operator is given by

$$\partial(w_I) = \sum_{i \in I} w_{I \setminus \{i\}}.$$

We also call the vectors w_I, the *standard basis* in $\mathcal{W}(w)$.

Let us now take the word $w = \mathsf{aba}$, and the standard basis in the chain complex $\mathcal{W}(\mathsf{aba})$. The associated basis poset, which we call P_{aba}, is shown in Figure 15.2. There we also mark with fat edges a certain fixed matching. We can verify directly that this matching is acyclic.

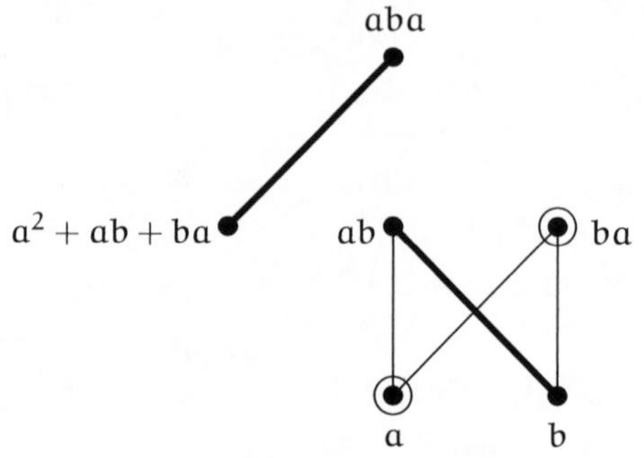

Figure 15.3. The poset associated to the basis $\Omega[1]$.

The proof of Theorem 15.11 is actually an algorithm. Let us now see how this algorithm transforms the poset P_{aba}. The first step is the bonding of a^2 and aba, with the resulting basis poset shown in Figure 15.3. The second, and final step is the bonding of b and ab, with the resulting basis poset shown in Figure 15.4. The critical chain complex in this case is

$$0 \longrightarrow \langle \mathsf{ab} + \mathsf{ba} \rangle \longrightarrow \langle \mathsf{a} \rangle \longrightarrow 0.$$

The boundary operator is trivial because there are two alternating paths from ba to a, so we have homology of rank 1 in dimensions 1 and 0.

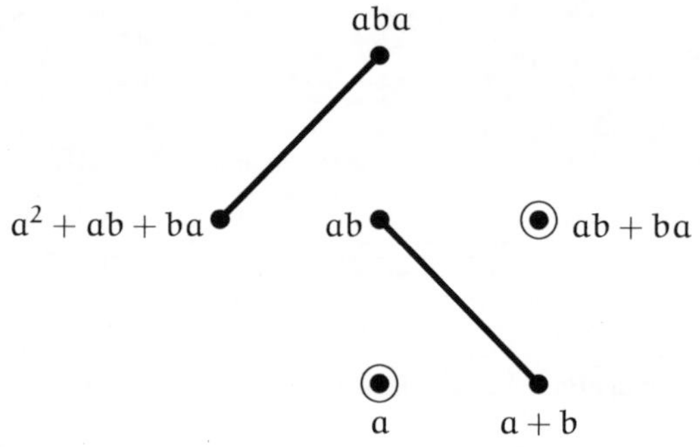

Figure 15.4. The poset associated to the basis $\Omega[2]$.

As an alternative, we could take the same chain complex $\mathcal{W}(\mathsf{aba})$, though this time equipped with the matching consisting of a single pair $(\mathsf{b}, \mathsf{ab})$. In this case, the bonding of $\mathfrak{b}$ and $\mathfrak{ab}$ results in the chain complex whose poset is shown in Figure 15.5. In this case, the critical chain complex is

$$0 \longrightarrow \langle \mathfrak{aba} \rangle \longrightarrow \langle \mathfrak{a}^2, \mathfrak{ab}+\mathfrak{ba} \rangle \longrightarrow \langle \mathfrak{a} \rangle \longrightarrow 0,$$

but it does not yet trivially compute the homology of $\mathcal{C}$. One of the boundary maps is trivial, but the other one is not. Instead, it takes $\mathfrak{aba}$ to $\mathfrak{a}^2 + (\mathfrak{ab} + \mathfrak{ba})$.

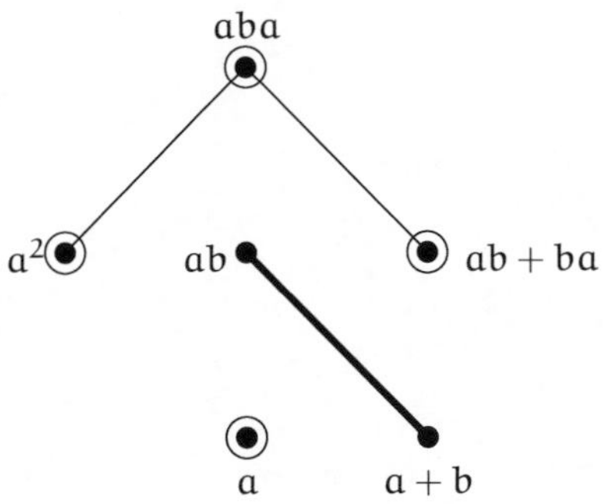

Figure 15.5. The poset obtained by bonding $\mathfrak{b}$ and $\mathfrak{ab}$.

As two final examples, we take the chain complexes associated to the words $\mathfrak{aba}^2$ and $\mathfrak{aba}^3$, with acyclic matchings as shown in Figures 15.6 and 15.7. In the first case, the matching is almost complete. The critical chain complex will consist of a single chain group generated by $\mathfrak{a}$. This is the situation corresponding to the collapsible complexes in the simplicial setting.

In the second case, there are two critical elements, $\mathfrak{a}$ and $\mathfrak{ba}^3$. The critical chain complex will therefore have two generators: $\mathfrak{a}[5] = \mathfrak{a}$ in dimension 0, and $\mathfrak{ba}^3[5] = \mathfrak{ba}^3 + \mathfrak{aba}^2$ in dimension 3. These generators are not in neighboring dimensions, so all the boundary operators are trivial.

15.5. Algebraic Morse theory for based free chain complexes of $\mathcal{R}$-modules

In this section we describe the general framework of algebraic Morse theory. The group $\mathbb{Z}_2$ will from now on be replaced by an arbitrary commutative ring with a unit, which, as before, is denoted by $\mathcal{R}$. Accordingly, we now consider a chain complex $\mathcal{C}$ consisting of finitely generated $\mathcal{R}$-modules:

$$\mathcal{C} = (\ \dots \xrightarrow{\partial^{\mathcal{C}}_{n+2}} C_{n+1} \xrightarrow{\partial^{\mathcal{C}}_{n+1}} C_n \xrightarrow{\partial^{\mathcal{C}}_{n}} C_{n-1} \xrightarrow{\partial^{\mathcal{C}}_{n-1}} \dots\ ).$$

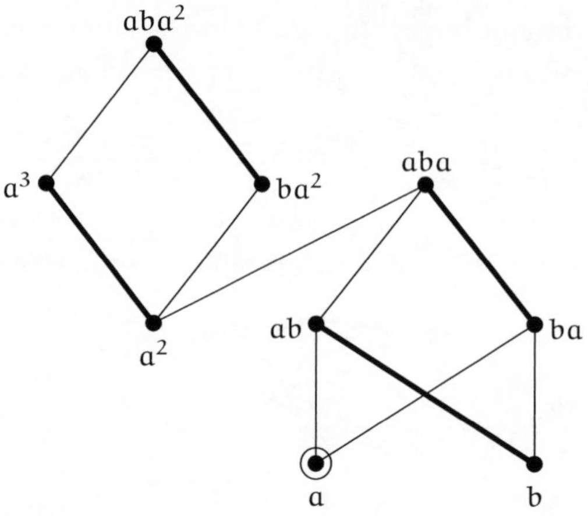

Figure 15.6. An acyclic matching for $w = aba^2$.

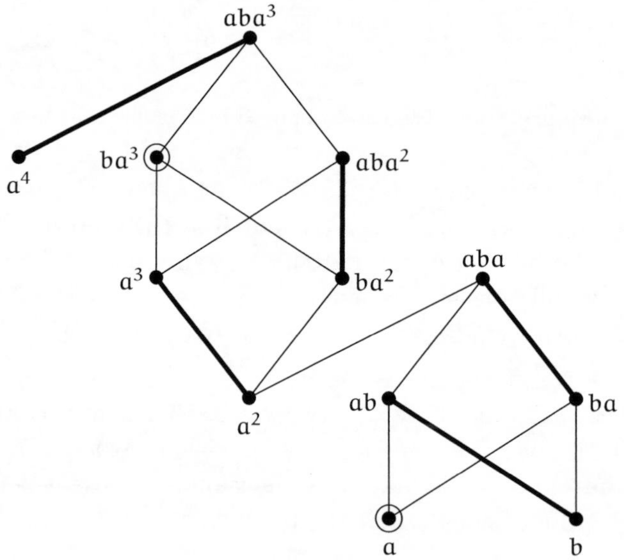

Figure 15.7. An acyclic matching for $w = aba^3$.

We shall now reasonably quickly go through the previous developments in this more general setting. For brevity, we shall skip some of the parts when the arguments are really verbatim to the previous ones.

Recall that $\mathcal{C}$ is called *free* if C_n is a finitely generated free $\mathcal{R}$-module for all n. When no confusion can occur, we simply write ∂ instead of ∂_n. Again, we assume that only finitely many of the chain groups of $\mathcal{C}$ are non-trivial.

As before, a free chain complex is called *based* if we have chosen a basis in each of the chain groups. These bases are again denoted by Ω_n, and their union is denoted by Ω.

The scalar product from Definition 15.2 can easily be extended to the setting of free modules over a commutative ring. Accordingly, given a based free chain complex $(\mathcal{C}, \Omega)$, and two elements $\alpha \in \Omega_{n-1}$ and $b \in \Omega_n$, the element $w_\Omega(b \succ a)$, or simply $w(b \succ a)$, can be defined in the same way as before, the only difference being that it is now an element of the commutative ring $\mathcal{R}$.

A based free chain complex $(\mathcal{C}, \Omega)$ of $\mathcal{R}$-modules can still be represented as a ranked poset $P(\mathcal{C}, \Omega)$, though now we need to add $\mathcal{R}$-valued weights on the order relations.

Definition 15.18. An *acyclic* matching M in a based free chain complex $(\mathcal{C}, \Omega)$ is an acyclic matching in the corresponding base poset $P(\mathcal{C}, \Omega)$, with the additional condition that, whenever $a \in \Omega_{n-1}$ is matched with $b \in \Omega_n$, the element $w_\Omega(b \succ a)$ has an inverse in $\mathcal{R}$.

Of course, when $\mathcal{R}$ is a field, the invertibility condition in Definition 15.18 gets replaced by the requirement that $w_\Omega(b \succ a) \neq 0$.

The definitions of the sets $R(\Omega)$ and $R_n(\Omega)$ do not change. Also, the notion of an alternating path is the same as before. However, we do need a new notion of the *weight* of an alternating path.

Definition 15.19. Given two basis elements $s \in \Omega_n$ and $t \in \Omega_{n-1}$, the *weight* of an alternating path

$$p = (s \succ \mu(b_1) \prec b_1 \succ \mu(b_2) \prec b_2 \succ \cdots \succ \mu(b_n) \prec b_n \succ t), \tag{15.19}$$

where $n \geqslant 0$ and all $b_i \in M^\uparrow$ are distinct, is defined to be the quotient

$$w(p) := (-1)^n \frac{w(s \succ \mu(b_1)) \cdot w(b_1 \succ \mu(b_2)) \cdot \cdots \cdot w(b_n \succ t)}{w(b_1 \succ \mu(b_1)) \cdot w(b_2 \succ \mu(b_2)) \cdot \cdots \cdot w(b_n \succ \mu(b_n))}. \tag{15.20}$$

The reader is invited to compare (15.20) with formula (14.2). Additionally, we shall use the notations $p^\bullet = s$ and $p_\bullet = t$.

Definition 15.20. Let $(\mathcal{C}, \Omega)$ be a based free chain complex, and let M be an acyclic matching. The *Morse complex*

$$\mathcal{C}^\mu : \ \dots \xrightarrow{\partial^\mu_{n+2}} C^\mu_{n+1} \xrightarrow{\partial^\mu_{n+1}} C^\mu_n \xrightarrow{\partial^\mu_n} C^\mu_{n-1} \xrightarrow{\partial^\mu_{n-1}} \dots$$

is defined as follows. The $\mathcal{R}$-module C^μ_n is freely generated by the elements indexed by the set R_n. The boundary operator is defined by

$$\partial^\mu_n(s) = \sum_p w(p) \cdot p_\bullet,$$

for all $s \in \mathcal{C}_n^\mu(\Omega)$, where the sum is taken over all alternating paths p satisfying $p^\bullet = s$. Again, if the degree is clear, we simply write ∂^μ instead of ∂_n^μ.

Given a based free chain complex $(\mathcal{C}, \Omega)$, we can choose a different basis $\widetilde{\Omega}$ by replacing each $a \in M^\downarrow$ by $\tilde{a} = w(\mu(a) \succ a) \cdot a$, because $w(\mu(a) \succ a)$ is required to be invertible. Since

$$\langle x \mid a \rangle_{\widetilde{\Omega}} = \langle x \mid a \rangle_{\Omega} / w(\mu(a) \succ a), \tag{15.21}$$

for any $x \in \Omega_n$, we see that the weights of those alternating paths, which do not begin with or end in an element from $M^\downarrow$, remain unaltered, as the quotient $w(x \succ z)/w(y \succ z)$ stays constant as long as $x, y \neq a$. In particular, the Morse complex will not change. On the other hand, by (15.21), $w_{\widetilde{\Omega}}(\mu(a) \succ a) = 1$, for all $a \in M^\downarrow$, so the total weight of the alternating path in (15.19) will simply become

$$w_{\widetilde{\Omega}}(p) = (-1)^n w_{\widetilde{\Omega}}(s \succ \mu(b_1)) \cdot w_{\widetilde{\Omega}}(b_1 \succ \mu(b_2)) \cdot \dots \cdot w_{\widetilde{\Omega}}(b_n \succ t).$$

Because of these observations, we may always replace any given basis of $\mathcal{C}$ with the basis $\widetilde{\Omega}$ satisfying $w_{\widetilde{\Omega}}(\mu(a) \succ a) = 1$, for all $a \in M^\downarrow$.

The *atomic* chain complex is defined as

$$\text{Atom}(d) : \ \dots \longrightarrow 0 \longrightarrow \mathcal{R} \xrightarrow{\text{id}} \mathcal{R} \longrightarrow 0 \longrightarrow \dots,$$

where the only non-trivial modules are in the dimensions d and $d-1$. The choice of a basis is no longer unique, but any basis poset will again consist of two comparable elements with the $\mathcal{R}$-weight on that unique edge equal to 1.

After all these reformulations, the main theorem of algebraic Morse theory has a pretty much identical formulation to the $\mathbb{Z}_2$-case.

Theorem 15.21 (Main theorem of algebraic Morse theory for free chain complexes). *Assume that $\mathcal{R}$ is a commutative ring with a unit, and $(\mathcal{C}, \Omega)$ is a based free chain complex with an acyclic matching M. Then $\mathcal{C}$ decomposes as a direct sum of chain complexes*

$$\mathcal{C} \simeq \mathcal{C}^\mu \oplus \mathcal{T}, \tag{15.22}$$

where $\mathcal{C}^\mu$ is the corresponding Morse complex and $\mathcal{T} \simeq \bigoplus_{(a,b) \in M} \text{Atom}(\dim b)$.

Proof. The proof is essentially the same as that of Theorem 15.11. The transformation described by Equation (15.2) now becomes

Transformation of the basis $\Omega[k-1]$ into the basis $\Omega[k]$: *we set*

- $a_k[k] := \partial(b_k[k-1])$.
- $x[k] := x[k-1] - w(x[k-1] \succ a_k[k-1]) \cdot b_k[k-1]$, *for all* $x \in \Omega_d$, $x \neq b_k$, *where* $d = \dim b_k$.

- $x[k] := x[k-1]$, *for all other* x.

Furthermore, we get

$$w(x[k] \succ y[k]) = w(x[k-1] \succ y[k-1]) \\ - w(x[k-1] \succ a_k[k-1]) \cdot w(b_k[k-1] \succ y[k-1]),$$

for $x \in \Omega_n[k]$, $y \in \Omega_{n-1}[k]$, $x \neq b_k$, $y \neq a_k$. □

Until now we have assumed that the chain complexes have only finitely many non-trivial chain groups, and that each of these chain groups is finitely generated. As a final remark, we note that both can be relaxed as long as we keep the requirement that the acyclic matching itself is assumed to be finite. The proof repeats verbatim the proof in the final case.

Exercises

(1) Compute homology groups of $\mathcal{W}(aba^3)$ by the explicit use of bonding transformations defined in this chapter.

(2) Give a precise formulation for a relaxed version of Theorem 15.21 for a chain complex $\mathcal{C}$ with possibly infinitely many non-trivial, not necessarily finitely generated, chain groups, with μ being finite. Prove your statement.

Chapter 16

Discrete Morse Theory for Posets

Recalling what we did in Chapter 10, where a connection was drawn between discrete Morse theory and the acyclic matchings in the Hasse diagrams of the face posets of the simplicial complexes, it is tempting to step back and to try to re-develop everything within a purely combinatorial or, better yet, categorical framework. This is what we do in the current chapter. The main idea is to recast acyclic matchings in functorial terms. The following three points illustrate some of the most important advantages of such an approach.

First, there is a one-to-one correspondence between acyclic matchings and sets of fibers of poset maps with small fibers; see Theorem 16.2. This provides a functorial tool to generate families of matchings, which are automatically acyclic.

Second, given an acyclic matching, one can construct a certain universal object. This object is a poset whose linear extensions enumerate all legal collapsing orders associated to this acyclic matching.

Third, using poset maps with small fibers allows us to gain a conceptual understanding of a very useful technique, the so-called Patchwork Theorem (see Theorem 16.8) for gluing a number of small acyclic matchings together in order to form a larger one.

16.1. Poset maps with small fibers

In what follows there is no real reason to restrict ourselves to exclusively considering the Hasse diagrams of face posets of simplicial complexes, so let us work with arbitrary posets from now on. Providing an acyclic matching in such a poset is an ad hoc construction which may or may not behave very naturally with respect to operations involving maps between posets. It is therefore rather useful to shift our attention from acyclic matchings to a special class of poset maps, which is described in the following definition.

Definition 16.1. Assume we are given two arbitrary posets P and Q, and a poset map $\varphi : P \to Q$. The map φ is called a *poset map with small fibers*, if for any $q \in Q$, one of the following three statements is true:

- the fiber $\varphi^{-1}(q)$ is empty;
- the fiber $\varphi^{-1}(q)$ consists of a single element;
- the fiber $\varphi^{-1}(q)$ consists of two comparable elements.

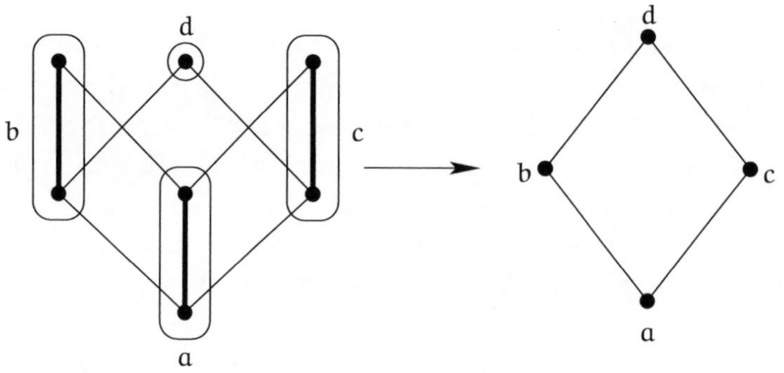

Figure 16.1. A poset map with small fibers.

An example of a poset map with small fibers is shown in Figure 16.1. We remark that if φ is a poset map, and for some $q \in Q$ the fiber $\varphi^{-1}(q)$ consists of two comparable elements, then one of these two elements must necessarily cover the other one. Therefore, to any given poset map with small fibers $\varphi : P \to Q$, we can associate a partial matching $M(\varphi)$ such that

- the matched pairs of $M(\varphi)$ are all fibers of φ of cardinality 2;
- the fibers of φ of cardinality 1 correspond to the critical elements of $M(\varphi)$; their set is denoted $C(P, M)$.

It turns out that poset maps with small fibers and acyclic matchings are equivalent as mathematical concepts. This is made precise by the following theorem.

Theorem 16.2 (Acyclic matchings via poset maps with small fibers). *The following two statements describe the close relation between poset maps with small fibers and acyclic matchings.*

(1) *For any poset map with small fibers* $\varphi : P \to Q$, *the partial matching* $M(\varphi)$ *is acyclic.*

(2) *Any acyclic matching on* P *can be represented as* $M(\varphi)$ *for some poset map with small fibers* $\varphi : P \to Q$. *In fact, the poset* Q *can be chosen to be a totally ordered set.*

Proof. The fact that $\varphi : P \to Q$ is a poset map implies that the induced matching $M(\varphi)$ is acyclic: for if it was not, there would exist a cycle as in (10.1), and φ would be mapping this cycle to a set of distinct elements $q_1 > q_2 > \cdots > q_t > q_1$ of Q, for some t, yielding a contradiction.

On the other hand, by Theorem 11.9, for any acyclic matching on P there exists a linear extension L of P, such that the elements a and b, where $(a, b) \in M$, follow consequently in L. Gluing together such a and b, in this order, yields a poset map with small fibers from P to a chain. □

As an example, let $n \geqslant k \geqslant 1$, and let $\mathcal{K}$ be the $(k-1)$-skeleton of the n-simplex whose $n+1$ vertices are indexed by the set $[n]$. Let P denote the face poset of $\mathcal{K}$. Clearly, the poset P consists of all subsets S of the set $[n]$ which have cardinality at most k. Let Q be the poset consisting of all subsets T of the set $[n-1]$ which have cardinality at most k. Consider the map $\varphi : P \to Q$ mapping each S to its restriction to the set $[n-1]$. Obviously, the map φ is order-preserving, and a direct check shows that φ has small fibers. In fact, the acyclic matching associated to φ is precisely the one described in Proposition 11.6. Figure 16.1 shows the case $n = 2$, $k = 2$.

16.2. Collapsing orders and the universal object associated to an acyclic matching

In Theorem 16.2 we have actually constructed a poset map with small fibers into a chain. These maps are especially important and we give them a separate name.

Definition 16.3. A poset map with small fibers $\varphi : P \to Q$ is called a *collapsing order* if φ is surjective as a set map and Q is a chain.

It is possible to drop the requirement that φ be surjective. For our purposes, for example, for the description of the universal object, we find it more convenient to keep that assumption.

Given an acyclic matching M, we say that a collapsing order φ is a *collapsing order for* M if it satisfies $M(\varphi) = M$. The etymology of this terminology is fairly clear: the chain Q gives us the order in which it is allowed to perform the prescribed collapses.

Clearly, such a collapsing order may not be unique. In fact, most of the time there are quite a few possible collapsing orders. There arises a natural question of developing an appropriate context for dealing with the totality of the collapsing orders. It turns out that, for any poset P and any acyclic matching on P, there exists a universal object - a poset whose linear extensions enumerate all allowed collapsing orders.

Definition 16.4. Let P be a poset, and let M be an acyclic matching on P. The poset $U(P, M)$ is defined as follows:

- the set of all elements of $U(P, M)$ is indexed by the union $M \cup C(P, M)$;
- the partial order in $U(P, M)$ is the transitive closure of the elementary relations given by:
  $S_1 \leqslant_{U(P,M)} S_2$, for $S_1, S_2 \in U(P, M)$ if and only if $x \leqslant y$, for some $x \in S_1$, $y \in S_2$. We also write $S_1 \leqslant_U S_2$ for brevity.

We call the poset $U(P, M)$ the *colimit of the matching* M.

Note that in the formulation of Definition 16.4, each pair of elements matched in M indexes a single element of $U(P, M)$. One can loosely say that Definition 16.4 states that $U(P, M)$ is obtained from P by gluing each matched pair together to form a single element, with the new partial order induced by the partial order of P in a natural way.

Of course, the first natural question is whether this new order is actually well-defined. The next theorem answers that question and also explains in what sense $U(P, M)$ is a universal object: its linear extensions encode all the collapsing order for M.

Theorem 16.5 (Universality of the colimit of a matching). *For any poset* P, *and for any acyclic matching* M *on* P, *we have:*

(1) *the partial order on* $U(P, M)$ *is well-defined;*

(2) *the induced quotient map* $q : P \to U(P, M)$ *is a poset map with small fibers;*

(3) *the linear extensions of* $U(P, M)$ *are in 1-to-1 correspondence with collapsing orders for* M*; this correspondence is given by the composition of the quotient map* q *with a linear extension map.*

Proof. To prove (1) we need to check the 3 axioms of being a partial order. The reflexivity is obvious, and the transitivity is automatic, since we have taken the transitive closure. The only property which needs to be proved is the antisymmetry. So assume it does not hold, and take $X, Y \in U(P, M)$, such that $X \leqslant_U Y$, $Y \leqslant_U X$, and $X \neq Y$. Choose a sequence

$$(16.1) \qquad X <_U S_1 <_U \cdots <_U S_p <_U Y <_U T_1 <_U \cdots <_U T_q <_U X,$$

with the minimal possible p and q. Since p and q are chosen to be minimal, all the sets $S_1, \ldots, S_p$ and $T_1, \ldots, T_q$ must have cardinality 2.

Let us first deal with the case $p = q = 0$ separately. If $|X| = |Y| = 1$, say $X = \{x\}$, $Y = \{y\}$, then we have $x \leqslant y$ and $y \leqslant x$, hence $x = y$, since P itself is a poset. If $|X| = 1$ and $|Y| = 2$, say $X = \{x\}$ and $Y = \{a, b\}$, then $b > x$ and $x > a$, since $x \neq b$ and $x \neq a$. This gives $b > x > a$, yielding a contradiction to the assumption that b covers a. By symmetry of (16.1) this argument covers the case $|X| = 2$, $|Y| = 1$ as well, so we can assume that $|X| = |Y| = 2$. In this case $X \leqslant_U Y \leqslant_U X$ is a cycle, contradicting the assumption that our matching is acyclic.

From now on, we have $p + q \geqslant 1$. Assume first that $|X| = |Y| = 1$, say $X = \{x\}$, $Y = \{y\}$. If $p = 0$ and $q = 1$, let $T_1 = (a, b)$, with $b \succ a$. On one hand, we have $x \leqslant y$, and on the other, $b \geqslant y$, $x \geqslant a$. Combining, we get $b \geqslant y \geqslant x \geqslant a$, implying $x = y$, since b covers a. Again, by symmetry this takes care of the case $p = 1$ and $q = 0$ as well.

Without loss of generality we may now assume that either $p + q \geqslant 2$, or $|Y| = 2$ and $p + q \geqslant 1$. In the first case

$$S_1 <_U \cdots <_U S_p <_U T_1 <_U \cdots <_U T_q$$

yields a cycle, contradicting the assumption that our matching was acyclic; in the second case such a cycle is given by

$$S_1 <_U \cdots <_U S_p <_U Y <_U T_1 <_U \cdots <_U T_q.$$

Part (2) is straightforward. If $x < y$ in P and $x \in X$, $y \in Y$, for $X, Y \in U(P, M)$, then $X \leqslant Y$ in $U(P, M)$ by the definition of the partial order on $U(P, M)$, though we may actually get equality. So q is a poset map and the fibers are small, since we have just proved that $X \leqslant_U Y$ together with $Y \leqslant_U X$ implies $X = Y$.

Let us now show (3). Given a linear extension $l : U(P, M) \to Q$, the composition $l \circ q : P \to Q$ is of course a poset map with small fibers, and it is surjective since both l and q are surjective.

Conversely, assume $\varphi : P \to Q$ is a collapsing order for M. Since φ is surjective, $\varphi^{-1}(x)$ is non-empty for every $x \in Q$; in fact we have a bijection between the sets $\varphi^{-1}(x)$, for $x \in Q$, and elements of $U(P, M)$. To factor φ through $U(P, M)$, we set $l(q(\varphi^{-1}(x))) := x$, for each $x \in Q$. We have $l \circ q = \varphi$ as set maps. To see that the map l is order-preserving, notice that an elementary relation $S \geqslant T$, for $S, T \in U(P, M)$, implies there exist $x \in S$, $y \in T$, such that $x \geqslant y$, which in turn implies $\varphi(x) \geqslant \varphi(y)$, since φ

is order-preserving, and notice furthermore that all relations $S \geqslant T$ are just the transitive closures of the elementary ones.

Thus, we get the desired 1-to-1 correspondence between the linear extensions of $U(P, M)$ and the collapsing orders for M. □

Let us return to our example of the standard matching on the $(k-1)$-skeleton of the simplex with n vertices. The universal poset $U(P, M)$ for that matching is the Boolean algebra B_k. Figure 16.1 shows the universal quotient map $q : P \to U(P, M)$.

16.3. Poset fibrations and the Patchwork Theorem

In this section we will see that viewing the posets with small fibers as the central notion of the combinatorial version of discrete Morse theory is also invaluable for the structural explanation of the so-called patchwork technique: a standard way to construct acyclic matchings as unions of acyclic matchings on fibers of a poset map. We start by defining a very simple notion.

Definition 16.6. A *poset fibration* is a pair (B, F), where

- B is a poset, thought of as the *base* of the fibration;
- $F = \{F_x\}_{x \in B}$ is a collection of posets, indexed by the elements of B, thought of as individual *fibers*.

Assume now we have such a fibration and define a poset $E(B, F)$, which is called the *total space* of the fibration, as follows:

- the set of elements of $E(B, F)$ is the union $\bigcup_{x \in B} F_x$;
- the order relation in $E(B, F)$ is given by requiring that $\alpha \geqslant \beta$ if
  - either $\alpha, \beta \in F_x$, and $\alpha \geqslant \beta$ in F_x, for some $x \in B$,
  - or $\alpha \in F_x$, $\beta \in F_y$, and $x > y$ in B.

In addition, we have a structural *projection map* of the total space to the base space, whose preimages are the fibers. This is a poset map $p : E(B, F) \to B$, defined by $p(\alpha) := x$, if $\alpha \in F_x$. In particular, we have $p^{-1}(x) = F_x$, for all $x \in B$.

The next theorem describes a universality property which the notion of poset fibrations satisfies.

Theorem 16.7 (Decomposition Theorem). *For an arbitrary poset fibration (B, F), where $F = \{F_x\}_{x \in B}$, and an arbitrary poset P, there is a 1-to-1 correspondence between*

- *poset maps $\varphi : P \to E(B, F)$;*

- *pairs* $(\psi, \{g_x\}_{x \in B})$, *where* ψ *and the* g_x*'s are poset maps* $\psi : P \to B$, *and* $g_x : \psi^{-1}(x) \to F_x$, *for each* $x \in B$.

Under this bijection, the fibers of φ *are the same as the fibers of the maps* g_x.

Proof. One direction of this bijection is trivial: given a poset map $\varphi : P \to E(B, F)$, we obtain the poset map $\psi : P \to B$ by composing φ with the structural projection map $p : E(B, F) \to B$, and we obtain the poset maps g_x by taking the appropriate restrictions of the map φ.

In the opposite direction, assume that we have a poset map $\psi : P \to B$ and a collection of poset maps $g_x : \psi^{-1}(x) \to F_x$, for all $x \in B$. Define $\varphi : P \to E(B, F)$ by taking the value of the appropriate fiber map:

$$\psi(\alpha) := g_{\varphi(\alpha)}(\alpha),$$

for all $\alpha \in P$. Let us see that this defines a poset map. For $\alpha > \beta$, $\alpha, \beta \in P$, we have $\varphi(\alpha) \geqslant \varphi(\beta)$, since φ is a poset map. If $\varphi(\alpha) = \varphi(\beta)$, then $g_{\varphi(\alpha)}(\alpha) \geqslant g_{\varphi(\beta)}(\beta)$, since $g_{\varphi(\alpha)}$ $(= g_{\varphi(\beta)})$ is a poset map. Otherwise, we have $\varphi(\alpha) > \varphi(\beta)$, and hence $g_{\varphi(\alpha)}(\alpha) > g_{\varphi(\beta)}(\beta)$, by the definition of the partial order on the total space $E(B, F)$. □

The Decomposition Theorem 16.7 provides us with a blueprint to construct an acyclic matching on a poset P in two steps as follows:

- first, map P to some other poset Q,
- second, construct acyclic matchings on the fibers of this map.

As was mentioned earlier, these acyclic matchings will automatically *patch together* to form an acyclic matching for the whole poset. The next theorem makes this observation formal.

Theorem 16.8 (Patchwork of acyclic matchings). *Assume that* $\varphi : P \to Q$ *is an order-preserving map, and assume that we have acyclic matchings on subposets* $\varphi^{-1}(q)$, *for all* $q \in Q$. *Then the union of these matchings is itself an acyclic matching on* P.

Proof. The role of the base space here is played by the poset Q, and the fiber maps g_q are given by the acyclic matchings on the subposets $\varphi^{-1}(q)$. The Decomposition Theorem 16.7 tells us that there exists a poset map from P to the total space of the corresponding poset fibration, and that the fibers of this map are the same as the fibers of the fiber maps g_q. Since the latter ones are given by acyclic matchings, we conclude that we have a poset map from P with small fibers, which corresponds precisely to the patching of acyclic matchings on the subposets $\varphi^{-1}(q)$, for $q \in Q$. □

Note that viewing acyclic matchings as preimages of poset maps with small fibers yields a special case of Theorem 16.8. The fibers in this case consist of either one element or two comparable elements. Accordingly, the acyclic matchings on these fibers are either empty or consist of a single pair of matched elements.

As an example, let us return to the order complex of the partition lattice, considered in Subsection 11.5.2. First, let n be a positive integer, say $n \geqslant 2$. The partition lattice for the base set $[n]$ was denoted by Π_n. Its reduced order complex was denoted by $\widetilde{\Delta}(\Pi_n)$, and, for brevity, let P_n denote the face poset of $\widetilde{\Delta}(\Pi_n)$. The elements of P_n are chains of Π_n that are refining sequences of partitions of the set $[n]$.

Given such a chain σ, we have introduced in Subsection 11.5.2 the notions *special prefix* and *prefix height* $h(\sigma)$. According to this notation, setting $h := h(\sigma)$, we have

$$\sigma = (\alpha_1 n) < (\alpha_1 \alpha_2 n) < \cdots < (\alpha_1 \dots \alpha_h n) < \pi_{h+1} < \dots,$$

such that $\pi_{h+1} \neq (\alpha_1 \dots \alpha_{h+1} n)$, for any α_{h+1}. We then call the chain

$$(\alpha_1) < (\alpha_1 \alpha_2) < \cdots < (\alpha_1 \dots \alpha_h)$$

the *pivot chain* of σ, and denote it by $\text{Piv}(\sigma)$. Note that it is allowed for the pivot chain to be empty.

Let $B_{[n-1]}$ be the Boolean algebra with the basis set $[n-1]$, and set $\text{Bd}(B_{[n-1]}) := \mathcal{F}(\text{Bd}\,\mathcal{K})$, where $\mathcal{K}$ is a simplex with n vertices. This poset is called the *barycentric subdivision of* $B_{[n-1]}$. The elements of $\text{Bd}(B_{[n-1]})$ are sequences $(S_1, \dots, S_m)$ of subsets $[n-1]$ such that $S_1 \subset \cdots \subset S_m$. Let Q_n denote the subset of $\text{Bd}(B_{[n-1]})$ consisting of all such sequences satisfying the additional condition $|S_i| = i$, for $1 \leqslant i \leqslant m$.

The pivot chain $\text{Piv}(\sigma)$ can be considered as an element of the poset Q_n, so Piv is a map from P_n to Q_n. The order relation in P_n is given by the deletion of partitions from the chain. Clearly, deleting some partitions from σ either preserves $\text{Piv}(\sigma)$ or decreases the prefix height of σ while truncating its pivot chain. This observation shows that Piv is a poset map.

In order to apply the patchwork theorem we need to investigate the preimages of this map. Let us fix an element of Q, say

$$q := ((\alpha_1) < \cdots < (\alpha_1 \dots \alpha_m)),$$

and describe the poset $\text{Piv}^{-1}(q)$. Each element α of this poset has the form

$$\alpha := (\alpha_1 n) < (\alpha_1 \alpha_2 n) < \cdots < (\alpha_1 \dots \alpha_m n) < \pi_{m+1} < \cdots < \pi_t, \tag{16.2}$$

such that $\pi_{m+1} \neq (\alpha_1 \dots \alpha_{m+1} n)$, for any $\alpha_{m+1} \in [n-1] \setminus \{\alpha_1, \dots, \alpha_m\}$. We have $|[n] \setminus \{\alpha_1, \dots, \alpha_m\}| = n - m + 1$, so let ν denote the unique order-preserving bijection $\nu : [n] \setminus \{\alpha_1, \dots, \alpha_m\} \to [n-m]$.

Assume π is a partition of $[n]$ such that the elements $\alpha_1, \ldots, \alpha_m$ and n are all contained in the same block. Let $\nu(\pi)$ denote the partition of $[n-m]$ obtained by deleting the elements $\alpha_1, \ldots, \alpha_m$, and replacing each $x \in [n] \setminus \{\alpha_1, \ldots, \alpha_m\}$ with $\nu(x)$. This can be extended by taking the element $\alpha \in \mathrm{Piv}^{-1}(q)$, as in Equation (16.2), and mapping it to

$$\nu(\alpha) := (\nu(\pi_{m+1}) < \cdots < \nu(\pi_t)).$$

This is well-defined, since the elements $\alpha_1, \ldots, \alpha_m$ and n are all contained in the same block in each of the partitions $\pi_{m+1}, \ldots, \pi_t$.

Furthermore, if $\alpha \neq \beta$, then $\nu(\alpha) \neq \nu(\beta)$, so the map ν is injective. It is however not surjective. The reason for this is our condition that $\pi_{m+1} \neq (\alpha_1 \ldots \alpha_{m+1} n)$, for any $\alpha_{m+1} \in [n-1] \setminus \{\alpha_1, \ldots, \alpha_m\}$. This translates into saying that in the image of ν we will get all the chains $\rho_1 < \cdots < \rho_s$, such that $\rho_1 \neq (a, n-m)$, for any $a \in [n-m-1]$. This also includes the empty chain.

We can therefore conclude that ν is a poset isomorphism between $\mathrm{Piv}^{-1}(q)$ and the face poset of $\Pi_{n-m} \setminus \{\tau_1, \ldots, \tau_{n-m-1}\}$, where $\tau_1 = (1, n-m), \tau_2 = (2, n-m), \ldots, \tau_{n-m-1} = (n-m-1, n-m)$. Note now that Π_{n-m} is a lattice, and that the set of elements $\{\tau_1, \ldots, \tau_{n-m-1}\}$ is precisely the set of all the complements of the coatom indexed by the partition $(n-m)([n-m-1])$. These complements are atoms. It is well known that removing an atom from a lattice will again yield a lattice. So the obtained poset is a lattice where one of the elements, namely the coatom $(n-m)([n-m-1])$, does not have any complements. These were called non-complemented lattices in Subsection 10.7.2, where we have seen that the order complexes of non-empty noncomplemented lattices are collapsible. Specifically, the complete acyclic matching is given by taking the meet with the non-complemented coatom; see Theorem 10.31.

We can now use the patchwork Theorem 16.8 to glue these matchings together and to recover our acyclic matching from Subsection 11.5.2. Note that the critical elements will correspond to those fibers of the map ν which have cardinality 1. This is the case precisely when the non-complemented lattice above is empty, i.e., when $m = n-1$. Thus we recover our enumeration of the critical elements by all possible permutations of the set $[n-1]$.

As a final remark of this chapter, let us note that there is a certain degree of flexibility connected to our choice of the set of allowed fibers. For instance, we can take any Boolean algebra as a fiber. This would correspond to the theory of all collapses, not just the elementary ones, which we get when considering the small fibers.

Exercises

(1) Show that for the simplicial complex of all disconnected graphs on 4 vertices, the poset $\mathsf{U}(\mathsf{P}, \mathsf{M})$ will be the face poset of the complete graph on 5 vertices.

Chapter 17

Discrete Morse Theory for CW Complexes

17.1. Cellular collapses and topological consequences

Let us recall that collapses of abstract simplicial complexes, as defined in Chapter 9, have two aspects. On the combinatorial side, a simplicial collapse corresponds to the removal of a pair of simplices σ and τ in neighboring dimensions, subject to two conditions: σ is a maximal simplex, and it is the only simplex containing τ. On the topological side, this could be seen as a strong deformation retraction which removed the two simplices in the geometric realization of the original abstract simplicial complex.

It is tempting to generalize this topological picture to encompass a larger class of strong deformation retractions, so that Definition 9.1 becomes a special case. For the purposes of the current text, we feel this is best done in the context of CW complexes. In that case, we could talk about *cellular*, rather than *simplicial*, collapses.

For the sake of brevity, this short chapter is not self-contained and the interested reader is invited to check other sources for the concepts which we use but do not define here.

Intuitively, a cellular collapse should be a strong deformation retract which pushes the interior of a maximal cell in, using one of its free boundary cells as the starting point, much like compressing a body made of clay. The highest generality is clearly achieved by the following definition of what we call an *elementary topological collapse*.

Definition 17.1. Let X be a topological space and let Y be a subspace of X. We say that Y is obtained from X by an *elementary topological collapse* if X can be represented as a result of attaching a ball B^n to Y along one of the hemispheres. In other words, if there exists a map $\varphi : B^{n-1}_{-} \to Y$, such that $X = B^n \cup_\varphi Y$, where B^{n-1}_{-} denotes one of the closed hemispheres on the boundary of B^n.

For practical reasons, it is useful to restrict ourselves to the cellular collapses for arbitrary CW complexes; see Definition 3.10.

Definition 17.2. Let X be a CW complex, and Y its subcomplex. We say that X *cellularly collapses* to Y if X is obtained from Y by attaching a $(d-1)$-cell e^{d-1} and a d-cell e^d, subject to certain restrictions.

Specifically, let Δ^d denote the standard d-simplex, let $\tilde{\Delta}$ be one of its boundary $(d-1)$-simplices, and set $\Lambda := \Delta^d \setminus \operatorname{Int}\tilde{\Delta}$. We require that there exists a continuous map $f : \Delta^d \to X$ such that the following conditions are satisfied:

(1) f is a characteristic map for the cell e^d, and $f|_{\tilde{\Delta}}$ is a characteristic map for the cell e^{d-1};

(2) $f(\Lambda) \subseteq Y_{d-1}$.

Cellular collapses generalize the simplicial ones, but they also include *cubical* and more generally *polyhedral collapses.*

Proposition 17.3. *A cellular collapse yields a strong deformation retraction.*

Proof. Exercise (1). □

When one is only interested in the homological conclusions, there is no difference between the simplicial and the cellular setting. One can simply consider the cellular chain complex of the corresponding CW complex. On one hand, it is a standard fact of algebraic topology that this cellular chain complex computes the homology groups of the original complex. On the other hand, the developments of Section 15.1 can be applied to this chain complex directly, bypassing the topological framework.

However, if one would like to understand the homotopy type of a certain CW complex, given some matching on the set of its cells, one cannot make use of the chain complexes in the same way. Instead, we need to carefully proceed forward, checking what remains true under appropriate conditions.

It is easy to see that the proof of Theorem 14.5(b) actually works in greater generality: one can take arbitrary CW complexes, at the same time replacing cellular collapses by arbitrary homotopy equivalences. Let us note the following result.

Theorem 17.4. *Let* X *be a CW complex, and let*

$$F_0(X) \subset F_1(X) \subset \cdots \subset F_t(X) = X$$

be a CW filtration of X*, such that the subcomplex* $F_0(X)$ *is just a single vertex, and, for all* $i = 1, \ldots, t$*, either* $F_i(X) \backslash F_{i-1}(X)$ *consists of a single cell, in which case we call such a cell* critical*, or the inclusion map* $f_i : F_{i-1}(X) \hookrightarrow F_i(X)$ *is a homotopy equivalence.*

Then X *is homotopy equivalent to a CW complex whose cells are in dimension-preserving bijection with the critical cells of* X*.*

Proof. If the inclusion map $f_i : F_{i-1}(X) \hookrightarrow F_i(X)$ is a homotopy equivalence, then there exists $g_i : F_i(X) \to F_{i-1}(X)$ which is a homotopy equivalence as well. After this observation the proof of Theorem 14.5(b) can be repeated verbatim, with critical cells being replaced with $F_i(X) \setminus F_{i-1}(X)$ whenever the latter consists of a single cell, and with collapses being replaced by such maps g_i. □

17.2. Acyclic matchings yielding a wedge of spheres

Next, we are interested in acyclic matchings which allow us to conclude that the considered complex is in fact homotopy equivalent to a wedge of spheres which are enumerated by critical cells. First, we need some terminology.

Definition 17.5. Assume M is an acyclic matching on a poset P. A *generalized alternating path* is a sequence $(x_1, \ldots, x_t)$ of elements of P such that

(1) $x_{2k} < x_{2k+1}$, whenever $2 \leqslant 2k \leqslant t-1$,

(2) $x_{2k-1} > x_{2k}$, whenever $2 \leqslant 2k \leqslant t$,

(3) $\mu(x_{2k+1}) = x_{2k}$, whenever $2 \leqslant 2k \leqslant t-1$,

where μ is the matching function associated to M.

The alternating paths as well as the reaching paths defined before are generalized alternating paths.

Definition 17.6. Assume as above that M is an acyclic matching on a poset P, and let $x \in P$. The *feasibility domain* of x is the set of all endpoints of generalized alternating paths emanating from x.

We let $F(x)$ denote the feasibility domain of x. The following theorem gives a sufficient condition on an acyclic matching for the critical Morse complex to be homotopy equivalent to a wedge of spheres enumerated by critical cells.

Theorem 17.7. *Let* X *be a connected regular CW complex, and let* μ *be an acyclic partial matching on* $F(X)$*. Assume that for every critical cell*

c of dimension larger than 0, its feasibility domain $F(c)$ contains precisely two critical cells: c itself and one critical cell of dimension 0. Then X is homotopy equivalent to a wedge of spheres enumerated by critical cells.

Proof. Recall that the main theorem of discrete Morse theory for simplicial complexes was proved by considering a sequence of attachments, where at each step we either attached a critical simplex or a pair of simplices matched by μ. The study of this sequence was accompanied by a parallel explicit construction of a Morse homotopy map. Let us do the same here. The corresponding stepwise attachment is done along a certain linear extension of the face poset of X, which we denote by l. When a pair of matched cells is attached, we simply have a strong deformation retraction of the obtained complex to what we have had before that attachment, so we just need to understand the case of attaching a critical cell.

Assume now that a critical cell c of dimension at least 1 is being attached. The cells in $F(c) \setminus \{c\}$ form a subcomplex C of X. The assumption of the theorem implies that C is collapsible along the matching μ. It means that prior to the attachment of c, the Morse homotopy has already shrunk the complex C to a point a, where a is the critical 0-dimensional cell of $F(c)\setminus\{c\}$. Since the image of the attaching map of the cell c lies inside C, we conclude that in the critical Morse complex the attaching map of c will simply map everything to the point a. Thus we can conclude that all the attaching maps in the critical Morse complex are trivial.

Finally, we need to see that under the assumptions of the theorem, the matching μ has exactly one 0-dimensional critical cell, which will imply that all the critical cells will be attached to the same vertex. Assume we have another critical 0-dimensional cell b, and assume that b occurs after a in the linear extension l. Then, when b is added, it will form a new connected component. So, since the total complex X is connected, at some point in the inductive process of adding critical cells and pairs of matched cells we will have to connect this connected component to the connected component containing a. This can only be achieved by adding a critical 1-dimensional cell, which we call e. The set $F(e)$ cannot contain any critical 0-dimensional cells other than b. Let v_1 denote the vertex of e which does not lie in the same connected component as b. The vertex v_1 is not critical, and we set $e_1 := \mu(v_1)$. Both v_1 and e_1 were added before e. We now proceed, starting with $k = 1$ by letting v_{k+1} be the vertex of e_k other than v_k. Since $v_{k+1} \in F(e)$, we see that v_{k+1} is not critical, and set $e_{k+1} := \mu(v_{k+1})$. Both v_{k+1} and e_{k+1} were added before e. Eventually we will have to conclude that for some $k \geqslant 1$ the vertex v_{k+1} lies in the same connected component as b. But this means that b was connected to the vertex v_1 even before adding e, yielding a contradiction to the choice of e. □

17.3. An example using Hopf fiber bundles

Contrary to what one might intuitively believe, having an acyclic matching with no critical cells in neighboring dimensions will not guarantee that the CW complex X is homotopy equivalent to a wedge of spheres. A counterexample which is described below makes use of the fact that the third homotopy group of S^2 is isomorphic to $\mathbb{Z}$.

Start by considering the set $A := \{(z_1, z_2) \,|\, z_1, z_2 \in \mathbb{C}, |z_1|^2 + |z_2|^2 = 1\}$, equipped with the diagonal action $z : (z_1, z_2) \mapsto (zz_1, zz_2)$ by the multiplicative group $G = \{z \,|\, |z| = 1\} \subseteq \mathbb{C}$. Note that A is homeomorphic to the 3-sphere, while G is homeomorphic to the circle. The quotient space A/G is a naturally occurring model for the complex projective line $\mathbb{CP}^1$, and it is homeomorphic to the 2-sphere. The canonical quotient map $q : A \to A/G$ is given by $q : (z_1, z_2) \mapsto (z_1 : z_2)$.

As a side remark, in the situation of this sort one says that one has a *fiber bundle*, which is denoted by $S^1 \to S^3 \to S^2$, with S^1 called the *fiber*, S^2 the *base space*, and S^3 the *total space* of the bundle. What we have here is the first example of the so-called *Hopf bundle*.

A CW structure on the space A is obtained by intersecting it with the real coordinate hyperplanes $\operatorname{Re} z_1 = 0$, $\operatorname{Im} z_1 = 0$, $\operatorname{Re} z_2 = 0$, and $\operatorname{Im} z_2 = 0$. What we obtain is a regular CW complex with the face vector $(8, 24, 32, 16)$. Furthermore, consider the CW structure on A/G consisting of the two vertices $v_1 = (1 : 0)$ and $v_2 = (0 : 1)$, four edges $e_1 = \{(1 : r) \,|\, r > 0\}$, $e_2 = \{(1 : ir) \,|\, r > 0\}$, $e_3 = \{(1 : -r) \,|\, r > 0\}$, $e_4 = \{(1 : -ir) \,|\, r > 0\}$, and four 2-cells denoted s_1, s_2, s_3, s_4, where s_i is bound by e_i and e_{i+1}, for $i = 1, 2, 3$, and s_4 is bound by e_1 and e_4. This describes a regular CW complex with the face vector $(2, 4, 4)$. It is easy to see that q is a cellular map.

Now we choose a CW structure on the mapping cylinder $\operatorname{Cyl} q$ by taking all the cells of the cylinder base A/G, then subdividing $A \times \{0\}$, the top copy of A, as described above, and taking the open cells $\tilde{\sigma} := \operatorname{Int} \sigma \times (0, 1)$, for all cells σ of A. Finally, let X be the regular CW complex obtained from $\operatorname{Cyl} q$ by attaching a 4-cell k along $A \times \{0\} \cong S^3$.

Consider the following acyclic matching: $\mu(\tilde{\sigma}) = \sigma$, whenever σ is a cell of $A \times \{0\}$, $\mu(s_i) = e_i$, for $i = 1, 2, 3$, $\mu(e_4) = v_2$. This partial matching has three critical cells: v_1, k, and s_4, in dimensions 0, 2, and 4. It is easily verified directly that all the matched pairs are cellular collapses. In particular, the main theorem of discrete Morse theory can be applied, and we can conclude that X is homotopy equivalent to a CW complex with one cell in each of the dimensions 0, 2, and 4.

The crucial observation now is that the space X is not homotopy equivalent to $S^2 \vee S^4$. One way to see this is to show that X and $S^2 \vee S^4$ have different π_3 groups. Namely $\pi_3(X) = 0$, while $\pi_3(S^2 \vee S^4) = \mathbb{Z}$. We leave the verification of this as an exercise for the reader who is familiar with homotopy groups.

The technique using fibrations can be used to produce further examples which might be needed to test various hypotheses.

Exercises

(1) Prove Proposition 17.3.

(2) Give an example showing that the condition of Theorem 17.7 is not necessary for getting a wedge of spheres enumerated by critical cells.

(3) Finish the justification for our counterexample in Section 17.3 by showing that $\pi_3(X) = 0$ and $\pi_3(S^2 \vee S^4) = \mathbb{Z}$.

(4) Take the barycentric subdivision of X in the counterexample above. Show that the obtained simplicial complex has an acyclic matching with one critical cell of dimensions 0, 2, and 4 each. Of course the underlying topological spaces is still not homotopy equivalent to $S^2 \vee S^4$.

Chapter 18

Discrete Morse Theory and Persistence

18.1. Persistent homology of filtered simplicial complexes

In this section we touch upon persistence which is a central object of study in applied topology. The idea of persistence is to measure the change of algebraic invariants in a 1-parameter indexed family of topological spaces.

For simplicity of the presentation, we shall limit ourselves to the case of based chain complexes. All of the cases occurring in applications are of this type.

As a toy example, assume we are given S - a set of points in a Euclidean space. Fix a non-negative number λ. We can then construct a simplicial complex $\Delta_\lambda(S)$ whose vertices are the elements of S, and whose simplices are all sets of points from S which can be fit into a ball of radius λ. When $\lambda = 0$ we shall just get the set of isolated vertices. On the other hand, when λ is sufficiently large, we will get the whole simplex whose vertex set is S. As λ varies between these two extremes, we can observe an evolution of a simplicial complex, as simplices get added one after another. The homology groups of these complexes will come and go, and the persistent homology will try to measure how long the specific homology classes survive. Those classes which are present for a long time will reflect some kind of persistent features of the original set S.

Formally, the process of consequent growing is reflected in the abstract notion of a *filtration*. To start with, assume S is a finite set. A filtration[1]

[1] All considered filtrations will be finite.

on S is a sequence of subsets $\{S_k\}_{k=0}^t$, where t is a non-negative integer, such that $\emptyset = S_0 \subseteq \cdots \subseteq S_t = S$. Now consider the free abelian group generated by S, denoted by $\langle S \rangle$ earlier in the book. A filtration on S induces one on $\langle S \rangle$ in the sense that we have a nested sequence of abelian subgroups $0 = \langle S_0 \rangle \subseteq \cdots \subseteq \langle S_t \rangle = \langle S \rangle$. Of course, given a commutative ring $\mathcal{R}$, the same can be done for any free $\mathcal{R}$-modules, but we restrict ourselves to considering the free abelian groups.

This can be generalized to the based chain complexes as follows.

Definition 18.1. Let $\mathcal{C} = (C_*, \partial_*)$ be a based chain complex of free abelian groups, where for each d we have fixed a basis S_d for C_d. Assume furthermore that there is a filtration $\emptyset = S_d^0 \subseteq \cdots \subseteq S_d^t = S_d$, for each d.

We say that we have a *base filtration* on $\mathcal{C}$ if the following condition is satisfied:

$$\partial S_d^k \subseteq \left\langle S_{d-1}^k \right\rangle, \text{ for all } k \text{ and } d.$$

Note that in Definition 18.1 we require that t does not depend on d, but of course we allow that $S_d^k = S_d^{k+1}$ for some d and k.

Given a base filtration on $\mathcal{C}$, set $\mathcal{F}_k C_d := \left\langle S_d^k \right\rangle$, for all k and d. In this notation, we have $0 = \mathcal{F}_0 C_d \subseteq \cdots \subseteq \mathcal{F}_k C_d \subseteq \cdots \subseteq \mathcal{F}_t C_d = C_d$, for all $d \geqslant 0$, and $\partial_d(\mathcal{F}_k C_d) \subseteq \mathcal{F}_k C_{d-1}$, for all k and d.

For each k, the last property allows us to define the chain complex $\mathcal{F}_k \mathcal{C}$ by setting

$$\mathcal{F}_k \mathcal{C} := (\ \dots \longrightarrow \mathcal{F}_k C_{d+1} \longrightarrow \mathcal{F}_k C_d \longrightarrow \mathcal{F}_k C_{d-1} \longrightarrow \dots\ ),$$

where the boundary operators are the restrictions of those in $\mathcal{C}$. It is then customary to say that we have a nested sequence of chain complexes $0 = \mathcal{F}_0 \mathcal{C} \subseteq \cdots \subseteq \mathcal{F}_t \mathcal{C} = \mathcal{C}$, which we denote by $\mathcal{F}\mathcal{C}$.

In the example above, increasing the parameter λ results in a series of discrete transformations corresponding to a filtration of the chain complex of a simplex by chain complexes of $\Delta_\lambda(S)$.

Definition 18.2. Given a d-chain $\gamma \in C_d$, we set $h(\gamma)$ to be the minimal $0 \leqslant k \leqslant t$, such that $\gamma \in \mathcal{F}_k C_d$.

We shall refer to $h(\gamma)$ as the *height* of γ in the filtration $\mathcal{F}\mathcal{C}$. For future reference, we make the following remarks.

Remark 18.3. For any $\gamma \in C_d$ and any $\alpha \in \operatorname{supp} \gamma$, we have $h(\gamma) \geqslant h(\alpha)$, in fact,

$$h(\gamma) = \max_{\alpha \in \operatorname{supp} \gamma} h(\alpha). \tag{18.1}$$

Remark 18.4. For any $\gamma \in C_d$, we have $h(\gamma) \geqslant h(\partial_d \gamma)$.

These can be combined to obtain our last remark.

Remark 18.5. If we are given $\alpha \in \operatorname{supp}(\partial\gamma)$, then $h(\gamma) \geqslant h(\alpha)$.

Let us now proceed with defining the actual persistent homology groups. We set

$$Z_d^p := \operatorname{Ker} \partial_d \cap \mathcal{F}_p C_d = \{\alpha \in C_d \mid \partial\alpha = 0, h(\alpha) \leqslant p\}$$

and

$$B_d^{p,q} := \partial_{d+1}(\mathcal{F}_{p+q} C_{d+1}) \cap \mathcal{F}_p C_d$$
$$= \{\partial\beta \mid \beta \in C_{d+1},\ h(\beta) \leqslant p+q,\ h(\partial\beta) \leqslant p\}.$$

In other words, the group Z_d^p consists of all d-cycles which are present in $\mathcal{F}_p\mathcal{C}$. Sometimes one says that these d-cycles are *detected* by the p-th layer of filtration; note that any d-cycle detected by an earlier layer is included in this set. Similarly, the elements of $B_d^{p,q}$ are the boundaries of $(d+1)$-chains, such that the chains themselves are present at the $(p+q)$th filtration step $\mathcal{F}_{p+q}\mathcal{C}$, while their boundaries are in $\mathcal{F}_p\mathcal{C}$. One can imagine that we are increasing q and trying to see whether some d-cycle σ in $\mathcal{F}_p\mathcal{C}$ is actually a boundary. We then proceed through layers $p+1$, $p+2$, $\dots$, $p+q$, etc., and try to find a chain which will have σ as its boundary. This procedure gives an answer to the question of how long the cycle σ survives.

Definition 18.6. Assume we are given a based chain complex $\mathcal{C}$ equipped with a base filtration $\{S_k\}_k$. The *persistent homology groups* of $\mathcal{F}\mathcal{C}$ are defined by the formula

$$PH_d^{q,p}(\mathcal{F}\mathcal{C}) := Z_d^p / B_d^{p,q}.$$

Following our intuition above, the persistent homology group $PH_d^{q,p}(\mathcal{F}\mathcal{C})$ is obtained by taking all the d-cycles detected in $\mathcal{F}_p\mathcal{C}$ and dividing by the all the boundaries of the elements detected in $\mathcal{F}_{p+q}\mathcal{C}$, such that these boundaries themselves are present in $\mathcal{F}_p\mathcal{C}$.

Accordingly, when $q = 0$, we simply recover the homology groups of the chain complex $\mathcal{F}_p\mathcal{C}$. At the other extreme, when q is large, we are looking at the group of all d-cycles in $\mathcal{F}_p\mathcal{C}$ quotiented by the group of all d-chains which are boundaries of some chain, not necessarily at the filtration level p. In algebraic topology, the standard way to visualize this last group is to view it as the image of the d-th homology group of $\mathcal{F}_p\mathcal{C}$ in the d-th homology group of $\mathcal{C}$ under the homology map which is induced by the inclusion map of the chain complexes.

The last observation can be generalized as follows. For any non-negative integers p and q we have an inclusion chain map $\mathcal{F}_p\mathcal{C} \hookrightarrow \mathcal{F}_{p+q}\mathcal{C}$. It induces a homology map $f_d^{p,q} : H_d(\mathcal{F}_p\mathcal{C}) \to H_d(\mathcal{F}_{p+q}\mathcal{C})$. Unfolding the definition tells us that *the persistent homology group* $PH_d^{p,q}(\mathcal{F}\mathcal{C})$ *is precisely the image of the map* $f_d^{p,q}$. This is sometimes taken as an alternative definition of persistent homology.

18.2. Combining persistence with discrete Morse theory

Let us now investigate the interplay of filtrations and discrete Morse theory. Assume $\mathcal{C}$ is a based chain complex, with the bases S_d, for all d, as above. Set $P_{\mathcal{C}} := P(\mathcal{C}, \bigcup_d S_d)$ to be the basis poset, as described in Definition 15.4. Its elements are $\bigcup_d S_d$, and x covers y if and only if y is contained in $\operatorname{supp} \partial x$. Let μ be an acyclic matching on $P_{\mathcal{C}}$.

Definition 18.7. We say that the matching μ *respects* the given filtration $\mathcal{F}\mathcal{C}$ if for all $\gamma \in P_{\mathcal{C}}$ we have $h(\gamma) = h(\mu(\gamma))$, in other words, $\gamma \in \mathcal{F}_k C_d$ if and only if $\mu(\gamma) \in \mathcal{F}_k C_d$, for all k.

When the matching respects filtration, following a reaching path will not increase the height function. This is formalized by the following lemma.

Lemma 18.8. *Assume* μ *is an acyclic matching which respects the filtration* $\mathcal{F}\mathcal{C}$, *and assume* p *is a reaching path with respect to that matching. Set* $\alpha := p_\bullet$ *and* $\beta := p^\bullet$. *Then we have* $h(\alpha) \geqslant h(\beta)$.

Proof. Assume that the reaching path in question is

$$\alpha \succ \mu(\beta_1) \prec \beta_1 \succ \mu(\beta_2) \prec \beta_2 \succ \cdots \succ \mu(\beta_m) \prec \beta_m = \beta.$$

Applying Remark 18.5, we then have

$$\begin{aligned} h(\alpha) \geqslant h(\mu(\beta_1)) = h(\beta_1) \geqslant h(\mu(\beta_2)) \\ = h(\beta_2) \geqslant \cdots \geqslant h(\mu(\beta_m)) = h(\beta_m) = h(\beta), \end{aligned}$$

which proves the lemma. □

In Chapter 12 we have associated a closure function φ to an arbitrary acyclic matching μ. It turns out that when the matching respects the given filtration, the closure function preserves the height.

Lemma 18.9. *For* $\gamma \in S_d$, *we have* $\gamma \in \mathcal{F}_k C_d$ *if and only if* $\varphi(\gamma) \in \mathcal{F}_k C_d$. *In other words,* $h(\gamma) = h(\varphi(\gamma))$.

Proof. Assume first that $\varphi(\gamma) \in \mathcal{F}_k C_d$. We know that $\gamma \in \operatorname{supp}(\varphi(\gamma))$, hence, by Remark 18.3, we have $\gamma \in \mathcal{F}_k C_d$.

Reversely, assume $\gamma \in \mathcal{F}_k C_d$. By Proposition 12.7 we have $\varphi(\gamma) = \sum_p p^\bullet$, where the sum is taken over all reaching paths p, such that $p_\bullet = \gamma$. By Lemma 18.8 we then have $h(\gamma) \geqslant h(p^\bullet)$, for each such reaching path p, and hence $\varphi(\gamma) \in \mathcal{F}_k C_d$. □

Recall the Morse complex $\mathcal{C}rit(\mathcal{K}, \mu) \approx \mathcal{C}^{\mu}(\mathcal{K}; \mathbb{Z}_2)$ that was defined in Section 13.4. Its chain groups are generated by the critical basis elements, and the boundary operator is defined in a combinatorial way.

Let us now see that when the original based chain complex $\mathcal{C}$ has a base filtration $\{S_k\}$, and the acyclic matching respects $\mathcal{F}\mathcal{C}$, then the base filtration can be extended to that Morse complex as well.

Definition 18.10. By construction, the group $\mathcal{C}rit_d(\mathcal{K}, \mu)$ is generated by $\varphi(\gamma)$, for all $\gamma \in R_d$. We define a filtration on $\mathcal{C}rit_d(\mathcal{K}, \mu)$ by taking $\mathcal{F}_k\mathcal{C}rit_d(\mathcal{K}, \mu)$ to be the group generated by $\varphi(\gamma)$, for $\gamma \in R_d$, such that $h(\gamma) = k$.

Note that since $h(\gamma) = h(\varphi(\gamma))$, the group $\mathcal{F}_k\mathcal{C}rit_d(\mathcal{K}, \mu)$ is generated by $\varphi(\gamma)$, such that $\gamma \in R_d$ and $h(\varphi(\gamma)) = k$.

In general it is possible that taking the boundary will lower the filtration height of the element. This however cannot happen if our element is a linear combination of the basis elements which are matched downwards, as the next lemma explains.

Lemma 18.11. *Let $\mathcal{C}$ be the chain complex as above. Assume $\gamma \in C_{d+1}$, such that* $\operatorname{supp}\gamma \subseteq M^{\uparrow}$ *then* $h(\partial\gamma) = h(\gamma)$.

Proof. For brevity, set $k := h(\gamma)$. By Remark 18.4, we already know that $h(\partial\gamma) \leqslant h(\gamma)$. What we need is to find $w \in \operatorname{supp}\partial\gamma$, such that $h(w) = k$.

By construction, the element γ is a linear combination of basis elements of C_{d+1}. Let us split it as a sum $\gamma = \gamma_1 + \gamma_2$, where γ_1 is the part of that linear combination corresponding to the basis elements of height k, and γ_2 is the part corresponding to the basis elements of height less than k.

Clearly, we still have $\operatorname{supp}\gamma_1 \subseteq M^{\uparrow}$, so Proposition 12.2(2) can be applied. We obtain $\operatorname{supp}\partial\gamma_1 \cap \mu(\operatorname{supp}\gamma_1) \neq \emptyset$, so there exists $v \in \operatorname{supp}\gamma_1$, such that $\mu(v)$ belongs to $\operatorname{supp}\partial\gamma_1$. Since the matching μ respects the filtration, we have $h(\mu(v)) = h(v) = k$.

On the other hand, by construction $\gamma_2 \in \mathcal{F}_{k-1}C_{d+1}$, hence $\partial\gamma_2 \in \mathcal{F}_{k-1}C_d$. It follows that $\mu(v) \in \operatorname{supp}\partial(\gamma_1 + \gamma_2) = \operatorname{supp}\partial\gamma$. We can now set $w := \mu(v)$ and the proof is finished. □

We are now ready for the main result of this chapter. Let $\mathcal{C}$ be a chain complex with a base filtration $\{S_k\}_k$ as above, and let μ be an acyclic matching respecting the filtration $\mathcal{F}\mathcal{C}$. To start with, assume k is an arbitrary index between 0 and t. The matching μ gives us a decomposition

$$S_d = R_d \cup M_d^{\uparrow} \cup M_d^{\downarrow}.$$

Furthermore, since the matching μ respects our filtration, it can be restricted to $\mathcal{F}_k\mathcal{C}$, so we have a decomposition

$$S_d^k = R_d(k) \cup M_d^{\uparrow}(k) \cup M_d^{\downarrow}(k),$$

where $R_d(k) = R_d \cap \mathcal{F}_d C_k$, $M_d^{\uparrow}(k) = M_d^{\uparrow} \cap \mathcal{F}_d C_k$, and $M_d^{\downarrow}(k) = M_d^{\downarrow} \cap \mathcal{F}_d C_k$.

In Chapter 13 we described a change of bases. The new basis $\mathcal{B}_d^R \cup \mathcal{B}_d^{\uparrow} \cup \mathcal{B}_d^{\downarrow}$ was obtained from the old one using the formulae

$$\mathcal{B}_d^R := \{\varphi(\gamma) \mid \gamma \in R_d\}, \quad \mathcal{B}_d^{\uparrow} := M_d^{\uparrow}, \quad \mathcal{B}_d^{\downarrow} := \left\{\partial\beta \mid \beta \in M_{d+1}^{\uparrow}\right\}.$$

As the filtered analog we define three sets. First, we set

$$\mathcal{B}_d^R(k) := \{\varphi(\gamma) \mid \gamma \in R_d \cap \mathcal{F}_k C_d\} = \mathcal{B}_d^R \cap \mathcal{F}_k C_d, \tag{18.2}$$

where the second equality is a consequence of Lemma 18.9. Second, we set

$$\mathcal{B}_d^{\downarrow}(k) := M_d^{\downarrow}(k) \cap \mathcal{F}_k C_d = \mathcal{B}_d^{\downarrow} \cap \mathcal{F}_k C_d. \tag{18.3}$$

Third, we set

$$\mathcal{B}_d^{\uparrow}(k) := \left\{\partial\beta \mid \beta \in M_{d+1}^{\uparrow}(k)\right\} = \mathcal{B}_d^{\uparrow} \cap \mathcal{F}_k C_d, \tag{18.4}$$

where the second equality is a consequence of Lemma 18.11.

Since the matching μ respects our filtration, it can be restricted to $\mathcal{F}_k\mathcal{C}$. Considering the first equality in Equations (18.2) to (18.4) tells us that the set $\mathcal{B}_d^R(k) \cup \mathcal{B}_d^{\uparrow}(k) \cup \mathcal{B}_d^{\downarrow}(k)$ is a basis for $\mathcal{F}_k C_d$. On the other hand, using the second equality in Equations (18.2) to (18.4) allows us to extend the original filtration to this new basis, so that the formula (18.1) still holds.

Recall that we have $Z_d^p = \operatorname{Ker} \partial_d \cap \mathcal{F}_p C_d$ and $B_d^{p,q} := \partial_{d+1}(\mathcal{F}_{p+q} C_{d+1}) \cap \mathcal{F}_p C_d$. We let $\widetilde{Z}_d^p$ and $\widetilde{B}_d^{p,q}$ denote the analogs of Z_d^p and $B_d^{p,q}$ for the extension of our initial filtration to the Morse complex $\mathcal{C}^{\mu}$. Accordingly, the persistence homology $PH_d^{p,q}(\mathcal{C}^{\mu})$ is well-defined.

Theorem 18.12. *The persistent homology of the filtered Morse complex is isomorphic to the persistent homology of the original complex, i.e.,*

$$PH_d^{p,q}(\mathcal{F}\mathcal{C}) \approx PH_d^{p,q}(\mathcal{C}^{\mu}), \tag{18.5}$$

for all p, q, *and* d.

Proof. As mentioned above, we have the direct sum decomposition

$$\mathcal{F}_p C_d = \langle \mathcal{B}_d^R(p) \rangle \oplus \left\langle \mathcal{B}_d^{\uparrow}(p) \right\rangle \oplus \left\langle \mathcal{B}_d^{\downarrow}(p) \right\rangle. \tag{18.6}$$

Take $\sigma \in Z_d^p$ and split it as a sum $\sigma = \alpha + \beta + \gamma$, according to the decomposition (18.6), i.e., $\alpha \in \langle \mathcal{B}_d^R(p) \rangle$, $\beta \in \left\langle \mathcal{B}_d^{\uparrow}(p) \right\rangle$, and $\gamma \in \left\langle \mathcal{B}_d^{\downarrow}(p) \right\rangle$.

We have $0 = \partial\sigma = \partial\alpha + \partial\beta + \partial\gamma$. By definition of $\mathcal{B}_d^{\downarrow}(p)$, we have $\partial\gamma = 0$ independently of the actual γ. Furthermore, the sum of chain complexes in decomposition (13.1) is direct, so $\partial\alpha + \partial\beta = 0$ implies $\partial\alpha = 0$ and $\partial\beta = 0$. By Proposition 12.2(1), $\partial\beta = 0$ implies $\beta = 0$. We thus conclude that $\alpha \in \widetilde{Z}_d^p$ and $\gamma \in L$, where $L = \partial\left\langle \mathcal{B}_{d+1}^{\uparrow}(p)\right\rangle$. Indeed we have a direct sum decomposition $Z_d^p = \widetilde{Z}_d^p \oplus L$.

Next, we show that $B_d^{p,q} = \widetilde{B}_d^{p,q} \oplus L$. An arbitrary element of $B_d^{p,q}$ can be written as $\partial(\sigma) \in \mathcal{F}_p C_d$, where $\sigma \in \mathcal{F}_{p+q} C_{d+1}$. Write $\sigma = \alpha + \beta + \gamma$, such that $\alpha \in \langle \mathcal{B}_{d+1}^{R}(p+q)\rangle$, $\beta \in \left\langle \mathcal{B}_{d+1}^{\uparrow}(p+q)\right\rangle$, and $\gamma \in \left\langle \mathcal{B}_{d+1}^{\downarrow}(p+q)\right\rangle$. By construction, $\partial\gamma = 0$, so $\partial\sigma = \partial\alpha + \partial\beta$. By Lemma 18.11, we have $h(\partial\beta) = h(\beta)$. Again using the fact that the decomposition in (13.1) is direct, and that $h(\partial\sigma) \leqslant p$, we conclude that $\beta \in \partial\left\langle \mathcal{B}_{d+1}^{\uparrow}(p)\right\rangle$. It follows that $B_d^{p,q} \subseteq \widetilde{B}_d^{p,q} \oplus L$, and the reverse inclusion is obvious.

We can now summarize the argument by writing

$$PH_d^{p,q}(\mathcal{F}\mathcal{C}) = Z_d^p / B_d^{p,q} = (\widetilde{Z}_d^p \oplus L)/(\widetilde{B}_d^{p,q} \oplus L) \approx \widetilde{Z}_d^p / \widetilde{B}_d^{p,q} = PH_d^{p,q}(\mathcal{C}^{\mu}),$$

and the proof is finished. □

Exercises

(1) Consider the simplicial complex introduced as a sample application in the preface. Take the filtration obtained by adding one vertex at a time in their indexing order. Compute the corresponding persistent homology. Can you simplify the calculations using discrete Morse theory?

(2) Generalize the results of this chapter to integer coefficients.

Suggested further reading for Part 4

Original sources on algebraic Morse theory are [**Ko05b**, **SK06**, **JW09**]. Our presentation here follows [**Ko05b**], focusing on the sequence of basis changes as the essence of the subject. Further references are [**BW02**, **We07**].

The reader who is intrigued by the notion of poset maps with small fibers is invited to consult [**Ko08**, Section 11.1]. Furthermore, it would help to get immersed into the functorial way of thinking. Here any standard text in category theory, such as [**McL98**], is helpful.

Interesting developments on the crossroads between discrete Morse theory and combinatorics can be found in, e.g., [**AMSSS**, **AFFV**].

We recommend [**LW69**] as a standard, and still excellent, reference for topology of CW complexes. In addition to that, much of Chapter 17 is adapted from [**Koz11**], and the reader may want to look at the original paper.

The standard reference on the subject of persistent homology is [**EH10**], but see also [**Zo09**]. A very readable introduction can also be found in [**Ca09**]. There are a number of papers, many of them recent, considering the mixture of persistent homology and discrete Morse theory. We recommend [**MN13**] as a good starting point.

Further sources for discrete Morse theory and persistence, shape analysis, and computational complexity include [**BE17**, **BLPS**, **FFI16**, **HMMN**, **KKM17**, **MS19**, **RGHPH**].

Separately, we would like to mention recent applications of discrete Morse theory to stochastic geometry; see, e.g., [**ENÖS**, **ENR17**].

Finally, for reasons of space, several very interesting developments involving discrete Morse theory were not treated in this book. For instance, the reader interested in random discrete Morse theoy should consult, [**ABL17**, **BL14**]. Further, scattered reading recommendations are [**Be16**, **Be12**, **Fo02b**, **Fr09**, **GBMR**, **Ku13**, **Na19**].

Index

List of Figures

List of Tables

Bibliography

[AMSSS] Seth E. Aaronson, Marie E. Meyer, Nicholas A. Scoville, Mitchell T. Smith, and Laura M. Stibich, *Graph isomorphisms in discrete Morse theory*, AKCE Int. J. Graphs Comb. **11** (2014), no. 2, 163–176. MR3243115

[ABL17] Karim A. Adiprasito, Bruno Benedetti, and Frank H. Lutz, *Extremal examples of collapsible complexes and random discrete Morse theory*, Discrete Comput. Geom. **57** (2017), no. 4, 824–853, DOI 10.1007/s00454-017-9860-4. MR3639606

[AGORS] Michael Agiorgousis, Brian Green, Alex Onderdonk, Kim Rich, and Nicholas A. Scoville, *Homologically equivalent discrete Morse functions*, Topology Proc. **54** (2019), 283–294. MR3949263

[AFFV] R. Ayala, L. M. Fernández, D. Fernández-Ternero, and J. A. Vilches, *Discrete Morse theory on graphs*, Topology Appl. **156** (2009), no. 18, 3091–3100, DOI 10.1016/j.topol.2009.01.022. MR2556069

[BK03a] Eric Babson and Dmitry N. Kozlov, *Topological obstructions to graph colorings*, Electron. Res. Announc. Amer. Math. Soc. **9** (2003), 61–68, DOI 10.1090/S1079-6762-03-00112-4. MR2029466

[BK03b] Eric Babson and Dmitry N. Kozlov, *Complexes of graph homomorphisms*, Israel J. Math. **152** (2006), 285–312, DOI 10.1007/BF02771988. MR2214465

[BK04] Eric Babson and Dmitry N. Kozlov, *Proof of the Lovász conjecture*, Ann. of Math. (2) **165** (2007), no. 3, 965–1007, DOI 10.4007/annals.2007.165.965. MR2335799

[BW02] E. Batzies and V. Welker, *Discrete Morse theory for cellular resolutions*, J. Reine Angew. Math. **543** (2002), 147–168, DOI 10.1515/crll.2002.012. MR1887881

[BE17] Ulrich Bauer and Herbert Edelsbrunner, *The Morse theory of Čech and Delaunay complexes*, Trans. Amer. Math. Soc. **369** (2017), no. 5, 3741–3762, DOI 10.1090/tran/6991. MR3605986

[BR18] Fernando Benavides and Sergio Rajsbaum, *Collapsibility of read/write models using discrete Morse theory*, J. Appl. Comput. Topol. **1** (2018), no. 3-4, 365–396, DOI 10.1007/s41468-018-0011-7. MR3975558

[Be16] Bruno Benedetti, *Smoothing discrete Morse theory*, Ann. Sc. Norm. Super. Pisa Cl. Sci. (5) **16** (2016), no. 2, 335–368. MR3559605

[Be12] Bruno Benedetti, *Discrete Morse theory for manifolds with boundary*, Trans. Amer. Math. Soc. **364** (2012), no. 12, 6631–6670, DOI 10.1090/S0002-9947-2012-05614-5. MR2958950

[BL14] Bruno Benedetti and Frank H. Lutz, *Random discrete Morse theory and a new library of triangulations*, Exp. Math. **23** (2014), no. 1, 66–94, DOI 10.1080/10586458.2013.865281. MR3177457

[Bj96] A. Björner, *Topological methods*, Handbook of combinatorics, Vol. 1, 2, Elsevier Sci. B. V., Amsterdam, 1995, pp. 1819–1872. MR1373690

[BM60] A. Borel and J. C. Moore, *Homology theory for locally compact spaces*, Michigan Math. J. **7** (1960), 137–159. MR131271

[Br97] Glen E. Bredon, *Sheaf theory*, 2nd ed., Graduate Texts in Mathematics, vol. 170, Springer-Verlag, New York, 1997. MR1481706

[BLPS] Benjamin A. Burton, Thomas Lewiner, João Paixão, and Jonathan Spreer, *Parameterized complexity of discrete Morse theory*, Computational geometry (SoCG'13), ACM, New York, 2013, pp. 127–136, DOI 10.1145/2462356.2462391. MR3208204

[CM17] Nicolas Ariel Capitelli and Elias Gabriel Minian, *A simplicial complex is uniquely determined by its set of discrete Morse functions*, Discrete Comput. Geom. **58** (2017), no. 1, 144–157, DOI 10.1007/s00454-017-9865-z. MR3658332

[Ca09] Gunnar Carlsson, *Topology and data*, Bull. Amer. Math. Soc. (N.S.) **46** (2009), no. 2, 255–308, DOI 10.1090/S0273-0979-09-01249-X. MR2476414

[Ch00] Manoj K. Chari, *On discrete Morse functions and combinatorial decompositions* (English, with English and French summaries), Formal power series and algebraic combinatorics (Vienna, 1997). Discrete Math. **217** (2000), no. 1-3, 101–113, DOI 10.1016/S0012-365X(99)00258-7. MR1766262

[CJ05] Manoj K. Chari and Michael Joswig, *Complexes of discrete Morse functions*, Discrete Math. **302** (2005), no. 1-3, 39–51, DOI 10.1016/j.disc.2004.07.027. MR2179635

[Co73] Marshall M. Cohen, *A course in simple-homotopy theory*, Graduate Texts in Mathematics, Vol. 10. Springer-Verlag, New York-Berlin, 1973. MR0362320

[CK04a] Sonja Lj. Čukić and Dmitry N. Kozlov, *The homotopy type of complexes of graph homomorphisms between cycles*, Discrete Comput. Geom. **36** (2006), no. 2, 313–329, DOI 10.1007/s00454-006-1245-z. MR2252107

[CK04b] Sonja Lj. Čukić and Dmitry N. Kozlov, *Higher connectivity of graph coloring complexes*, Int. Math. Res. Not. **25** (2005), 1543–1562, DOI 10.1155/IMRN.2005.1543. MR2152894

[CGN16] Justin Curry, Robert Ghrist, and Vidit Nanda, *Discrete Morse theory for computing cellular sheaf cohomology*, Found. Comput. Math. **16** (2016), no. 4, 875–897, DOI 10.1007/s10208-015-9266-8. MR3529128

[DK01] James F. Davis and Paul Kirk, *Lecture notes in algebraic topology*, Graduate Studies in Mathematics, vol. 35, American Mathematical Society, Providence, RI, 2001. MR1841974

[FFI16] Leila De Floriani, Ulderico Fugacci, and Federico Iuricich, *Homological shape analysis through discrete Morse theory*, Perspectives in shape analysis, Math. Vis., Springer, [Cham], 2016, pp. 187–209. MR3822076

[EH10] Herbert Edelsbrunner and John L. Harer, *Computational topology*, American Mathematical Society, Providence, RI, 2010. An introduction. MR2572029

[ENÖS] H. Edelsbrunner, A. Nikitenko, K. Ölsböck, P. Synak, *Radius functions on Poisson-Delaunay mosaics and related complexes experimentally*, preprint.

[ENR17] Herbert Edelsbrunner, Anton Nikitenko, and Matthias Reitzner, *Expected sizes of Poisson-Delaunay mosaics and their discrete Morse functions*, Adv. in Appl. Probab. **49** (2017), no. 3, 745–767, DOI 10.1017/apr.2017.20. MR3694316

[FS05] Daniel Farley and Lucas Sabalka, *Discrete Morse theory and graph braid groups*, Algebr. Geom. Topol. **5** (2005), 1075–1109, DOI 10.2140/agt.2005.5.1075. MR2171804

[FFG86] A. T. Fomenko, D. B. Fuchs, and V. L. Gutenmacher, *Homotopic topology*, Akadémiai Kiadó (Publishing House of the Hungarian Academy of Sciences), Budapest, 1986. Translated from the Russian by K. Mályusz. MR873943

[Fo02a] Robin Forman, *A user's guide to discrete Morse theory*, Sém. Lothar. Combin. **48** (2002), Art. B48c, 35. MR1939695

[Fo02b] Robin Forman, *Discrete Morse theory and the cohomology ring*, Trans. Amer. Math. Soc. **354** (2002), no. 12, 5063–5085, DOI 10.1090/S0002-9947-02-03041-6. MR1926850

[Fo98] Robin Forman, *Morse theory for cell complexes*, Adv. Math. **134** (1998), no. 1, 90–145, DOI 10.1006/aima.1997.1650. MR1612391

[Fr09] Ragnar Freij, *Equivariant discrete Morse theory*, Discrete Math. **309** (2009), no. 12, 3821–3829, DOI 10.1016/j.disc.2008.10.029. MR2537376

[Fu95] William Fulton, *Algebraic topology: A first course*, Graduate Texts in Mathematics, vol. 153, Springer-Verlag, New York, 1995. MR1343250

[GMS11] G. Gaiffi, F. Mori, and M. Salvetti, *Minimal CW-complexes for complements to line arrangements via discrete Morse theory*, Topology of algebraic varieties and singularities, Contemp. Math., vol. 538, Amer. Math. Soc., Providence, RI, 2011, pp. 293–308, DOI 10.1090/conm/538/10607. MR2777826

[Ga10] Étienne Gallais, *Combinatorial realization of the Thom-Smale complex via discrete Morse theory*, Ann. Sc. Norm. Super. Pisa Cl. Sci. (5) **9** (2010), no. 2, 229–252. MR2731156

[GM03] Sergei I. Gelfand and Yuri I. Manin, *Methods of homological algebra*, 2nd ed., Springer Monographs in Mathematics, Springer-Verlag, Berlin, 2003. MR1950475

[GBMR] Aldo Gonzalez-Lorenzo, Alexandra Bac, Jean-Luc Mari, and Pedro Real, *Allowing cycles in discrete Morse theory*, Topology Appl. **228** (2017), 1–35, DOI 10.1016/j.topol.2017.05.008. MR3679072

[GH81] Marvin J. Greenberg and John R. Harper, *Algebraic topology: A first course*, Mathematics Lecture Note Series, vol. 58, Benjamin/Cummings Publishing Co., Inc., Advanced Book Program, Reading, Mass., 1981. MR643101

[Har69] Frank Harary, *Graph theory*, Addison-Wesley Publishing Co., Reading, Mass.-Menlo Park, Calif.-London, 1969. MR0256911

[HMMN] Shaun Harker, Konstantin Mischaikow, Marian Mrozek, and Vidit Nanda, *Discrete Morse theoretic algorithms for computing homology of complexes and maps*, Found. Comput. Math. **14** (2014), no. 1, 151–184, DOI 10.1007/s10208-013-9145-0. MR3160710

[Hat02] Allen Hatcher, *Algebraic topology*, Cambridge University Press, Cambridge, 2002. MR1867354

[HKR14] Maurice Herlihy, Dmitry Kozlov, and Sergio Rajsbaum, *Distributed computing through combinatorial topology*, Elsevier/Morgan Kaufmann, Waltham, MA, 2014. MR3292637

[HS97] P. J. Hilton and U. Stammbach, *A course in homological algebra*, 2nd ed., Graduate Texts in Mathematics, vol. 4, Springer-Verlag, New York, 1997. MR1438546

[JW09] Michael Jöllenbeck and Volkmar Welker, *Minimal resolutions via algebraic discrete Morse theory*, Mem. Amer. Math. Soc. **197** (2009), no. 923, vi+74, DOI 10.1090/memo/0923. MR2488864

[KMM04] Tomasz Kaczynski, Konstantin Mischaikow, and Marian Mrozek, *Computational homology*, Applied Mathematical Sciences, vol. 157, Springer-Verlag, New York, 2004. MR2028588

[KKM17] Henry King, Kevin Knudson, and Neža Mramor Kosta, *Birth and death in discrete Morse theory*, J. Symbolic Comput. **78** (2017), 41–60, DOI 10.1016/j.jsc.2016.03.007. MR3535328

[Kn15] Kevin P. Knudson, *Morse theory: Smooth and discrete*, World Scientific Publishing Co. Pte. Ltd., Hackensack, NJ, 2015. MR3379451

[Ko99] Dmitry N. Kozlov, *Complexes of directed trees*, J. Combin. Theory Ser. A **88** (1999), no. 1, 112–122, DOI 10.1006/jcta.1999.2984. MR1713484

[Ko00] Dmitry N. Kozlov, *Collapsibility of $\Delta(\Pi_n)/\mathcal{S}_n$ and some related CW complexes*, Proc. Amer. Math. Soc. **128** (2000), no. 8, 2253–2259, DOI 10.1090/S0002-9939-99-05301-0. MR1662257

[Ko02] D.N. Kozlov, *Trends in Topological Combinatorics*, Habilitationsschrift, Bern University, 2002.

[Ko05b] Dmitry N. Kozlov, *Discrete Morse theory for free chain complexes* (English, with English and French summaries), C. R. Math. Acad. Sci. Paris **340** (2005), no. 12, 867–872, DOI 10.1016/j.crma.2005.04.036. MR2151775

[Ko04] Dmitry N. Kozlov, *A simple proof for folds on both sides in complexes of graph homomorphisms*, Proc. Amer. Math. Soc. **134** (2006), no. 5, 1265–1270, DOI 10.1090/S0002-9939-05-08105-0. MR2199168

[Ko05a] Dmitry N. Kozlov, *Chromatic numbers, morphism complexes, and Stiefel-Whitney characteristic classes*, Geometric combinatorics, IAS/Park City Math. Ser., vol. 13, Amer. Math. Soc., Providence, RI, 2007, pp. 249–315. MR2383129

[Ko08] Dmitry Kozlov, *Combinatorial algebraic topology*, Algorithms and Computation in Mathematics, vol. 21, Springer, Berlin, 2008. MR2361455

[Koz11] Dmitry N. Kozlov, *Discrete Morse theory and Hopf bundles*, Pacific J. Math. **249** (2011), no. 2, 371–376, DOI 10.2140/pjm.2011.249.371. MR2782674

[Ko12] Dmitry N. Kozlov, *Chromatic subdivision of a simplicial complex*, Homology Homotopy Appl. **14** (2012), no. 2, 197–209, DOI 10.4310/HHA.2012.v14.n2.a12. MR3007093

[KST] Johannes Köbler, Uwe Schöning, and Jacobo Torán, *The graph isomorphism problem: its structural complexity*, Progress in Theoretical Computer Science, Birkhäuser Boston, Inc., Boston, MA, 1993. MR1232421

[Ku13] Michał Kukieła, *The main theorem of discrete Morse theory for Morse matchings with finitely many rays*, Topology Appl. **160** (2013), no. 9, 1074–1082, DOI 10.1016/j.topol.2013.04.025. MR3049255

[LPV13] F. Larrión, M. A. Pizaña, and R. Villarroel-Flores, *Discrete Morse theory and the homotopy type of clique graphs*, Ann. Comb. **17** (2013), no. 4, 743–754, DOI 10.1007/s00026-013-0204-7. MR3129782

[Lo78] L. Lovász, *Kneser's conjecture, chromatic number, and homotopy*, J. Combin. Theory Ser. A **25** (1978), no. 3, 319–324, DOI 10.1016/0097-3165(78)90022-5. MR514625

[Lo86] László Lovász and Michael D. Plummer, *Matching theory*, AMS Chelsea Publishing, Providence, RI, 2009. Corrected reprint of the 1986 original [MR0859549]. MR2536865

[LW69] Albert T. Lundell and Stephen Weingram, *The topology of CW complexes*, The University Series in Higher Mathematics, Van Nostrand Reinhold Co., New York, 1969. MR3822092

[McL98] Saunders Mac Lane, *Categories for the working mathematician*, 2nd ed., Graduate Texts in Mathematics, vol. 5, Springer-Verlag, New York, 1998. MR1712872

[McL67] Saunders Mac Lane, *Homology*, 1st ed., Die Grundlehren der mathematischen Wissenschaften, Band 114. Springer-Verlag, Berlin-New York, 1967. MR0349792

[MS19] Clément Maria and Hannah Schreiber, *Discrete Morse theory for computing zigzag persistence*, Algorithms and data structures, Lecture Notes in Comput. Sci., vol. 11646, Springer, Cham, 2019, pp. 538–552. MR3992985

[May92] J. Peter May, *Simplicial objects in algebraic topology*, Chicago Lectures in Mathematics, University of Chicago Press, Chicago, IL, 1992. Reprint of the 1967 original. MR1206474

[May99] J. P. May, *A concise course in algebraic topology*, Chicago Lectures in Mathematics, University of Chicago Press, Chicago, IL, 1999. MR1702278

[McC01] John McCleary, *A user's guide to spectral sequences*, 2nd ed., Cambridge Studies in Advanced Mathematics, vol. 58, Cambridge University Press, Cambridge, 2001. MR1793722

[MSTY] Oleg Melnikov, Regina Tyshkevich, Vladimir Yemelichev, and Vladimir Sarvanov, *Lectures on graph theory*, Bibliographisches Institut, Mannheim, 1994. Translated from the 1990 Russian original by N. Korneenko with the collaboration of the authors. MR1388513

[Mi63] J. Milnor, *Morse theory*, Based on lecture notes by M. Spivak and R. Wells. Annals of Mathematics Studies, No. 51, Princeton University Press, Princeton, N.J., 1963. MR0163331

[MS74] John W. Milnor and James D. Stasheff, *Characteristic classes*, Annals of Mathematics Studies, No. 76. Princeton University Press, Princeton, N. J.; University of Tokyo Press, Tokyo, 1974. MR0440554

[MN13] Konstantin Mischaikow and Vidit Nanda, *Morse theory for filtrations and efficient computation of persistent homology*, Discrete Comput. Geom. **50** (2013), no. 2, 330–353, DOI 10.1007/s00454-013-9529-6. MR3090522

[MS11] Francesca Mori and Mario Salvetti, *(Discrete) Morse theory on configuration spaces*, Math. Res. Lett. **18** (2011), no. 1, 39–57, DOI 10.4310/MRL.2011.v18.n1.a4. MR2770581

[Mu84] James R. Munkres, *Elements of algebraic topology*, Addison-Wesley Publishing Company, Menlo Park, CA, 1984. MR755006

[Na19] Vidit Nanda, *Discrete Morse theory and localization*, J. Pure Appl. Algebra **223** (2019), no. 2, 459–488, DOI 10.1016/j.jpaa.2018.04.001. MR3850551

[NTT18] Vidit Nanda, Dai Tamaki, and Kohei Tanaka, *Discrete Morse theory and classifying spaces*, Adv. Math. **340** (2018), 723–790, DOI 10.1016/j.aim.2018.10.016. MR3886179

[No55] P. S. Novikov, *Ob algoritmičeskoĭ nerazrešimosti problemy toždestva slov v teorii grupp* (Russian), Trudy Mat. Inst. im. Steklov. no. 44, Izdat. Akad. Nauk SSSR, Moscow, 1955. MR0075197

[Os00] M. Scott Osborne, *Basic homological algebra*, Graduate Texts in Mathematics, vol. 196, Springer-Verlag, New York, 2000. MR1757274

[Oz17] Viktoriya Ozornova, *Discrete Morse theory and a reformulation of the* $K(\pi, 1)$*-conjecture*, Comm. Algebra **45** (2017), no. 4, 1760–1784, DOI 10.1080/00927872.2016.1226852. MR3576693

[RGHPH] Jan Reininghaus, David Günther, Ingrid Hotz, Steffen Prohaska, and Hans-Christian Hege, *TADD: a computational framework for data analysis using discrete Morse theory*, Mathematical software—ICMS 2010, Lecture Notes in Comput. Sci., vol. 6327, Springer, Berlin, 2010, pp. 198–208. MR3663192

[RW10] Konstanze Rietsch and Lauren Williams, *Discrete Morse theory for totally non-negative flag varieties*, Adv. Math. **223** (2010), no. 6, 1855–1884, DOI 10.1016/j.aim.2009.10.011. MR2601003

[Ro09] Joseph J. Rotman, *An introduction to homological algebra*, 2nd ed., Universitext, Springer, New York, 2009. MR2455920

[SW12] Bruce E. Sagan and Robert Willenbring, *Discrete Morse theory and the consecutive pattern poset*, J. Algebraic Combin. **36** (2012), no. 4, 501–514, DOI 10.1007/s10801-012-0347-3. MR2984154

[Sc19] Nicholas A. Scoville, *Discrete Morse theory*, Student Mathematical Library, vol. 90, American Mathematical Society, Providence, RI, 2019. MR3970274

[Sh01] John Shareshian, *Discrete Morse theory for complexes of 2-connected graphs*, Topology **40** (2001), no. 4, 681–701, DOI 10.1016/S0040-9383(99)00076-2. MR1851558

[SK06] Emil Sköldberg, *Morse theory from an algebraic viewpoint*, Trans. Amer. Math. Soc. **358** (2006), no. 1, 115–129, DOI 10.1090/S0002-9947-05-04079-1. MR2171225

[Sp95] Edwin H. Spanier, *Algebraic topology*, Springer-Verlag, New York, 1994. Corrected reprint of the 1966 original. MR1325242

[Sw02] Robert M. Switzer, *Algebraic topology—homotopy and homology*, Classics in Mathematics, Springer-Verlag, Berlin, 2002. Reprint of the 1975 original [Springer, New York; MR0385836 (52 #6695)]. MR1886843

[Tu01] Vladimir Turaev, *Introduction to combinatorial torsions*, Lectures in Mathematics ETH Zürich, Birkhäuser Verlag, Basel, 2001. Notes taken by Felix Schlenk. MR1809561

[Vi94] James W. Vick, *Homology theory: An introduction to algebraic topology*, 2nd ed., Graduate Texts in Mathematics, vol. 145, Springer-Verlag, New York, 1994. MR1254439

[We94] Charles A. Weibel, *An introduction to homological algebra*, Cambridge Studies in Advanced Mathematics, vol. 38, Cambridge University Press, Cambridge, 1994. MR1269324

[We07] Volkmar Welker, *Discrete Morse theory and free resolutions*, Algebraic combinatorics, Universitext, Springer, Berlin, 2007, pp. 81–172. MR2321838

[Wh50] J. H. C. Whitehead, *Simple homotopy types*, Amer. J. Math. **72** (1950), 1–57, DOI 10.2307/2372133. MR35437

[Zh18] A. Zhukova, *Discrete Morse theory for the barycentric subdivison*, Zap. Nauchn. Sem. S.-Peterburg. Otdel. Mat. Inst. Steklov. (POMI) **462** (2017), no. Teoriya Predstavleniĭ, Dinamicheskie Sistemy, Kombinatornye Metody. XXVIII, 52–64, DOI 10.1007/s10958-018-3863-4; English transl., J. Math. Sci. (N.Y.) **232** (2018), no. 2, 129–137. MR3743406

[ZhP17] A. M. Zhukova and G. Yu. Panina, *Discrete Morse theory for moduli spaces of flexible polygons, or a solitaire game on the circle* (Russian, with Russian summary), Mat. Sb. **208** (2017), no. 9, 100–115, DOI 10.4213/sm8677; English transl., Sb. Math. **208** (2017), no. 9, 1353-1367. MR3691717

[Zo09] Afra J. Zomorodian, *Topology for computing*, Cambridge Monographs on Applied and Computational Mathematics, vol. 16, Cambridge University Press, Cambridge, 2009. Reprint of the 2005 original [MR2111929]. MR2549932

[Zi97] Rade T. Živaljević, *Topological methods*, Handbook of discrete and computational geometry, CRC Press Ser. Discrete Math. Appl., CRC, Boca Raton, FL, 1997, pp. 209–224. MR1730167

Selected Published Titles in This Series

207 **Dmitry N. Kozlov,** Organized Collapse: An Introduction to Discrete Morse Theory, 2020
204 **Sarah J. Witherspoon,** Hochschild Cohomology for Algebras, 2019
203 **Dimitris Koukoulopoulos,** The Distribution of Prime Numbers, 2019
202 **Michael E. Taylor,** Introduction to Complex Analysis, 2019
201 **Dan A. Lee,** Geometric Relativity, 2019
200 **Semyon Dyatlov and Maciej Zworski,** Mathematical Theory of Scattering Resonances, 2019
199 **Weinan E, Tiejun Li, and Eric Vanden-Eijnden,** Applied Stochastic Analysis, 2019
198 **Robert L. Benedetto,** Dynamics in One Non-Archimedean Variable, 2019
197 **Walter Craig,** A Course on Partial Differential Equations, 2018
196 **Martin Stynes and David Stynes,** Convection-Diffusion Problems, 2018
195 **Matthias Beck and Raman Sanyal,** Combinatorial Reciprocity Theorems, 2018
194 **Seth Sullivant,** Algebraic Statistics, 2018
193 **Martin Lorenz,** A Tour of Representation Theory, 2018
192 **Tai-Peng Tsai,** Lectures on Navier-Stokes Equations, 2018
191 **Theo Bühler and Dietmar A. Salamon,** Functional Analysis, 2018
190 **Xiang-dong Hou,** Lectures on Finite Fields, 2018
189 **I. Martin Isaacs,** Characters of Solvable Groups, 2018
188 **Steven Dale Cutkosky,** Introduction to Algebraic Geometry, 2018
187 **John Douglas Moore,** Introduction to Global Analysis, 2017
186 **Bjorn Poonen,** Rational Points on Varieties, 2017
185 **Douglas J. LaFountain and William W. Menasco,** Braid Foliations in Low-Dimensional Topology, 2017
184 **Harm Derksen and Jerzy Weyman,** An Introduction to Quiver Representations, 2017
183 **Timothy J. Ford,** Separable Algebras, 2017
182 **Guido Schneider and Hannes Uecker,** Nonlinear PDEs, 2017
181 **Giovanni Leoni,** A First Course in Sobolev Spaces, Second Edition, 2017
180 **Joseph J. Rotman,** Advanced Modern Algebra: Third Edition, Part 2, 2017
179 **Henri Cohen and Fredrik Strömberg,** Modular Forms, 2017
178 **Jeanne N. Clelland,** From Frenet to Cartan: The Method of Moving Frames, 2017
177 **Jacques Sauloy,** Differential Galois Theory through Riemann-Hilbert Correspondence, 2016
176 **Adam Clay and Dale Rolfsen,** Ordered Groups and Topology, 2016
175 **Thomas A. Ivey and Joseph M. Landsberg,** Cartan for Beginners: Differential Geometry via Moving Frames and Exterior Differential Systems, Second Edition, 2016
174 **Alexander Kirillov Jr.,** Quiver Representations and Quiver Varieties, 2016
173 **Lan Wen,** Differentiable Dynamical Systems, 2016
172 **Jinho Baik, Percy Deift, and Toufic Suidan,** Combinatorics and Random Matrix Theory, 2016
171 **Qing Han,** Nonlinear Elliptic Equations of the Second Order, 2016
170 **Donald Yau,** Colored Operads, 2016
169 **András Vasy,** Partial Differential Equations, 2015
168 **Michael Aizenman and Simone Warzel,** Random Operators, 2015
167 **John C. Neu,** Singular Perturbation in the Physical Sciences, 2015
166 **Alberto Torchinsky,** Problems in Real and Functional Analysis, 2015

For a complete list of titles in this series, visit the
AMS Bookstore at **www.ams.org/bookstore/gsmseries/**.